Abstract Algebra

Abstract Algebra

An Active Learning Approach

Neil Davidson

Frances Gulick

University of Maryland

Houghton
Mifflin
Company

Boston

Atlanta
Dallas
Geneva, Illinois
Hopewell, New Jersey
Palo Alto
London

Chapter-opening illustrations were prepared by
George C. Sumerack. Photographs of Niels
Henrik Abel, Arthur Cayley, William R. Hamilton,
and Heinrich Weber courtesy of Columbia
University Library.

Printed in the U.S.A.

Library of Congress Catalog Card Number:
75-19537

ISBN: 0-395-20663-4

In memory of my uncle
George Segal and friend
Michael Bogart
ND

To all those students
who have contributed
in thought and time to the
many versions of this book
FG

Contents

Preface

This book has grown out of our concern over the traditional method of teaching, accompanied all too frequently by passive learning for the student. After much searching into possible alternatives, we decided on a small-group method of learning in which students would work through course material such as abstract algebra in groups of approximately four members, with the teacher's role evolving primarily into that of trouble-shooter rather than lecturer.

Under this small-group method the students work cooperatively in groups at the blackboard, proving theorems, solving problems, working out details of given examples, and constructing new examples and counterexamples as well as creating conjectures. The teacher moves from group to group as he sees the need for his help, giving suggestions and encouragement in addition to checking proofs and solutions. (Details of the small-group method of learning are given in the Instructor's Manual.)

The idea of the small-group method is to create a cooperative environment *with* a mutual understanding in which criticism is offered in such a way that no one is afraid of it and *without* classroom competition (except occasionally between groups). As a result, for the teacher there is no longer the need of continually acting on stage, trying to hold students' attention with his performance at the blackboard. He has the time and opportunity to observe his students, to get to know them better as individuals, to identify those having trouble (without the delay caused by the wait for results from an examination), and to act as a catalyst for those creative students who can benefit from extra challenges. Although students generally cover somewhat less material than in traditional lecture courses on abstract algebra, we believe that the benefits to the teacher and student alike should compensate more than adequately.

Although this book has been designed especially for the small-group method, we believe it can be used with two other types of teaching. One of these is the teacher-directed class discovery method with its Socratic dialogues between the teacher and the entire class, in the manner exemplified by George Polya. The second would be a modified form of R. L. Moore's individual discovery approach for bright students.

The book includes the standard subjects of a first (junior-senior) one-semester course in abstract algebra and we envisage a wide range of abilities among the readers. There are numerous examples which we regard as vehicles for genuine understanding of the concepts and theorems.

The appendixes include short discussions of set theory, logic and types of proof, equivalence relations, induction and well-ordering, and number theory. The topics included are used at various points in the book and as a result they should be studied early in the term. They appear in a form designed for reading outside the classroom and, consequently, the class time spent discussing the ideas contained in the appendixes should be kept at a minimum.

The flow chart shows various sequences in which the material can be used. For a typical course we recommend reading the appendixes and working through Chapter 1, Sections 2.1 through 2.5, 2.7 through 2.9, and Chapter 3, omitting Sections 3.5 and 3.8 if needed. In past experience such a course (with an average class) has required about 42 hours of class time. If it appears that there will not be enough time for this material, one alternative is to omit temporarily Sections 2.7 through 2.9, saving a couple hours at the end of the course for lectures on the material included there. We have included in the Instructor's Manual several suggestions for shortening the amount of time needed to cover this amount of material.

Chapters 4 and 5 contain optional subjects. In Chapter 4 the sections fall into three disconnected sets: Sections 4.1 and 4.2 on permutation groups, Section 4.3 on groups of automorphisms, and Sections 4.4 and 4.5 on direct sums

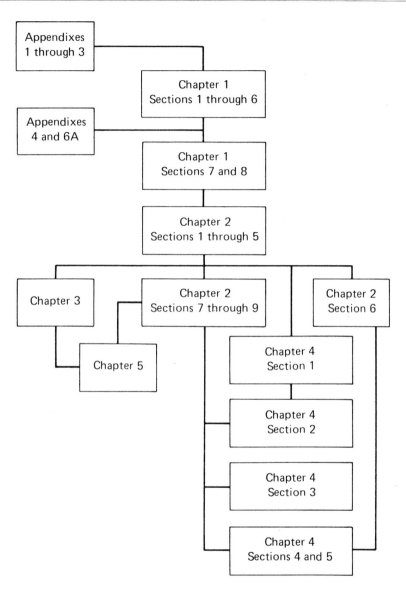

of groups and subgroups. Section 5.1 on polynomial rings provides many interesting examples for later sections and is of interest by itself, while Sections 5.2 through 5.5 form a unit on ideals.

Many people have helped us in the preparation of this book. We are especially grateful to Professor Warren Persons, who offered many incisive and constructive suggestions on two versions. We acknowledge with appreciation the helpful comments of Professors David E. Zitarelli and Lee M. Sonneborn on an earlier version, and we wish to thank Susan Grant and Elliott Rosenthal for working through the entire set of problems and exercises. We have a growing and continuing indebtedness to our students both at the University of Maryland and at the Catholic University of America, who have patiently worked through the various versions of the manuscript during the past four years. We are grateful to the staff of Houghton Mifflin for their help in speeding along this project. Our spouses, Jan D. and Denny G., have supported us through several long years and have occasionally offered their own good ideas to the project.

Letter
To The
Student

Dear Student,

You may have little or no experience working in groups. The rapport established within your group will have a great effect on both your ability to work and your enjoyment of the work. For these reasons we suggest the following guidelines:

Work with your fellow students in a *cooperative* manner.

Share the leadership of the group; everyone should participate and no one should dominate a discussion.

Achieve a single group solution to each problem.

Solve each problem on the blackboard; take turns writing on the blackboard.

Be certain that everyone in the group understands a solution before beginning a new problem.

Ask questions if you do not understand the ideas under consideration; answer questions if you do understand.

Listen carefully; try to expand and clarify ideas.

Do not worry about the work of the other groups; each group should proceed at its own pace.

In order to ease your way through the book, let us explain the conventions we have used.

Throughout each chapter, definitions, problems, propositions, theorems, and lemmas are numbered consecutively. Thus you will find sequences of items such as the following:

1
Definition

2
Problem

3
Problem   Prove the following theorem:

Theorem

4
Definition

5
Problem

In such a sequence there may be no Problem 1 or 4 and no Definition 2 or 3. The consecutive numbering of all items is done to aid the reader in locating a particular item.

We often mention items in chapters other than the one being read. In such cases we simply say, for example, Problem 5 of Chapter 1. If an item is mentioned without a chapter number (for example, Problem 5), then the reference is to an item in that chapter. To simplify references to theorems and lemmas which appear in problems, we use the number of the problem and do not give the theorem a separate number. Thus, if we want to refer to the theorem which appears in

Problem 3, we simply say Theorem 3. References to theorems, definitions, etc., in the appendixes are treated in a similar manner. Thus we might mention Theorem 10 in Appendix 6.

In addition to problems there are exercises. Problems are included in the text and are intended for group work in class. Exercises are given at the end of each section and are intended for work at home, either individually or in groups, depending on the preference of your teacher. When we refer to an exercise at the end of the section being read, we simply say, for example, Exercise 8. If we refer to an exercise in another section, whether in the chapter being read or not, the section number precedes the exercise number. Thus a reference to Exercise 3.1–6 means that you should look at Exercise 6 in the set of homework exercises at the end of Section 3.1. References to exercises in the appendixes are given in full, as in Exercise 2 in Appendix 6.

Some of the appendixes are divided into sections, which are referred to by capital letters. When we refer to a section in the appendix being read, we say, for example, Section E. When reference is made to a section in another appendix, or when the reference appears in the text, the section letter directly follows the appendix number as in Appendix 4E.

Occasionally you will find the symbol ▲ at the end of a problem or the symbol ● at the end of an exercise. These symbols indicate that a hint for that particular problem or exercise is given at the back of the book. Hints for problems begin on page 320 and hints for exercises begin on page 323.

A star (*) before the number of an exercise indicates that the exercise is referred to or used in a later exercise or (rarely) a problem.

Lines are often provided so that you can write answers in your copy of the book.

ND and FG

Chapter 1   Groups: Definitions And Examples

What is abstract algebra? The term "algebra" may bring back memories of a subject studied in high school, dealing with solutions to linear and polynomial equations. Historically, the study of solutions to such equations gave rise to what we now call abstract algebra. Let us briefly describe the development, as it evolved historically.

The original, fundamental question which absorbed mathematicians since ancient times concerned the solutions of general polynomial equations of the form

$$a_n x^n + a_{n-1} x^{n-1} + \cdots + a_1 x + a_0 = 0$$

where $a_0, a_1, \ldots, a_n$ are real numbers and $a_n \neq 0$. The problem was to determine those values of n for which these equations have solutions which can be expressed in terms of a formula involving only the operations of addition, subtraction, multiplication, division, and the taking of kth roots regardless of the choice of coefficients $a_0, a_1, \ldots, a_n$.

Already by the ninth century the Arabs had published the solutions when $n = 2$

1

(that is, to the equations of the form $ax^2+bx+c=0$), these solutions deriving from the quadratic formula

$$x = \frac{-b \pm \sqrt{b^2-4ac}}{2a}$$

when b^2-4ac is nonnegative. The next step was a long time coming. In fact, it was only in the sixteenth century that the Italian mathematicians Niccolò Tartaglia and Lodovico Ferrari found general solutions and the associated formulas for the third- ($n=3$) and fourth- ($n=4$) degree equations. However, through the seventeenth and eighteenth centuries the fifth-degree equations defied all attempts at a general solution and for good reason. Indeed, in 1828 the Norwegian mathematician Niels Henrik Abel proved definitively that the general fifth-degree equation (that is, $n=5$) does *not* have a solution involving only algebraic methods.

In his study of the problem some fifty years earlier, Joseph-Louis Lagrange used "substitutions," which we now call permutations, to arrive at the formulas for the third- and fourth-degree equations. It took later mathematicians to translate his work on permutations and that of such nineteenth-century mathematicians as Evariste Galois and Augustin-Louis Cauchy into the terminology we meet in this and other abstract algebra books. Yet the foundations are there, particularly in the work of these three men. In fact, Cauchy and Galois both used the French word *groupe* in their study of "substitutions" (permutations) and the solutions of the polynomial equations. Step by step the work of these great mathematicians led to the study of groups, rings, and fields, which are the main topics of abstract algebra.

In this book we study the basic ideas of groups, rings, and fields. We begin with groups, and after we have stated the definition of a group and given relevant examples of groups, we move right on to permutations, investigating in particular grouplike properties of functions. Later in Chapter 1 we see other examples of finite groups based on geometry and on number theory.

1.1 Binary Operations

One of the basic notions of mathematics is that of an operation, such as the addition or multiplication of real numbers, which assigns to two elements of a set a third element of the set. In order to define precisely this notion of an operation, we need to consider two other concepts. The first, that of a function, may be familiar from algebra or the calculus.

1
Definition
A *function* from a set X to a set Y is a rule which assigns to every $x \in X$ exactly one element $y \in Y$; this element y is denoted by $f(x)$. The set X is the *domain* of f and the set Y is the *range* of f.

It is common practice to denote a function by $f: X \to Y$ or $X \xrightarrow{f} Y$, where f is the symbol for the rule, X is the domain, and Y is the range.

Examples of functions include the following: f from the set of all real numbers into itself defined by

$$f(x) = x^4 + x^2$$

and $g: \{1, 2, 3\} \to \{1, 2\}$ defined by $g(1) = 1$, $g(2) = 2$, $g(3) = 2$. The rule $h: \{1, 2\} \to \{1, 2, 3\}$ defined by setting $h(1) = 1$, $h(2) = 2$, and $h(2) = 3$ certainly is not a function. (Why?)

Throughout the book the symbols **Z**, **Q**, and **R** denote the following sets:

$$\textbf{Z} = \text{the set of all integers}$$
$$= \{..., -3, -2, -1, 0, 1, 2, 3, ...\}$$
$$\textbf{Q} = \text{the set of all rational numbers}$$
$$= \{m/n: m, n \in \textbf{Z}, n \neq 0\}$$
$$\textbf{R} = \text{the set of all real numbers}$$

In addition, we often use the sets

$$\textbf{Z}^+ = \{x: x \in \textbf{Z} \text{ and } x > 0\}$$

$$\mathbf{Q}^+ = \{x: x \in \mathbf{Q} \text{ and } x > 0\}$$
$$\mathbf{R}^+ = \{x: x \in \mathbf{R} \text{ and } x > 0\}$$

Certain properties of addition and multiplication of real numbers are taken for granted throughout the book. A summary of these properties is found in Appendix 3. The properties may be used in the problems that follow. For a summary of set theory notation see Appendix 1.

2

Problem   Which of the following rules defines a function f from $\mathbf{R}^+$ into $\mathbf{R}$? Justify your answer.

a $f(x) = x^2$
b $f(x) = y$, where $y^2 = x$
c $f(x) = y$, where $y^2 = x$, $y \geq 0$

The rules for functions may be given in many different ways. For example, a function $f: \mathbf{R} \to \mathbf{R}$ might be given by a single rule such as $f(x) = 3x^2 - x$ or we might define a function $f: \mathbf{R} \to \mathbf{R}$ by a fairly complicated rule such as

$$f(x) = \begin{cases} 2x & (x \leq 0) \\ x^3 & (0 < x \leq 1) \\ 2x - 1 & (x \geq 1) \end{cases}$$

On the other hand, if a finite set has a small number of elements, we might state a rule by listing the elements of the set and the corresponding images. Thus, if $S = \{a, b, c\}$, we can define a function $f: S \to S$ by setting $f(a) = b$, $f(b) = c$, and $f(c) = a$ or by a table such as

$$\begin{pmatrix} a & b & c \\ b & c & a \end{pmatrix}$$

or by a table such as Table 1.1.

Table 1.1

x	$f(x)$
a	b
b	c
c	a

3
Definition
Let X and Y be sets. The *cartesian product* of X and Y is the set

$$X \times Y = \{(x, y) : x \in X \text{ and } y \in Y\}$$

The elements of the cartesian product are called *ordered pairs*.

The familiar coordinate plane $\mathbf{R}^2$ is an example of a cartesian product, in this case the cartesian product of the set $\mathbf{R}$ of the real numbers with itself. Examples of elements of $\mathbf{R}^2$ are $(0, 1)$, $(\pi, 2)$, $\left(-\sqrt{2}, -\sqrt{3}\right)$, $(\frac{1}{2}, -2)$, etc.

A function from a cartesian product $G \times G$ into the set G is given a special name.

4
Definition
A *binary operation* on a set G is a function from $G \times G$ into G. Thus a binary operation is a rule $\circ$ which assigns to every ordered pair (a, b) in $G \times G$ exactly one element of G; this element is denoted $a \circ b$. Unless otherwise specified the image $a \circ b$ of the pair (a, b) will be called the *composite* of the pair and the operation $\circ$ will be called *composition*.

The most familiar examples of binary operations are addition and multiplication of real numbers. These are the functions $\mathbf{R} \times \mathbf{R} \xrightarrow{+} \mathbf{R}$ defined by $(a, b) \to a + b$ and $\mathbf{R} \times \mathbf{R} \xrightarrow{\cdot} \mathbf{R}$ defined by $(a, b) \to a \cdot b$ (or ab), respectively. As usual, $a + b$ is called the sum of a and b and ab is called the product.

Note that there are *two* points which must be checked in determining whether or not a rule defines a binary operation on a set G.

First, the rule must be a *properly defined function*: it must assign to every ordered pair $(a, b) \in G \times G$ exactly one element $a \circ b$.

One example of this requirement is provided by the set $\mathbf{Q}$ of rational numbers. In $\mathbf{Q}$ the element $\frac{1}{2}$ can also be written as $\frac{3}{6}, \frac{4}{8}, \frac{10}{20}$, and so on, while the element $\frac{3}{4}$ can also be written as $\frac{6}{8}, \frac{9}{12}, \frac{18}{24}$, etc. Any binary operation defined on the rational numbers must assign to the pair $(\frac{1}{2}, \frac{3}{4})$ the same number it assigns to the pairs $(\frac{3}{6}, \frac{6}{8})$, $(\frac{4}{8}, \frac{9}{12})$, $(\frac{10}{20}, \frac{18}{24})$, etc. The answer must not depend on the particular names chosen for the elements of the pair. This is usually stated by saying that the function is properly defined or well defined. Thus, if the operation is addition in $\mathbf{Q}$, we must have

$$\tfrac{1}{2} + \tfrac{3}{4} = \tfrac{3}{6} + \tfrac{6}{8} = \tfrac{4}{8} + \tfrac{9}{12}, \text{ etc.}$$

For most, but not all, proposed operations on an arbitrary set G, the requirement of being a properly defined function will be quite apparent and will not need any proof.

The second condition in the definition of a binary operation is that for every pair $(a, b) \in G \times G$ the image $a \circ b$ is an element of G. In other words, this condition asserts that for every $a, b \in G$, $a \circ b \in G$. A phrase historically used for this property is that G is *closed* under the operation $\circ$. For any proposed operation this closure property must be checked.

In summary, to prove that a proposed rule defines a binary operation $\circ$ on G we must show that the rule is a properly defined function and that G is closed under the rule $\circ$.

5

Problem   a   Is the correspondence defined by

$$(a, b) \rightarrow a - b$$

for every $(a, b) \in \mathbf{Z} \times \mathbf{Z}$ a binary operation on $\mathbf{Z}$? In other words, is subtraction a binary operation on $\mathbf{Z}$?

b   Is division a binary operation on the set $\mathbf{Z} - \{0\}$ of nonzero integers? That is, if a rule of correspondence is defined on $(\mathbf{Z} - \{0\}) \times (\mathbf{Z} - \{0\})$ by

$$(a, b) \rightarrow a/b$$

then does this define a binary operation on $\mathbf{Z} - \{0\}$?

In our later study we are concerned with binary operations which enjoy special properties. For this reason we introduce the concepts of associative and commutative binary operations.

6

Definition a A binary operation ∘ on a set G is *associative* if and only if for every $a, b, c \in G$,

$$a \circ (b \circ c) = (a \circ b) \circ c$$

b A binary operation ∘ on a set G is *commutative* if and only if for every pair $a, b \in G$,

$$a \circ b = b \circ a$$

7

Problem Determine whether or not each of the following operations on the set of real numbers is associative or commutative. (Use the properties in Appendix 3 for a quick solution to this problem.)

a Addition
b Multiplication
c Subtraction

We are familiar mainly with operations which are commutative, and consequently a person might ask whether there is any especially interesting set with a binary operation which is associative but *not* commutative. The first demonstration of a set of "numbers" with a noncommutative multiplication was in 1843 by William R. Hamilton, who was so impressed by the necessary axioms that he carved the critical portion on a bridge in Dublin (see Exercise 3.7–10). A second example appears in the work of Arthur Cayley, who is credited with the creation of matrices because he was the first to systematically explore the theory of matrices. We study here and in later sections one of the simplest sets of matrices.

8

Definition Let $M_2(\mathbf{R})$ be the set of all 2×2 matrices

$$\begin{pmatrix} a & b \\ c & d \end{pmatrix}$$

with real entries:

$$M_2(\mathbf{R}) = \left\{ \begin{pmatrix} a & b \\ c & d \end{pmatrix} : a, b, c, d \in \mathbf{R} \right\}$$

By definition, two 2×2 matrices are equal if and only if their corresponding entries are equal. Thus

$$\begin{pmatrix} a & b \\ c & d \end{pmatrix} = \begin{pmatrix} w & x \\ y & z \end{pmatrix}$$

if and only if $a = w$, $b = x$, $c = y$, and $d = z$.

Addition, denoted by $+$, is defined on $M_2(\mathbf{R})$ by setting

$$\begin{pmatrix} a & b \\ c & d \end{pmatrix} + \begin{pmatrix} e & f \\ g & h \end{pmatrix} = \begin{pmatrix} a+e & b+f \\ c+g & d+h \end{pmatrix}$$

9

Problem   a   Is the addition given in Definition 8 a binary operation on $M_2(\mathbf{R})$?

b   Is it an associative operation?

c   Is addition a commutative operation?

Justify your answers.

10

Definition   Multiplication, denoted by $\cdot$ or juxtaposition, is defined on $M_2(\mathbf{R})$ by setting

$$\begin{pmatrix} a & b \\ c & d \end{pmatrix} \cdot \begin{pmatrix} e & f \\ g & h \end{pmatrix} = \begin{pmatrix} ae+bg & af+bh \\ ce+dg & cf+dh \end{pmatrix}$$

This peculiar multiplication results from work with systems of linear equations and special functions $f: \mathbf{R}^2 \to \mathbf{R}^2$ of the form $f(x, y) = (ax+by, cx+dy)$. We explore this relationship between multiplication and the special functions further in Exercise 1.4–5.

11

Problem   a   Is multiplication a binary operation on $M_2(\mathbf{R})$? Explain.

b   Prove that matrix multiplication is an associative operation.

c   Is matrix multiplication a commutative operation? Justify your answer.

If G is a small finite set, it is often convenient to define a binary operation on G by means of a table, which is constructed as follows:

All the elements of the set G are written across the top line of the table. They also are written vertically in the same order down the left side of the table. In order to find the composite $x \circ y$, first find the row with x on the left. In this row $x \circ y$ appears in the column with y at the top. Thus $x \circ y$ is in the row determined by x (on the left of the table) and the column determined by y (at the top of the table), as shown in Table 1.2. This convention is used in all operations tables throughout the book.

Table 1.2

$\circ$	$\cdots$	y
$\vdots$		
x	$\cdots$	$x \circ y$

12

Problem   a   In reading Table 1.3 across the second row, note that $b \circ a = b,\, b \circ b = c,\, b \circ c = \underline{\hspace{1cm}},\, b \circ d = \underline{\hspace{1cm}}$.

Table 1.3

$\circ$	a	b	c	d
a	a	b	c	d
b	b	c	d	a
c	c	d	a	b
d	d	a	b	c

b   Show that Table 1.3 defines a binary operation on the set $G = \{a, b, c, d\}$. Recall that you must show (i) that the correspondence $(x, y) \to x \circ y$ as defined by Table 1.3 is a properly defined function and (ii) that G is closed under the correspondence.

c   Check a particular instance of the associative property of the operation by computing $b \circ (c \circ d)$ and $(b \circ c) \circ d$. Then check one more instance of the associative property.

d   Is the operation $\circ$ commutative? Describe a simple test for commutativity by inspection of Table 1.3.

EXERCISES 1   Let a and b be real numbers. Define $a \circ b$ to be the number

$$a \circ b = a + b - ab$$

Show that this defines a binary operation on **R**. Is the operation associative? commutative? Justify your answers.

*2   (The star indicates that this exercise is referred to or used in a later exercise.) For each of the following sets determine whether or not addition is a binary operation. Justify your answers.
a $\mathbf{Z}^+$, the set of all positive integers
b   The set of all even integers: $2\mathbf{Z} = \{2n: n \in \mathbf{Z}\}$
c   The set of all odd integers: $\{2n+1: n \in \mathbf{Z}\}$
d $\{\pm n^2: n \in \mathbf{Z}\}$
e $\{0\} \cup \{\pm 2^n: n \in \mathbf{Z}^+\}$

*3   Let $G = \{a, b, c, d\}$. Define a correspondence $(x, y) \to x \circ y$ by Table 1.4.
a   Show that this correspondence defines a binary operation on G.
b   Is the operation commutative?
c   Check two particular instances of the associative property of the operation.

Table 1.4

$\circ$	a	b	c	d
a	a	b	c	d
b	b	a	d	c
c	c	d	a	b
d	d	c	b	a

*4   Let $\mathbf{R}^2 = \mathbf{R} \times \mathbf{R}$. Define a correspondence $\mathbf{R}^2 \times \mathbf{R}^2 \overset{+}{\to} \mathbf{R}^2$ by setting

$$(a,b) + (c,d) = (a+c, b+d)$$

for every $(a,b), (c,d) \in \mathbf{R}^2$.

a   Show that $+$ is a binary operation on $\mathbf{R}^2$. This operation is called addition, and $(a,b) + (c,d)$ is called the sum of (a,b) and (c,d).

b   Prove that addition is an associative operation on $\mathbf{R}^2$.

c   Prove that addition is a commutative operation on $\mathbf{R}^2$.

d   Fix (a,b) and (c,d) in $\mathbf{R}^2$. Let A be the line segment from $(0,0)$ to (a,b) and let B be the line segment from $(0,0)$ to (c,d). Complete the parallelogram with sides A and B and vertices (a,b), $(0,0)$, (c,d) as shown in Figure 1.1. Show that $(a,b) + (c,d)$ is the fourth vertex of this parallelogram.

Figure 1.1

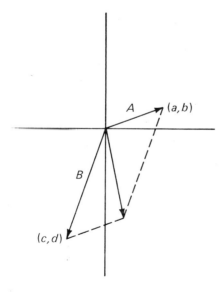

5   For every $(a,b) \in \mathbf{Q} \times \mathbf{Q}$ let $a * b$ be defined by

$$a * b = \begin{cases} a & \text{if } a > b \\ b & \text{if } b > a \\ a & \text{if } a = b \end{cases}$$

Then $a * b$ is the maximum of a and b.

a   Find $a * b$ for several values of a and b.

Justify your answers to the following questions:

b   Is $*$ a binary operation on $\mathbf{Q}$?

c   Is $*$ an associative operation?

d   Is $*$ a commutative operation?

6   For every $a, b \in \mathbf{Q}$ let

$$a \circ b = \frac{a+b}{k}$$

where k is a fixed positive integer. (If $k = 2$, $a \circ b$ is the average of a and b.) Justify your answers to the following questions:

a   Is $\circ$ a binary operation on $\mathbf{Q}$?

b   Is $\circ$ an associative operation?

c   Is $\circ$ a commutative operation?

d   For which values of k is $\circ$ a binary operation on $\mathbf{Z}$?

1.2 Groups

We have seen several examples of sets which have a binary operation which is at least associative though not always commutative. In fact, on the sets **R** of real numbers, **Q** of rational numbers, or **Z** of integers the binary operation of addition is associative, there is a zero element, and there are additive inverses (i.e., numbers $-a$ such that $a + (-a) = 0$). We wish to consider these properties first abstractly in the following definition and later through examples and deeper exploration.

13
Definition

A *group* $(G, \circ)$ is a set G with a binary operation $\circ$ which satisfies the following axioms:

a   The operation is associative: for every $a, b, c \in G$,

$$a \circ (b \circ c) = (a \circ b) \circ c$$

b   There exists an identity: there is an element $e \in G$ such that

$$e \circ a = a \circ e = a$$

for every $a \in G$.

c   There exist inverses: for every $a \in G$ there is an element $a' \in G$ such that

$$a \circ a' = a' \circ a = e$$

The element a' is called the *inverse* of a.

Note that there are four conditions which must be checked for any system $(G, \circ)$ which is thought to be a group. We give these conditions here as a check-list for any set G with a correspondence $(a, b) \to a \circ b$ defined on $G \times G$.

Checklist a
for
Group
Structure

Is the correspondence a binary operation on G? In particular, is G closed under $\circ$; that is, does $a \circ b$ belong to G for every $a, b \in G$? Occasionally the correspondence $\circ$ is not known to be a properly defined function. In that case it is necessary also to check that *exactly one* element of G is assigned to the pair (*a, b*) regardless of the names given to the elements *a* and *b*.

b   Is the operation associative? Is

$$a \circ (b \circ c) = (a \circ b) \circ c$$

for all $a, b, c \in G$?

c   Does there exist an identity? To show this it is necessary to find *one* element $e \in G$ such that $e \circ a = a \circ e = a$ for *every* $a \in G$. It is not enough to show that $e \circ a = a \circ e = a$ for a specific element of G.

d   Does every element of G have an inverse? This should be proved only after the identity has been found for the set G. To do so choose an arbitrary element $a \in G$ and then show that there exists an element $a' \in G$ such that $a \circ a' = a' \circ a = e$.

In Section 1.1 we considered the operations of addition, multiplication, and subtraction on **Z** and **R**. Now let us investigate whether or not the resulting systems are groups.

14

Problem   Determine which of the following systems are groups. Give reasons for your answers but do not attempt to prove any properties of **Z**, **Q**, and **R** under addition and multiplication. Wherever possible use properties from Appendix 3.

a   (**Z**, +)
b   (**Q**, +)
c   (**R**, +)
d   (**Z**, ·)
e   (**Q**, ·)
f   ($\mathbf{R}^{+}$, ·), where $\mathbf{R}^{+} = \{x: x \in \mathbf{R}, x > 0\}$
g   (**Z**, −), where − denotes the operation of subtraction
h   (**R** − {0}, /), where / denotes the operation of division

We have seen that some binary operations are commutative. If a group has a commutative binary operation, the group is given a special name.

15
Definition

A group $(G, \circ)$ is *commutative* or abelian if and only if the operation $\circ$ is commutative (that is, $a \circ b = b \circ a$ for every $a, b \in G$).

16
Problem

Which of the groups in Problem 14 are commutative groups? Justify your answers.

17
Problem

Let $M_2(\mathbf{R})$ be the set of all 2×2 matrices with the addition given in Definition 8. Prove or disprove that $(M_2(\mathbf{R}), +)$ is a group. Is it a commutative group? (See Problem 9.)

18
Problem

Answer the following questions using Definition 10 for multiplication in $M_2(\mathbf{R})$.

a   Is there an identity for multiplication in $M_2(\mathbf{R})$? If so, what is it?

b   Under what condition does a matrix in $M_2(\mathbf{R})$ have a multiplicative inverse? To answer this question find the multiplicative inverse of the matrix

$$\begin{pmatrix} a & b \\ c & d \end{pmatrix}$$

(if it exists) and complete the following statement: A matrix

$$\begin{pmatrix} a & b \\ c & d \end{pmatrix}$$

has a multiplicative inverse if and only if _____ _____. If

$$A = \begin{pmatrix} a & b \\ c & d \end{pmatrix}$$

then the multiplicative inverse, denoted by

$$\begin{pmatrix} a & b \\ c & d \end{pmatrix}^{-1} \text{ or } A^{-1}$$

is the matrix _____. ▲

(The symbol ▲ means that there is a hint for the problem. Hints for problems begin on page 320.)

19
Definition   A matrix which has a multiplicative inverse is said to be *non-singular*. A matrix which does not have a multiplicative inverse is said to be *singular*.

Using Problem 18 we see that a matrix

$$\begin{pmatrix} a & b \\ c & d \end{pmatrix}$$

is nonsingular if and only if it satisfies the condition _____.

20
Problem   Is $(M_2(\mathbf{R}), \cdot)$ a group? Explain.

Leave the proof of the following proposition for Exercise 4.

21
Proposition   Let $\mathscr{I}$ denote the set of all nonsingular 2×2 matrices. Then $(\mathscr{I}, \cdot)$ is a noncommutative group.

In Section 1.1 we saw that a binary operation can be defined by means of a table. Use the results of Problem 12 in the following problem.

22
Problem
Let $G = \{a, b, c, d\}$. Define a binary operation ∘ on G by means of Table 1.5.

a   Assuming that the operation is associative, determine whether or not $(G, \circ)$ is a group.

b   Is $(G, \circ)$ a commutative group?

Table 1.5

∘	a	b	c	d
a	a	b	c	d
b	b	c	d	a
c	c	d	a	b
d	d	a	b	c

23
Problem
Summarize your results. Make a list including each system considered in this section together with a statement of whether or not the system is a group. Which of the groups are not commutative?

EXERCISES 1   Determine which of the following subsets of **R** are groups under the usual addition of numbers. Justify your conclusions. (It will help you to list several elements of each set. Also see Exercise 1.1–2.)
a $\mathbf{Z}^+$, the set of all positive integers
*b The set of all even integers: $2\mathbf{Z} = \{2n: n \in \mathbf{Z}\}$
*c The set of all odd integers: $\{2n+1: n \in \mathbf{Z}\}$
d $\{\pm n^2: n \in \mathbf{Z}\}$
e $\{0\} \cup \{\pm 2^n: n \in \mathbf{Z}^+\}$

2   Determine which of the following sets are groups under the usual multiplication of numbers. Justify your conclusions.
*a $\mathbf{Q} - \{0\}$
*b $\mathbf{Q}^+ = \{x: x \in \mathbf{Q} \text{ and } x > 0\}$
c $\mathbf{Q}^- = \{x: x \in \mathbf{Q} \text{ and } x < 0\}$

d $\{\pm n^2 : n \in \mathbf{Z}^+\}$
e $\{2^n : n \in \mathbf{Z}\}$
f $\mathbf{R}$
*g $\mathbf{R} - \{0\}$
h $\mathbf{R}^- = \{x : x \in \mathbf{R} \text{ and } x < 0\}$

3a Is the set of all irrational numbers a group under addition?
    Explain.
b   Is the set of all irrational numbers a group under multiplica-
    tion? Justify your answer.

4   Prove that the set $\mathscr{I}$ of nonsingular 2×2 matrices is a non-
    commutative group under multiplication of matrices. In your
    proof it will be useful to employ the notation of determinants.
    For any matrix

$$A = \begin{pmatrix} a & b \\ c & d \end{pmatrix}$$

    the determinant of A, abbreviated $\det A$, is $ad - bc$. Problem
    18b asserts that a matrix A is nonsingular if and only if
    $\det A \neq 0$. ●

(The symbol ● indicates that there is a hint for the exercise. Hints for exercises
begin on page 323.)

*5 Let $\mathbf{Q}[\sqrt{2}] = \{a + b\sqrt{2} : a, b \in \mathbf{Q}\}$. Then $\mathbf{Q}[\sqrt{2}]$ is a subset
    of $\mathbf{R}$. You need to use this fact and the fact that $\sqrt{2}$ is
    irrational in the following problems:
a   Show that $a + b\sqrt{2} = c + d\sqrt{2}$, where $a, b, c, d \in \mathbf{Q}$, if and
    only if $a = c$ and $b = d$.
b   Since $\mathbf{Q}[\sqrt{2}]$ is a subset of $\mathbf{R}$, addition is defined for the
    elements of $\mathbf{Q}[\sqrt{2}]$. Is the addition of numbers a binary
    operation on $\mathbf{Q}[\sqrt{2}]$?
c   Prove or disprove that $(\mathbf{Q}[\sqrt{2}], +)$ is a group.

*6a Show that if · denotes the usual multiplication of real num-
    bers, then for every $a + b\sqrt{2}, c + d\sqrt{2} \in \mathbf{Q}[\sqrt{2}]$,

$$(a + b\sqrt{2}) \cdot (c + d\sqrt{2}) = \underline{\hspace{1cm}} + \underline{\hspace{1cm}}\sqrt{2}$$

    Be certain to show that the blanks are filled by rational
    numbers.

b   Prove or disprove that $(\mathbf{Q}[\sqrt{2}]-\{0\}, \cdot)$ is a group.

7   Let $G = \{m/7^n : m, n \in \mathbf{Z}$ and $n > 0\}$. Then G is a subset of $\mathbf{Q}$, and the usual addition and multiplication of numbers are defined on G.

a   Prove or disprove that $(G, +)$ is a group.

b   Prove or disprove that $(G-\{0\}, \cdot)$ is a group.

8   Let $G = \{m/p^n : m, n \in \mathbf{Z}$ and $n > 0\}$, where p is a fixed prime.

a   Prove or disprove that $(G, +)$ is a group.

b   Prove or disprove that $(G-\{0\}, \cdot)$ is a group.

*9   Let $G = \{a, b, c, d\}$ and define a binary operation $\circ$ on G by Table 1.6. (See Exercise 1.1–3.)

Table 1.6

$\circ$	a	b	c	d
a	a	b	c	d
b	b	a	d	c
c	c	d	a	b
d	d	c	b	a

a   Assuming that the operation is associative, prove that $(G, \circ)$ is a group. This group is known as Klein's Four-Group.

b   Is the operation commutative?

*10   Let $\mathbf{R}^2 = \mathbf{R} \times \mathbf{R}$ be the usual cartesian plane. A binary operation $+$ was defined in Exercise 1.1–4 by setting

$$(a, b) + (c, d) = (a+c, b+d)$$

for every $(a, b), (c, d) \in \mathbf{R}^2$. Is $(\mathbf{R}^2, +)$ a group? Justify your answer. You may use answers to Exercise 1.1–4.

1.3   Elementary Properties of Groups

In Section 1.2 we saw several examples of groups. In this section we establish a number of elementary properties which are true for any group $(G, \circ)$. Once these properties are proved in an arbitrary group, they can be used in any specific group. Hence this section indicates some of the power of abstract algebra: a theorem proved once in an arbitrary system can be used in any particular instance of this system.

In the work of this section you may want to use the following consequence of the definition of a binary operation:

**24
Proposition**
     If $(G, \circ)$ is a group, $w, x, y, z \in G$, $w = x$, and $y = z$, then $w \circ y = x \circ z$.

The proof of Proposition 24 follows immediately from the definition of a binary operation $\circ$ on G. Under this operation (w, y) is mapped onto $w \circ y$ and (x, z) is mapped onto $x \circ z$. Since $w = x$ and $y = z$, $(w, y) = (x, z)$. (Why?) Hence the images $w \circ y$ and $x \circ z$ are equal. (Why?)

**25
Problem**
     Let $(G, \circ)$ be a group. Prove the following propositions. Write each proof carefully with particular attention to such things as parentheses. Whenever possible use earlier results to prove later statements.

a   *Left Cancellation Law.* If $a, b, c \in G$ and $a \circ b = a \circ c$, then $b = c$.

b   *Right Cancellation Law.* If $a, b, c \in G$ and $a \circ c = b \circ c$, then $a = b$. (Why is it necessary to state two cancellation laws?)

c   The group $(G, \circ)$ has exactly one identity element. ▲

d   If $a \in G$, then a has exactly one inverse in G.

e   For every $a \in G$, $(a')' = $ _____ .

f   For every $a, b \in G$, $(a \circ b)' =$ _____. (Check your answer by finding the composite of $a \circ b$ and the proposed inverse.)

g   For every $a, b \in G$ there is exactly one element $x \in G$ such that $x \circ a = b$. The element $x =$ _____.   ▲

h   For every $a, b \in G$ there is exactly one $y \in G$ such that $a \circ y = b$. The element $y =$ _____.

26
Problem

Proposition g of Problem 25 can be reworded as follows: For every $a, b \in G$ the equation $x \circ a = b$ has exactly one solution $x =$ ____ $\in G$. Reword proposition h in this fashion.

We have seen several examples of groups such as $(\mathbf{Q} - \{0\}, \cdot)$, $(\mathbf{R} - \{0\}, \cdot)$, and $(\mathscr{I}, \cdot)$ in which the operation is called multiplication and is denoted by $\cdot$ or by juxtaposition. Any such group is called a *multiplicative group*. In a multiplicative group the identity element is written 1 or I and the inverse a' of an element a is denoted by a^{-1}.

We have also seen several examples of groups such as $(\mathbf{Q}, +)$, $(\mathbf{R}, +)$, and $(M_2(\mathbf{R}), +)$ in which the operation is called addition and is denoted by $+$. Such a group is called an *additive group*. In an additive group the identity element is written 0 and is called the zero element; the inverse a' of an element is denoted by $-a$.

Algebraists feel uncomfortable when a noncommutative operation is denoted by $+$ so we adopt the convention that the symbol $+$ is used for an operation only if the operation is commutative. Note, however, that $+$ is at times used for binary operations that are not like the usual addition in $\mathbf{Z}$, $\mathbf{Q}$, or $\mathbf{R}$ and that some commutative operations are denoted by symbols other than $+$.

27
Problem

Use the notational conventions mentioned above to translate the results of propositions g and h of Problem 25 as follows:

a   If $(G, \cdot)$ is a multiplicative group, write the solution of the equation $x \cdot a = b$. Then write the solution of the equation $a \cdot y = b$. Are the solutions x and y necessarily the same?

b   In the additive (and hence commutative) group $(G, +)$, write the solution of the equation $x + a = b$ and of the equation $a + y = b$. Is $x = y$?

Theorems 28 and 29 below show that the axioms of a group can be stated in several equivalent ways. The proofs of these theorems are difficult. Leave them for Exercises 7 and 8.

**28
Theorem**   Let G be a set with a binary operation $\circ$ which satisfies the following axioms:

a   The operation $\circ$ is associative.

b   There is an element $e \in G$, called the *left identity*, such that $e \circ a = a$ for every $a \in G$.

c   For every $a \in G$ there is an element $a' \in G$ such that $a' \circ a = e$. The element a' is called the *left inverse* of a.

Then $(G, \circ)$ is a group.

Naturally, there is a similar theorem involving the right identity and the right inverse.

**29
Theorem**   Let G be a set with a binary operation $\circ$ which satisfies the following axioms:

a   The operation $\circ$ is associative.

b   For every $a, b \in G$ the equation $x \circ a = b$ has a solution $x \in G$.

c   For every $a, b \in G$ the equation $a \circ y = b$ has a solution $y \in G$.

Then $(G, \circ)$ is a group.

EXERCISES 1   Let

$$A = \begin{pmatrix} 2 & 5 \\ 1 & 3 \end{pmatrix} \quad \text{and} \quad B = \begin{pmatrix} 1 & 2 \\ 3 & 4 \end{pmatrix}$$

Solve each of the equations $XA = B$ and $AY = B$ in the group of nonsingular 2×2 matrices. Do so by using the formula for the inverse of a matrix. Is $X = Y$?

2   In $M_2(\mathbf{R})$ let

$$A = \begin{pmatrix} 2 & 3 \\ 3 & 4 \end{pmatrix} \quad \text{and} \quad B = \begin{pmatrix} 1 & -1 \\ 0 & -2 \end{pmatrix}$$

Solve the following equations:
a $XA = B$
b $AY = B$
c $W + (A + W) = B$

3   Let $a = 1 + 2\sqrt{2}$ and $b = 3 + 4\sqrt{2}$. Solve the equation $x \cdot a = b$ in the group $(\mathbf{Q}[\sqrt{2}] - \{0\}, \cdot)$. (See Exercise 1.2–6.)

4   In a group $(G, \circ)$, are there any elements x such that $x \circ x = x$? What are they? Justify your answers.

*5   Prove that a group $(G, \circ)$ is commutative if and only if $(a \circ b) \circ (a \circ b) = (a \circ a) \circ (b \circ b)$ for every $a, b \in G$. (In a multiplicative group $(G, \cdot)$ the condition states that the square of a product is the product of the squares: $(ab)^2 = a^2 b^2$, where $a^2 = a \cdot a$, by definition.)

*6   Prove that if $(G, \circ)$ is a group and $x \circ x = e$ for every $x \in G$, then $(G, \circ)$ is a commutative group. Is the converse true? Why? ●

7   *Challenge.* Prove Theorem 28. To do so let $(G, \circ)$ be a set G with an associative binary operation such that (i) there exists a left identity $e \in G$ with $e \circ a = a$ for every $a \in G$ and (ii) every element $a \in G$ has a left inverse a' with $a' \circ a = e$. Prove that $(G, \circ)$ is a group by means of the following steps:
a   Prove that the left cancellation law holds in G.

    b   Prove that the left identity is actually an identity. (Prove that $a \circ e = a = e \circ a$.)

    c   Prove that every left inverse is actually an inverse. (Prove that $a \circ a' = e = a' \circ a$.)

8   *Challenge.* Prove Theorem 29. To do so let G be a set with an associative binary operation such that for every $a, b \in G$ there exist $x, y \in G$ with $x \circ a = b$ and $a \circ y = b$.

    a   Fix $b \in G$. Show that there exists an $e \in G$ such that $e \circ b = b$. Then show that e is a left identity for G. (Show that $e \circ a = a$ for *every* $a \in G$.)

    b   Show that $(G, \circ)$ is a group. To do so show that $(G, \circ)$ satisfies the hypotheses and hence the conclusion of Theorem 28.

1.4 A Binary Operation for Sets of Functions

We have seen examples of groups whose binary operations are a form of addition or multiplication. There are, however, less familiar binary operations for groups. One of these is composition of functions, which was previously met in the calculus. Before we construct new groups with the operation of composition, we consider some properties of functions. You may wish to review the definition of a function and the examples of functions and nonfunctions in Section 1.1.

30
Definition Two functions $f: X \to Y$ and $g: X \to Y$ are *equal* if and only if $f(x) = g(x)$ for every $x \in X$.

Note that Definition 30 states that equal functions must have the same domain and the same values.

We are interested in a particular class of functions, those which cannot map two or more elements of the domain onto a single element of the range and whose values in some sense cover all of the range. Much of this section and Section 1.5 are devoted to a study of functions with one or both of these properties.

31
Definition A function $f: X \to Y$ is *one-to-one* or *injective* if and only if the following condition holds:

For every $x_1, x_2 \in X$, if $x_1 \neq x_2$, then $f(x_1) \neq f(x_2)$.

In words, $f: X \to Y$ is one-to-one if and only if any two *distinct* elements of X have *distinct* images under f in Y. (See Figure 1.2.)

Figure 1.2

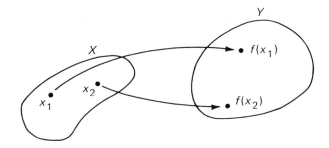

32

Problem

Each of the following functions has its rule specified by a table of values: $f: V \to U$ (Table 1.7), $g: U \to U$ (Table 1.8), $h: U \to V$ (Table 1.9), and $k: V \to V$ (Table 1.10). Determine whether or not each function is one-to-one. Let $U = \{1, 2, 3, 4\}$ and $V = \{1, 2, 3, 4, 5\}$.

Table 1.7 $f: V \to U$

v	$f(v)$
1	4
2	3
3	1
4	2
5	3

Table 1.8 $g: U \to U$

u	$g(u)$
1	2
2	4
3	1
4	3

Table 1.9 $h: U \to V$

u	$h(u)$
1	5
2	3
3	2
4	1

Table 1.10 $k: V \to V$

v	$k(v)$
1	5
2	3
3	1
4	2
5	1

It is often useful to work with another, equivalent, form of the definition of a one-to-one function: A function $f: X \to Y$ is one-to-one, or injective, if and only if the following condition holds:

A   For every $x_1, x_2 \in X$, if $f(x_1) = f(x_2)$, then _____.

(Use the results on logic given in Appendix 2 to write this equivalent form of the definition.)

To use condition A in proving that a particular function is one-to-one, assume $f(x_1) = f(x_2)$ and prove that $x_1 = x_2$.

We also need on occasion the negation of the definition of a one-to-one function:

B   A function f is not one-to-one if and only if _____

_____ .

33
Definition   A function $f: X \to Y$ maps X *onto* Y if and only if for every $y \in Y$ there exists $x \in X$ such that $f(x) = y$. If a function f maps X onto Y, we simply say at times that f is *onto* or *surjective*.

To prove that a particular function f maps X onto Y, begin with an arbitrary element $y \in Y$ and prove the existence of an element $x \in X$ such that $f(x) = y$. Sometimes it is possible to express x in terms of y.

34
Problem   Determine whether or not each of the functions in Problem 32 is surjective (onto).

35
Definition   Let $f: X \to Y$ be a function from X into Y. The set

$$f(X) = \{f(x): x \in X\}$$

is called the *image* of X under f or the *image set*.

36
Problem   Define $f: \mathbf{Z} \to \mathbf{Z}$ by $f(x) = 3x$ for every $x \in \mathbf{Z}$. Determine the elements of the image set $f(\mathbf{Z})$. Is the image set $f(\mathbf{Z})$ equal to the range $\mathbf{Z}$? Does f map $\mathbf{Z}$ onto $\mathbf{Z}$?

Leave the proof of the following proposition for Exercise 6.

37
Proposition   A function $f: X \to Y$ maps X onto Y if and only if $Y = f(X)$. In words, a function f is surjective if and only if the image of the domain is equal to the range.

On occasion we want to use the negation of the definition of a surjective (onto) function (see Figure 1.3):

C   A function $f: X \to Y$ does not map X onto Y (is not surjective) if and only if _____.

Figure 1.3

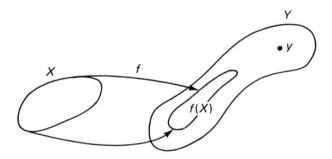

38
Problem   For each of the following functions the domain and the range are subsets of **R**. Determine whether or not each of these functions is one-to-one and/or onto. To justify your answers you may want to look at the graphs of these functions.

a $f: \mathbf{R} \to \mathbf{R}$ given by $f(x) = x^2$
b $f_1: \{x: x \geq 0\} \to \{x: x \geq 0\}$ given by $f_1(x) = x^2$
c $g: \mathbf{R} \to \mathbf{R}$ given by $g(x) = ax + b$, where a and b are fixed elements of **R** and $a \neq 0$

If $f: X \to Y$ and $g: Y \to Z$ are functions, then for every $x \in X$, $f(x) \in Y$ so that $g(f(x))$ is defined. We give the correspondence $x \to g(f(x))$ from X into Z a special name.

39
Definition

Let $f: X \to Y$ and $g: Y \to Z$ be functions. The *composite function*

$$g \circ f: X \to Z$$

is defined as follows: For every $x \in X$

$$(g \circ f)(x) = g(f(x))$$

The composite function $g \circ f$ is indicated in Figures 1.4 and 1.5.

Figure 1.4

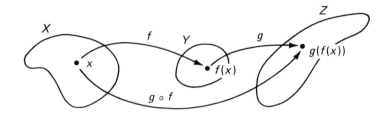

Figure 1.5

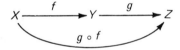

40
Problem

Let $f: V \to U$, $g: U \to U$, and $h: U \to V$ be the functions in Problem 32. Make tables of values for the composite functions $g \circ f: V \to U$ and $h \circ g: U \to V$.

41
Definition

For any nonempty set X, let $S(X)$ be the collection of all one-to-one functions from X *onto* itself.

$$f: X \to X$$

Note that a function f is in $S(X)$ if and only if f maps X *onto* X and f is *one-to-one*.

42
Problem   a

Let $X = \{1, 2, 3\}$. Determine which of the functions defined in Tables 1.11 through 1.14 are elements of $S(X)$.

Table 1.11

x	$f(x)$
1	3
2	1
3	2

Table 1.12

x	$g(x)$
1	3
2	3
3	2

Table 1.13

x	$h(x)$
1	2
2	4
3	1

Table 1.14

x	$k(x)$
1	2
2	1
3	3

b   Let $X = \mathbf{R}$. Let f, f_1, and g be the functions in Problem 38. Determine whether or not each of these functions is an element of $S(\mathbf{R})$.

The major result to be established in Sections 1.4 and 1.5 is that for any non-empty set X the collection $S(X)$ is a group under the operation of composition of functions. This result is proved with a series of lemmas which apply to elements of $S(X)$ and to other types of functions.

The following two lemmas are useful in proving that composition of functions is a binary operation on $S(X)$.

43
Problem   Prove the following lemma:

Lemma   Let $f: X \to Y$ and $g: Y \to Z$ be one-to-one functions. Then the composite function $g \circ f: X \to Z$ is one-to-one.

44
Problem   Prove the following lemma:

Lemma   If $f: X \to Y$ and $g: Y \to Z$ are functions such that f maps X onto Y and g maps Y onto Z, then $g \circ f$ maps X onto Z.

45
Problem   Prove that composition is a binary operation on $S(X)$.

Let $f: W \to X$, $g: X \to Y$, and $h: Y \to Z$ be functions. There are two natural ways to form a composite function from W into Z, as indicated in Figures 1.6 and 1.7. Complete Figure 1.7 with the appropriate arrows and letters.

Figure 1.6

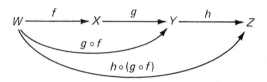

Figure 1.7

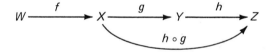

46
Problem   Prove the following lemma:

Lemma   *Associative Law for Composition of Functions.* Let $f: W \to X$, $g: X \to Y$, and $h: Y \to Z$ be functions. Then

$$h \circ (g \circ f) = (h \circ g) \circ f \quad \blacktriangle$$

47
Corollary   Composition of functions is an associative binary operation on the set $S(X)$ of all one-to-one functions which map X onto itself.

In Section 1.5 we prove that $S(X)$ actually is a group under the operation of composition of functions.

EXERCISES   1   For each of the following functions the domain and the range are subsets of $\mathbf{R}$. Determine whether or not each of these functions is one-to-one and/or onto.

     a $f: \mathbf{R}-\{0\} \to \mathbf{R}$ given by $f(x) = 1/x$

     b $f_1: \{x: x > 0\} \to \{x: x > 0\}$ given by $f_1(x) = 1/x$

     c $g: \{x: 0 < x < 1\} \to \{x: x > 0\}$ given by $g(x) = x/(1-x)$

2   Let $f: V \to U$, $g: U \to U$, and $h: U \to V$ be the functions in Problem 32. Using the tables from Problems 32 and 40, evaluate $[h \circ (g \circ f)](v)$ and $[(h \circ g) \circ f](v)$ for every $v \in V$.

3a   For the function $f_1: \{x: x > 0\} \to \{x: x > 0\}$ given by $f_1(x) = 1/x$, find $(f_1 \circ f_1)(x)$ for every $x > 0$.

     b   Let $X = \{x: 0 < x < 1\}$ and $Y = \{x: x > 0\}$. Define functions $g: X \to Y$ and $h: Y \to X$ by setting

$$g(x) = \frac{x}{1-x} \qquad \text{for } 0 < x < 1 \qquad \text{and}$$

$$h(y) = \frac{y}{1+y} \qquad \text{for } y > 0$$

Find $(g \circ h)(x)$, $(h \circ g)(x)$, and $(h \circ f_1)(x)$ for $0 < x < 1$, where f_1 is the function defined in part a.

4   Define $f: \mathbf{R} \to \mathbf{R}$ and $g: \mathbf{R} \to \mathbf{R}$ by $f(x) = x^2$ and $g(x) = ax + b$ for every $x \in \mathbf{R}$, where $a, b \in \mathbf{R}$ are fixed and $a \neq 0$. Define $h: \mathbf{R}-\{0\} \to \mathbf{R}$ by $h(x) = 1/x$ for every $x \in \mathbf{R}-\{0\}$. Verify by computation that $[f \circ (g \circ h)](x) = [(f \circ g) \circ h](x)$ for every $x \in \mathbf{R}-\{0\}$.

*5   Let $\mathbf{R}^2 = \mathbf{R} \times \mathbf{R}$. Then $\mathbf{R}^2$ is a commutative group with the addition defined by

$$(a, b) + (c, d) = (a+c, b+d)$$

for every $(a, b), (c, d) \in \mathbf{R}^2$. (See Exercise 1.2–10.)

     a   Let $f: \mathbf{R}^2 \to \mathbf{R}^2$ and $g: \mathbf{R}^2 \to \mathbf{R}^2$ be defined by setting

$$f(x, y) = (ax + by, cx + dy) \qquad \text{and}$$

$$g(x, y) = (a_1 x + b_1 y, c_1 x + d_1 y)$$

where $a, b, c, d, a_1, b_1, c_1, d_1 \in \mathbf{R}$. Find $(f \circ g)(x, y)$.

b To each function $f: \mathbf{R}^2 \to \mathbf{R}^2$ defined as in part a we assign a matrix

$$A_f = \begin{pmatrix} a & b \\ c & d \end{pmatrix}$$

Thus a matrix

$$A = \begin{pmatrix} a & b \\ c & d \end{pmatrix} \in M_2(\mathbf{R})$$

is assigned to a function $f: \mathbf{R}^2 \to \mathbf{R}^2$ if and only if

$$f(x, y) = (ax + by, cx + dy)$$

Let $f, g: \mathbf{R}^2 \to \mathbf{R}^2$ be the functions defined in part a. Let A_f and A_g be the corresponding matrices. Find the matrix $A_{f \circ g}$ which corresponds to the composite $f \circ g$. Show how $A_{f \circ g}$ is related to the matrices A_f and A_g. What can you say now about the motivation for the definition of matrix multiplication?

6 Prove Proposition 37.

7 Let $f: X \to Y$ and $g: Y \to Z$ be functions.
a Prove that if $g \circ f$ is one-to-one, then f is one-to-one.
b Either prove the converse of part a or find a counterexample to the converse.
c Give an example of functions $f: X \to Y$ and $g: Y \to Z$ such that g is not one-to-one and $g \circ f$ is one-to-one.

8 Let $f: X \to Y$ and $g: Y \to Z$ be functions.
a Prove that if $g \circ f$ is onto, then g is onto.
b Either prove the converse of part a or find a counterexample to the converse.
c Give an example of functions $f: X \to Y$ and $g: Y \to Z$ such that f is not onto and $g \circ f$ is onto.

9 For every positive integer n let

$$B_n = \{1, 2, \ldots, n\} = \{i: i \in \mathbf{Z} \text{ and } 1 \leq i \leq n\}$$

Answer the following questions. No proofs are required but plausibility arguments should be given.

a   Let $k < n$. Is there a function mapping B_k onto B_n?
b   Let $k < n$. Is there a one-to-one function from B_n into B_k?
c   Is there a function $f: B_n \to B_n$ which is one-to-one but not onto?
d   Is there a function $f: B_n \to B_n$ which is onto but not one-to-one?

1.5 Permutation Groups

We saw in Section 1.4 that the set $S(X)$ of all one-to-one functions from a set X onto itself has an associative binary operation, namely the operation of composition of functions. If this set is to be a group under that operation, then it must contain an identity function and every element of $S(X)$ must have an inverse under the operation of composition.

48

Problem

Let X be a nonempty set. Show that the set $S(X)$ has an identity element, i.e., a function e such that $e \in S(X)$ and $f \circ e = e \circ f = f$ for every $f \in S(X)$. To do so you must define a function $e: X \to X$ such that

$$(f \circ e)(x) = (e \circ f)(x) = f(x)$$

for all $x \in X$ and show that $e \in S(X)$.

Now let us fix an element $f \in S(X)$. If f has an inverse $f^{-1} \in S(X)$, then $f \circ f^{-1} = f^{-1} \circ f = e$ so that

$$(f \circ f^{-1})(x) = (f^{-1} \circ f)(x) = e(x) = \underline{\quad x \quad}$$

for every $x \in X$. Specifically, this means that

$$f^{-1}(f(x)) = \underline{\quad x \quad}$$

for every $x \in X$. Hence f^{-1} must return the element $f(x) \in X$ to the element $x \in X$.

Let $f: X \to Y$ be a function which is both one-to-one and onto. Then for any given element $y \in Y$ there is some element $x \in X$ such that $f(x) = y$. (Why?) In fact, there is only one element $x \in X$ such that $f(x) = y$. (Why?) It seems natural to define $f^{-1}(y) = x$ so that f^{-1} "retraces the path" from y back to x. Since f is both one-to-one and onto, it immediately follows that the rule f^{-1} defined in this way is a function from Y into X. (See Figure 1.8.)

49

Definition

If $f: X \to Y$ is one-to-one and onto, an *inverse function* $f^{-1}: Y \to X$ is defined as follows: For any given $y \in Y$, $f^{-1}(y)$ is the unique element $x \in X$ such that $f(x) = y$. Thus $f^{-1}(y) = x$ if and only if $f(x) = y$.

Figure 1.8

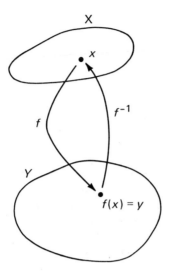

50
Problem   Find an inverse function for each function in Problem 32
                 which is both one-to-one and onto. (Note that not every
                 function has an inverse.)

We have already found an identity function $e \in S(X)$. Now we must prove that
if $f \in S(X)$, then the function f^{-1} defined above is truly an inverse and an element
of $S(X)$. This is the content of the following two lemmas.

51
Problem   Prove the following lemma:

Lemma   If f is a one-to-one function from X onto Y, then $f^{-1}(f(x)) = x$
                 for every $x \in X$ and $f(f^{-1}(y)) = y$ for every $y \in Y$.

Leave the proof of the following lemma for Exercise 6.

52
Lemma   If f is a one-to-one function from X onto Y, then f^{-1} is a one-
                 to-one function from Y onto X.

We have seen that composition of functions is an associative binary operation on $S(X)$. Let us combine this result with the work of this section to prove that $(S(X), \circ)$ is a group.

53
Problem

Use previous results including Lemmas 51 and 52 to prove the following theorem:

Theorem

Let $S(X)$ be the collection of all one-to-one functions which map a nonempty set X onto itself. Then $S(X)$ is a group with the operation of composition of functions.

Thus for each nonempty set X we have constructed a group $S(X)$ whose elements are one-to-one functions from X onto itself. We are particularly interested in the groups $S(X)$ when X is a finite set. For each positive integer n let

$$S_n = S(\{1, 2, ..., n\})$$

Then S_n is a group under the operation of composition of functions. For examples of elements of S_3 see Problem 42.

54
Definition

A *permutation* of a nonempty set is a one-to-one function from this set onto itself.

The group S_n of all permutations of $\{1, 2, ..., n\}$ is called the *full symmetric group* on the set $\{1, 2, ..., n\}$.

Remember that S_n is the collection of all permutations of the set $\{1, 2, ..., n\}$; it is *not* the set $\{1, 2, ..., n\}$ itself.

In working with permutations on finite sets it is quite useful and customary to employ a special two-line notation to designate the rule for a permutation. Let f be an element of S_n with $f(1) = a_1$, $f(2) = a_2$, ..., $f(n) = a_n$. In the two-line notation the function f is written

$$f = \begin{pmatrix} 1 & 2 & \cdots & n \\ a_1 & a_2 & \cdots & a_n \end{pmatrix}$$

In this notation the image $f(k) = a_k$ is written on the second line directly below k.

55

Problem   Let f be the function defined on $\{1,2,3,4\}$ by the rule $f(1) = 3$, $f(2) = 4$, $f(3) = 1$, and $f(4) = 2$. Thus $f \in S_4$. Write f in the two-line notation.

In computing a composite of two functions in S_n, remember that $(f \circ g)(k) = f(g(k))$ for every $k \in \{1, 2, ..., n\}$. For example, in S_4 let

$$f = \begin{pmatrix} 1 & 2 & 3 & 4 \\ 3 & 4 & 1 & 2 \end{pmatrix} \quad \text{and} \quad g = \begin{pmatrix} 1 & 2 & 3 & 4 \\ 3 & 1 & 2 & 4 \end{pmatrix}$$

In finding

$$f \circ g = \begin{pmatrix} 1 & 2 & 3 & 4 \\ 3 & 4 & 1 & 2 \end{pmatrix} \circ \begin{pmatrix} 1 & 2 & 3 & 4 \\ 3 & 1 & 2 & 4 \end{pmatrix}$$

one starts computing with the function on the right to obtain $(f \circ g)(1) = f(g(1)) = f(3) = 1$.

56

Problem   Compute $f \circ g$ for the functions f and g above and express your answer in the two-line notation

$$f \circ g = \begin{pmatrix} 1 & 2 & 3 & 4 \\ 1 & & & \end{pmatrix}$$

Then compute $g \circ f$. Is $f \circ g = g \circ f$?

Note that the function

$$f = \begin{pmatrix} 1 & 2 & 3 & 4 \\ 3 & 4 & 1 & 2 \end{pmatrix}$$

can be written in many ways in the two-line notation by rearranging the order of the entries on the top line. Thus

$$f = \begin{pmatrix} 1 & 2 & 3 & 4 \\ 3 & 4 & 1 & 2 \end{pmatrix} = \begin{pmatrix} 2 & 1 & 3 & 4 \\ 4 & 3 & 1 & 2 \end{pmatrix} = \begin{pmatrix} 4 & 3 & 2 & 1 \\ 2 & 1 & 4 & 3 \end{pmatrix}$$

and so on. Why do all of these expressions stand for the same function?

57

Problem   Use the two-line notation to list all the elements of S_3. How many elements are in S_3?

Before working Problem 58 you may want to review the conventions for operation tables given in Section 1.1.

58

Problem   Begin an operation table for $(S_3, \circ)$. For uniformity we have specified in Table 1.15 the arrangement of elements across the top line. Compute the entries in the first three rows and the first two columns of Table 1.15 and leave the rest for homework. Be careful with the order of composition of the elements. For example, note the entry given in the table.

59

Problem   Find an identity element for $(S_3, \circ)$ and find an inverse for every $f \in S_3$. Is $(S_3, \circ)$ commutative? ▲

We have seen that for every positive integer n, $(S_n, \circ)$ is a group. Now let us determine how large the groups S_n are and show that these groups give us other examples of noncommutative groups.

60

Problem   Let n be a fixed positive integer. How many elements are in the group S_n? Why?

61

Problem   Prove that for every integer $n \geq 3$ the group $(S_n, \circ)$ is not commutative. ▲

Composition of permutations provides us with a binary operation quite different from the multiplication and addition of numbers and matrices seen so far. We have seen that when X has three or more elements, the group $S(X)$ (or S_n) is noncommutative. Moreover, by varying the number of elements in X we obtain numerous different groups. These provide us with many useful examples and counterexamples in our study of the properties of groups in general.

Table 1.15

$\circ$	$\begin{pmatrix}1&2&3\\1&2&3\end{pmatrix}$	$\begin{pmatrix}1&2&3\\2&3&1\end{pmatrix}$	$\begin{pmatrix}1&2&3\\3&1&2\end{pmatrix}$	$\begin{pmatrix}1&2&3\\1&3&2\end{pmatrix}$	$\begin{pmatrix}1&2&3\\3&2&1\end{pmatrix}$	$\begin{pmatrix}1&2&3\\2&1&3\end{pmatrix}$
$\begin{pmatrix}1&2&3\\1&2&3\end{pmatrix}$				$\begin{pmatrix}1&2&3\\2&1&3\end{pmatrix}$		
$\begin{pmatrix}1&2&3\\2&3&1\end{pmatrix}$						

EXERCISES 1 Make an operation table for $(S_2, \circ)$. Is this group commutative?

2 Complete the operation table for $(S_3, \circ)$ and check your results at the next class meeting.

3 The operation table for S_3 is used later to illustrate many concepts in group theory. For this reason it is convenient to employ letter names for the permutations. Reconstruct Table 1.15 for S_3 using the letter names $e, \alpha_1, \alpha_2, \beta_1, \beta_2, \beta_3$ in that order, as indicated in Table 1.16. Check your results in class.

Table 1.16

$\circ$	e	α_1	α_2	β_1	β_2	β_3
e						
α_1						
α_2						
β_1						
β_2						
β_3						

4 In S_4 consider the collection $\overline{S}_3$ of all permutations which leave the element 4 fixed. Any such permutation in $\overline{S}_3$ has the form

$$\begin{pmatrix} 1 & 2 & 3 & 4 \\ a & b & c & 4 \end{pmatrix}$$

where a, b, c are distinct elements of the set $\{1, 2, 3\}$.

a How many elements are in $\overline{S}_3$?

b Describe a simple way to construct an operation table for $\overline{S}_3$. (Don't write out the entire table.)

5 We already know that $(S_n, \circ)$ is a group for every fixed integer $n \geq 1$. Let us illustrate some of the group axioms using the two-line notation.

a To show that S_n is closed under composition, compute

$$\begin{pmatrix} a_1 & a_2 & \cdots & a_n \\ b_1 & b_2 & \cdots & b_n \end{pmatrix} \circ \begin{pmatrix} 1 & 2 & \cdots & n \\ a_1 & a_2 & \cdots & a_n \end{pmatrix}$$

b   The identity element of S_n is

$$\Bigg(\hspace{4cm} \Bigg)$$

c   If

$$f = \begin{pmatrix} 1 & 2 & \cdots & n \\ a_1 & a_2 & \cdots & a_n \end{pmatrix},$$

then

$$f^{-1} = \Bigg(\hspace{3cm} \Bigg)$$

6   Prove Lemma 52.

7   Find an inverse function for each of the following functions which is one-to-one and onto. (See Exercise 1.4–1.)
a $f: \mathbf{R} - \{0\} \to \mathbf{R}$ given by $f(x) = 1/x$
b $f_1: \{x: x > 0\} \to \{x: x > 0\}$ given by $f_1(x) = 1/x$
c $g: \{x: 0 < x < 1\} \to \{x: x > 0\}$ given by $g(x) = x/(1-x)$

8   Let f be a one-to-one function from X onto Y. Let $g: Y \to X$ be a function such that $(g \circ f)(x) = x$ for every $x \in X$. Prove that $g = f^{-1}$. This shows that the inverse of a function is unique.

9   Let $f: X \to Y$ and $g: Y \to X$ be functions such that $(g \circ f)(x) = x$ for every $x \in X$ and $(f \circ g)(y) = y$ for every $y \in Y$.
a   Prove that f is a one-to-one function from X onto Y.
b   Prove that $g = f^{-1}$.

*10   Let $(G, *)$ be a group. Let X be a nonempty set and let $F(X, G)$ be the collection of all functions $f: X \to G$. For every pair $f, g \in F(X, G)$ define $f * g: X \to G$ by setting

$$(f * g)(x) = f(x) * g(x)$$

a Let $X = \{x: x \in \mathbf{R}, 0 \leq x \leq 1\}$ and let $(\mathbf{R}, +)$ be the group. Then $F(X, \mathbf{R})$ is the collection of all real-valued functions whose domain is the interval $[0, 1]$. In this case the operation on $F(X, \mathbf{R})$ is the usual operation of pointwise addition of functions. For example, let

$$f(x) = x^3 + 3x + 1 \qquad \text{and} \qquad g(x) = 2x^2 - 2x + 1$$

for $0 \leq x \leq 1$. Find $f + g$.

Define a function $O: X \to \mathbf{R}$ such that $f + O = f$ for every $f \in F(X, \mathbf{R})$: $O(x) = \underline{\hspace{2cm}}$ for $x \in [0, 1]$.

For $f \in F(X, \mathbf{R})$ define a function $f' \in F(X, \mathbf{R})$ such that $f + f' = O$.

b Let X be a nonempty set and $(G, *)$ a group. Show that if f and g are functions from X into G, then $f * g$ is a function from X into G. Show that the correspondence $(f, g) \to f * g$ defines a binary operation $*$ on $F(X, G)$.

c Prove that if X is a nonempty set and $(G, *)$ is a group, then $(F(X, G), *)$ is a group, where $*$ is the operation defined above on $F(X, G)$.

1.6   Groups of Symmetries of Geometrical Figures

Certain collections of permutations can be pictured as symmetries, or rigid motions, of a regular geometrical figure. These motions carry vertices of the figure onto vertices. In any rigid motion, or symmetry, the figure (for example, a square or an equilateral triangle) cannot be cut or bent or distorted out of shape in any way. It may, however, be turned over or rotated so long as vertices are carried onto vertices.

Let us study the symmetries of a square.

For convenience in visualizing the symmetries of a square, use a cardboard or paper square with its vertices labeled counterclockwise, as shown in Figure 1.9. At each vertex write the same number on both sides of the cardboard square.

Figure 1.9

Trace the square on a sheet of paper or the blackboard and label the positions of the vertices of this sketch, as shown in Figure 1.10.

Figure 1.10
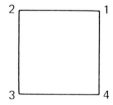

Place the cardboard square on top of the traced square, with like-numbered vertices matched, as shown in Figure 1.11. Now rotate the cardboard 90° counterclockwise (until vertices correspond again). (See Figure 1.12.)

Figure 1.11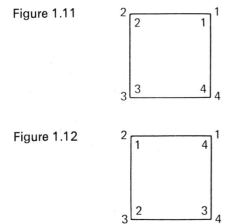

Figure 1.12

In this rotation a vertex has been carried from position 1 into position 2, another vertex from position 2 into position 3, etc. Thus this rotation, which we call ρ_1, can be described by the permutation

$$\rho_1 = \begin{pmatrix} 1 & 2 & 3 & 4 \\ 2 & 3 & 4 & 1 \end{pmatrix}$$

(The Greek letter ρ, rho, denotes a rotation.)

Continue rotating the square counterclockwise, sketching the result after each rotation. Write down the permutation corresponding to each rotation. Label these new permutations in turn ρ_2, ρ_3, etc. Let e denote the permutation for the initial position (Figure 1.11). *Save all sketches for later use!*

Now revolve the square around the diagonal joining vertices 1 and 3 to obtain Figure 1.13. Write down the corresponding permutation, which we label δ_1. (The Greek letter δ, delta, designates a revolution about a diagonal.) What is the result of performing this revolution again, starting with the position of Figure 1.13?

Figure 1.13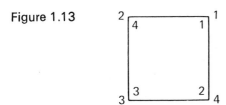

Starting in the initial position (Figure 1.11), revolve the square around the diagonal joining vertices 2 and 4. Sketch the result and write down the corresponding permutation, which we label δ_2. What is the result of continuing this revolution around the diagonal?

62

Problem   Find the remaining symmetries of the square. Describe each motion, draw a picture showing the result of performing the motion, and write each symmetry in permutation notation.

63

Problem   Show that there are exactly _____ symmetries of the square. ▲

The composite or product, $x \circ y$, of two symmetries x and y is defined by first performing y and then performing x on that result. This agrees with our notation for the composition of permutations.

Caution   In finding any composite $x \circ y$ always begin with the square in its initial position.

64

Problem   Begin an operation table for the symmetries of the square. For consistency ask your teacher to assign a letter name to each of your symmetries and to specify the order of elements in the top line of the operation table. Use the letters e, ρ, δ, and μ (mu, for mirror image) with suitable subscripts attached.

Compute the entries in the first four rows and the first two columns of Table 1.17 and leave the rest for homework. In making the table use movements of your cardboard square. To find the composite of two motions, simply perform the motions in succession, always beginning with the square in its initial position (Figure 1.11). Then compare the result with the pictures you have made of the motions. If you wish, check some of your answers by computing composites of permutations.

Table 1.17   Composition Table for the Symmetries of the Square

∘ |
_____

65
Problem   Let D_4 denote the set of all symmetries of the square. Prove that $(D_4, \circ)$ is a group. Is this group commutative?

We have now seen that the collection of all symmetries of the square is a group under the operation of composition. In fact, for any regular plane polygon with n sides, the collection D_n of all symmetries forms a group under composition. This is the essence of the exercises.

EXERCISES 1   Complete the operation table for the symmetries of the square (see Problem 64) and check your results at the next class meeting.

2   Let D_3 be the set of all symmetries of an equilateral triangle.

a   With pictures and words describe each symmetry in D_3. Then write each symmetry in permutation notation.

b   Make an operation table for D_3 and prove that $(D_3, \circ)$ is a group. Is it a commutative group?

3   Let D_5 be the set of symmetries of a regular pentagon. Describe the elements of D_5 and prove that $(D_5, \circ)$ is a group.

4   Let D_6 be the set of symmetries of a regular hexagon. Describe the elements of D_6 and prove that $(D_6, \circ)$ is a group.

*5   *Challenge.* Let $n \geq 3$ be a fixed integer. Let D_n be the set of all symmetries of a regular plane figure with n sides.

a   Describe the elements of D_n. You will need to consider cases with n even and with n odd.   ●

b   How many elements are in D_n?

c   Show that $(D_n, \circ)$ is a group.   ●

d   Show that for every $n \geq 3$, D_n is not a commutative group.   ●

6   We shall consider the set of symmetries for one nonregular plane figure, namely a general rectangle. With pictures and words describe each symmetry for a general rectangle. Then write each symmetry in permutation notation. Make a composition table and show that the set of all symmetries of a rectangle is a group under the operation of composition.

1.7 Congruence Modulo n

As any clock watcher knows, clocks operate on an unusual counting system. A clock hand moves around the dial from 1 to 12 and then, instead of going on to 13, starts over again at 1. So far as the clock is concerned, 1 A.M. and 1 P.M., whether yesterday, today, tomorrow or 30 days ago, are all the same. Thus the clock gives us one example of the mathematical notion of congruence modulo n (in the special case $n = 12$).

The section requires familiarity with equivalence relations and with divisibility notation and the division algorithm (see Appendixes 4 and 6).

66
Definition

Let n be a positive integer. Two integers a and b are said to be *congruent modulo n* if and only if their difference $a - b$ is divisible by n. This means that a is congruent to b modulo n if and only if there exists an integer k such that $b - a = kn$. In symbols we write $a \equiv b \pmod{n}$ if and only if $n \mid (b - a)$.

For the definition with $n = 0$ see Exercise 1.8–5.

67
Problem

Choose values for a, b, and n to obtain several examples of $a \equiv b \pmod{n}$.

If integers a and b are not congruent modulo n, we write $a \not\equiv b \pmod{n}$.

68
Problem

Give several examples in which $a \not\equiv b \pmod{n}$.

The following two problems show that congruence modulo n behaves much like equality.

69
Problem

Prove the following lemma:

Lemma

The relation of congruence modulo n in **Z** is an equivalence relation.

First state the reflexive, symmetric, and transitive properties for congruence modulo n (see Definition 1 in Appendix 4) and then prove that they hold for this relation.

70
Problem

Prove the following lemma as directed in part a.

Lemma

Let $a, b, c \in$ **Z** with $a \equiv b \pmod{n}$. Then

$$a + c \equiv b + c \pmod{n}$$
$$ac \equiv bc \pmod{n} \qquad \text{and}$$
$$-a \equiv -b \pmod{n}$$

Moreover, if $a, b, c, d \in$ **Z** with $a \equiv b \pmod{n}$ and $c \equiv d \pmod{n}$, then

$$a + c \equiv b + d \pmod{n} \qquad \text{and}$$
$$ac \equiv bd \pmod{n}$$

a   Prove the first statement $(a + c \equiv b + c \pmod{n})$. The proofs of the remaining statements are left for Exercise 2.

b   State the results of the lemma in words. For example, any integer can be added to both members of a congruence and the congruence is preserved.

Whenever we have an equivalence relation we can form equivalence classes. These classes are given a special name for congruence modulo n.

71
Definition

Let n be a fixed positive integer. For every $a \in$ **Z**, let

$$a_n = \{x : x \in \mathbf{Z} \text{ and } x \equiv a \pmod{n}\}$$

Note that each class a_n is just the equivalence class to which the element a belongs.

72

Problem   a   In the class

$$0_5 = \{x: x \in \mathbf{Z} \text{ and } x \equiv 0 \,(\text{mod } 5)\}$$

find several positive elements and several negative elements. Develop a formula which generates all elements of the class. Illustrate the class on the number line. How many elements are there in the class 0_5?

b   Find several positive and several negative elements of the class 1_5. State a formula that gives all elements of the class.

c   Continue describing classes for congruence modulo 5 until every integer belongs to one of the classes. How many classes are necessary? Do any of the classes have common elements? Explain.

Recall that two equivalence classes are equal if they have at least one element in common.

73

Problem   a   List several elements of each of the classes $(-4)_5, 1_5, 6_5, 11_5$. Show that these classes are actually the same, that is,

$$(-4)_5 = 1_5 = 6_5 = 11_5$$

Thus the symbols $(-4)_5, 1_5, 6_5, 11_5$ are just different names for the same class.

b   Find several values of $b \in \mathbf{Z}$ such that $b_5 = 2_5$.

For each of the following lemmas try to construct a very short proof which uses properties of an equivalence relation. You may wish to use Theorem 6 in Appendix 4. In both problems let n be a fixed positive integer.

74

Problem   Complete the statement and prove the following lemma.

Lemma   For every $a, b \in \mathbf{Z}$, $a_n = b_n$ if and only if _____ .

75

Problem   Prove the following lemma:

Lemma   If $a, b \in \mathbf{Z}$ and $a_n \cap b_n \neq \varnothing$, then $a_n = b_n$.

Lemma 75 shows that if $a_n \neq b_n$, then $a_n \cap b_n = \varnothing$. Thus two different classes, a_n and b_n, can have no common elements.

We have seen that an equivalence class such as 1_5 has many names (for example, $(-4)_5$, 6_5, 11_5, and so on). It is frequently useful to specify a class by means of its smallest nonnegative element (for example, 1_5 in Problem 73a). In order to do this for an arbitrary class a_n, we can use the division algorithm to find the remainder when a is divided by n. This remainder is the number we seek.

76

Problem   Let $a \in \mathbf{Z}$ and let n be a positive integer. Prove that if $a = nq + r$ and $0 \leq r < n$, then $a_n = r_n$.

This number r, the remainder when a is divided by n, is actually the smallest nonnegative element of a_n. (See Exercise 4.)

77

Problem   For a fixed positive integer n, how many distinct equivalence classes are there? List these classes, starting with 0_n. Use Problem 76 to show that every equivalence class a_n appears somewhere in your list.

EXERCISES 1   For every equivalence class

$$a_6 = \{x : x \in \mathbf{Z} \text{ and } x \equiv a \;(\mathrm{mod}\, 6)\}$$

in $\mathbf{Z}_6$ find several positive elements and several negative elements. Develop a formula which gives all the elements of the class a_6 and then illustrate each class on the number line.

2   Finish the proof of Lemma 70.

*3   Consider the following cancellation property: If $ac \equiv bc \pmod{n}$ and $c \not\equiv 0 \pmod{n}$, then $a \equiv b \pmod{n}$.

a   Illustrate the cancellation property when $n = 5$.

b   Investigate the cancellation property when $n = 6$. Does this property hold? Explain.

c   Give a counterexample to the cancellation property with $n = 10$.

d   Prove that the cancellation property holds if n is a prime. ●

4   Let n be a fixed positive integer and $a \in \mathbf{Z}$. Show that if $a = nq + r$, $0 \le r < n$, then r is the smallest nonnegative element of the class a_n. ●

5   Let n be a fixed positive integer and $a, b \in \mathbf{Z}$. Prove that $a \equiv b \pmod{n}$ if and only if the remainder when a is divided by n is the same as the remainder when b is divided by n.

1.8   The Additive Groups $\mathbf{Z}_n$

We have now seen that for a fixed positive integer n an equivalence relation known as congruence modulo n can be defined. In this section we continue our study of the equivalence classes of this relation. First we want to consider the collection of all these classes for a fixed integer n and then define an "addition" of classes to build a new group.

78
Definition
For any fixed positive integer n let $\mathbf{Z}_n$ be the collection of all distinct equivalence classes a_n with $a \in \mathbf{Z}$:

$$\mathbf{Z}_n = \{a_n : a \in \mathbf{Z}\}$$

Note that every element of $\mathbf{Z}_n$ is an *equivalence class* (with many different names), not a number.

79
Problem
a   List the distinct elements of $\mathbf{Z}_5$, of $\mathbf{Z}_6$, of $\mathbf{Z}_7$.

b   List the distinct elements of $\mathbf{Z}_n$ with n fixed. Is $\mathbf{Z}_n$ a finite set or an infinite set?

80
Definition
Let n be a fixed positive integer. For every $a, b \in \mathbf{Z}$ the sum $a_n + b_n$ of the classes $a_n, b_n \in \mathbf{Z}_n$ is the equivalence class of the integer sum $a + b$. Thus

$$a_n + b_n = (a+b)_n$$

81
Problem
Use Definition 80 to compute $3_5 + 4_5$, $3_6 + 4_6$, and $3_7 + 4_7$.

We must prove that the addition on $\mathbf{Z}_n$ given in Definition 80 is a properly defined binary operation. It is clear that the correspondence $(a_n, b_n) \to (a+b)_n$ maps the pair (a_n, b_n) onto an element of $\mathbf{Z}_n$. However, since the elements of $\mathbf{Z}_n$ have many names, it is not immediately obvious that the correspondence is a function. It is necessary to prove that the correspondence maps each pair (a_n, b_n) onto exactly one element of $\mathbf{Z}_n$, regardless of the names chosen for a_n and b_n. For example, we know that $2_5 = 1027_5$ and $4_5 = 2134_5$. (Why?) If addition, as defined above, is a binary operation, then we must have

$$(2+4)_5 = (1027 + 2134)_5$$

82

Problem   a   Use Definition 80 to calculate $2_5 + 4_5$ and $1027_5 + 2134_5$. Are the answers the same?

          b   Show that $2_5 = (-8)_5$ and $3_5 = 18_5$. Use Definition 80 to find $2_5 + 3_5$ and $(-8)_5 + 18_5$. Are the answers the same?

83

Problem   To prove that addition is a properly defined function from $\mathbf{Z}_n \times \mathbf{Z}_n$ into $\mathbf{Z}_n$, prove the following lemma:

Lemma   If $a, b, \bar{a}, \bar{b} \in \mathbf{Z}$ with $a_n = \bar{a}_n$ and $b_n = \bar{b}_n$, then $a_n + b_n = \bar{a}_n + \bar{b}_n$. ▲

Lemma 83 shows that the addition given in Definition 80 is a binary operation on $\mathbf{Z}_n$. Before proving that $(\mathbf{Z}_n, +)$ is a group, let us consider an example.

84

Problem   a   Construct an addition table for $\mathbf{Z}_5$ using Table 1.18.

          b   Find an identity element in $\mathbf{Z}_5$.

          c   Find an additive inverse for every element in $\mathbf{Z}_5$.

          d   Is addition commutative in $\mathbf{Z}_5$? Justify your answer.

e Verify one particular instance of the associative property in $\mathbf{Z}_5$.

Table 1.18

+	0_5	1_5		
0_5				

85
Problem   Prove the following theorem:

Theorem   Let n be a fixed positive integer. Then $(\mathbf{Z}_n, +)$ is a group.

86
Problem   Is addition commutative in $\mathbf{Z}_n$? Prove that your answer is correct.

We now have available a variety of examples of groups, both commutative and noncommutative. We have seen groups specified by tables, groups consisting of numbers, of matrices, of permutations, of symmetries, and finally groups of integers modulo n. In the next chapter we use these examples repeatedly to illustrate theorems, to provide some counterexamples, and to aid us in the discovery of important results.

EXERCISES 1 Construct an addition table for $\mathbf{Z}_6$. Find an identity element in $\mathbf{Z}_6$. Find an additive inverse for every element in $\mathbf{Z}_6$. Verify one instance of the associative property in $\mathbf{Z}_6$.

2a Let p be a prime greater than 2. Complete the following proposition: The sum of all the elements in $\mathbf{Z}_p$ is equal to _____. In symbols,

$$\sum_{a=0}^{p-1} a_p = \text{_____} \bullet$$

b Prove the proposition.

c Is the proposition true in $\mathbf{Z}_n$ for any values of n other than primes? If so, which ones? Is it true if $n = 2$?

d Prove that if p is a prime greater than 2, then p divides the sum of the first $p-1$ integers:

$$p \left| \sum_{a=0}^{p-1} a \right.$$

Is this true for any nonprimes?

*3 From number theory we know that if k is a positive integer and $a \in \mathbf{Z}$, then the symbol ka means the sum $a+a+\cdots+a$ with k summands. We can define a corresponding symbol ka_n if n is a fixed positive integer and $a_n \in \mathbf{Z}_n$. We do so inductively as follows:

$$1 \cdot a_n = a_n \quad \text{and} \quad 2a_n = a_n + a_n$$

If $k \cdot a_n$ is defined, then

$$(k+1) \cdot a_n = k \cdot a_n + a_n$$

a Show that $k \cdot a_n = (ka)_n$ for $k \in \mathbf{Z}^+$. Thus the multiple $k \cdot a_n$ of a congruence class a_n is the class of the multiple ka.

b Calculate $6(3_{12})$, $6(4_{12})$, $5(2_{12})$, $121(2_{12})$.

4 *Challenge.* The equation $kx = 0$ with $k \neq 0$ has exactly one solution, $x = 0$, in the real numbers. In this exercise we study

the corresponding equation, $kx_n = 0_n$, in the additive group $\mathbf{Z}_n$. We want to show that this equation $kx_n = 0_n$ with k a fixed positive integer may have as many as k solutions for x_n in $\mathbf{Z}_n$.

a   For each of the integers $k = 2, 3, 7, 8$, find all the elements $a_{12} \in \mathbf{Z}_{12}$ such that $ka_{12} = 0_{12}$. Use the definition of ka_n in Exercise 3.

b   Let n and k be fixed positive integers. Show that the set

$$H_k = \{a_n: a_n \in \mathbf{Z}_n, \, ka_n = 0_n\}$$

is a group under addition. Note that H_k is the set of all solutions in $\mathbf{Z}_n$ of the equation $kx_n = 0_n$.

Let n and k be fixed positive integers. Let $d = \gcd(n, k)$, $n = jd$, and $k = k_1 d$. (The symbol gcd means "greatest common divisor"; see Appendix 6C.)

c   Show that $kj_n = 0_n$.

d   Show that if $a \in \mathbf{Z}$ and $ka_n = 0_n$, then $j \mid a$.   ●

e   Find an element $b_n \in \mathbf{Z}_n$ such that the solution group

$$H_k = \{a_n: a_n \in \mathbf{Z}_n, \, ka_n = 0_n\}$$

can be written

$$H_k = \{mb_n: m \in \mathbf{Z}^+\}$$

How many elements are in H_k?

5   Define a relation of congruence modulo 0 on $\mathbf{Z}$ by setting $x \equiv y \pmod{0}$ (read "x is congruent to y modulo zero") if and only if $x - y = 0$.

a   Prove that the relation of congruence modulo 0 on $\mathbf{Z}$ is an equivalence relation, namely the relation of equality.

b   Define

$$[a]_0 = \{b: b \in \mathbf{Z}, \, b \equiv a \pmod{0}\}$$

Then $[a]_0$ is the equivalence class of a for this equivalence relation. Find explicitly $[0]_0$, $[2]_0$, $[-3]_0$, and $[a]_0$, where $a \in \mathbf{Z}$. Describe all the equivalence classes for this relation.

c   Let

$$\mathbf{Z}_0 = \{[a]_0 : a \in \mathbf{Z}\}$$

Is $\mathbf{Z}_0$ a finite set or an infinite set? Justify your answer.

d   Define a function $f: \mathbf{Z} \to \mathbf{Z}_0$ by setting $f(a) = [a]_0$. If $a = b$, then why is $f(a) = f(b)$? Show that f is a one-to-one function and that f maps $\mathbf{Z}$ onto $\mathbf{Z}_0$.

REVIEW

Important Phrases

function	associative binary operation
domain	commutative binary operation
range	operation table
equality of functions	2×2 matrix
one-to-one or injective function	nonsingular matrix
	group
onto or surjective function	commutative group
composite function	identity element
image set	inverse element
cartesian product	permutation
binary operation	full symmetric group
composition	symmetry
composite	congruence modulo n
closure property	

Symbols

$f(x)$	$M_2(\mathbf{R})$
$f: X \to Y$ or $X \xrightarrow{f} Y$	$(G, \circ),\ (G, +),\ (G, \cdot)$
$\mathbf{Z}$	$(\mathscr{I}, \cdot)$
$\mathbf{Q}$	$a',\ a^{-1},\ -a$
$\mathbf{R}$	$f \circ g$ (functions)
$\mathbf{Z}^+$	$S(X)$
$\mathbf{R}^+$	$a \equiv b \pmod{n}$
S_n	a_n
D_4	$\mathbf{Z}_n$
$X \times Y$	

Questions 1   What are the cancellation laws for a group? List some other properties of a group. For example, can a group have more than one identity element?

2   State two theorems which provide alternate sets of axioms for a group.

3   Let $f: X \to Y$ and $g: Y \to Z$ be functions. How is the composite function $g \circ f$ defined? Under what conditions does f have an inverse $f^{-1}: Y \to X$ and how is the inverse function defined? Under what conditions on f and g is $g \circ f$ one-to-one? Under what conditions on f and g does $g \circ f$ map X onto Z?

4   How many elements are in the group S_n? For what values of n is S_n noncommutative?

5   If

$$f = \begin{pmatrix} 1 & 2 & \cdots & n \\ a_1 & a_2 & \cdots & a_n \end{pmatrix}$$

is an element of S_n, then what is $f(j)$? What is $f^{-1}(a_j)$?

6   Let $n \in \mathbf{Z}^+$ be fixed. If $a \in \mathbf{Z}$, what integers x satisfy the relation $x \equiv a \pmod{n}$? What is a typical element of the additive group $\mathbf{Z}_n$? How many elements are in the group $\mathbf{Z}_n$? How is addition defined in $\mathbf{Z}_n$?

7   List several additive groups.

8   List several multiplicative groups.

Several useful examples of groups appear in the exercises of this chapter. These include the following systems:

$(2\mathbf{Z}, +)$ $(\mathbf{R}^+, \cdot)$
$(\mathbf{Q}(\sqrt{2}), +)$ $(\mathbf{Q}^+, \cdot)$
$(\mathbf{R}^2, +)$ $(D_n, \circ)$ (the dihedral
$(\mathbf{R} - \{0\}, \cdot)$ group)
$(\mathbf{Q} - \{0\}, \cdot)$ $(F(X, G), *)$

Chapter 2 Theory Of Groups, I

A subset of a group *G* might itself be a group with the operation borrowed from *G*; any such subset is called a subgroup of *G*. However, not every subset is a subgroup.

In this chapter we develop a general theory pertaining to subgroups of an arbitrary group. We establish criteria for deciding whether or not a given subset is actually a subgroup. We find certain arithmetical conditions on the number of elements which can be in a subgroup and formulate some techniques for constructing subgroups of a group. We illustrate and apply these theoretical considerations in determining subgroups of the particular groups described in Chapter 1.

We also examine some special mappings from one group into another group and show that certain subgroups are associated with these mappings. Moreover, we use these mappings to determine whether or not two groups with the same number of elements are essentially alike or essentially different as groups.

Finally, we study a method for constructing a new group from a given group and a certain type of subgroup. We show that the special mappings mentioned above are closely related to these new groups.

2.1 Subgroups

In this section we see how to form some interesting new groups from the groups already at our disposal. One way to do this is to consider subsets of the known groups. Of course, we can determine whether or not a subset is a group by checking all the group axioms, but there is a more efficient way. In this section we establish criteria which guarantee that a subset of a known group G is itself a group with the operation borrowed from G. But first let us explain what we mean by the binary operation on a subset.

Let $(G, \circ)$ be a group and let H be a subset of G. Then for every $a, b \in H$ the composite $a \circ b$ is an element of G. If the closure property holds for H so that $a \circ b \in H$ for every $a, b \in H$, then there is a function $(a, b) \to a \circ b$ from $H \times H$ into H. This function is called the *binary operation induced on H* (by the operation on G). If the closure property fails for H, then for some $a, b \in H$, $a \circ b$ is not in H. Thus the function defined on $H \times H$ by $(a, b) \to a \circ b$ is *not* a binary operation on H.

For example, in the additive group **R** of real numbers let H be the set $2\mathbf{Z}$ of all even integers. From Exercise 1.1–2 we see that the operation of addition on **R** induces a binary operation of addition on the set $2\mathbf{Z}$. On the other hand, the operation of addition on **R** does not induce a binary operation on the set of all odd integers since this set is not closed under addition.

In summary, if $(G, \circ)$ is a group and H is a subset of G, then the following two statements are equivalent:

a   There is a binary operation induced on H by the original binary operation $\circ$ on G.

b H is closed under the operation $\circ$ (i.e., for every $a, b \in H$, $a \circ b \in H$).

With the preceding discussion in mind, we can now define the notion of a subgroup of a group.

1
Definition   Let $(G, \circ)$ be a group. A nonempty subset H of G is a *subgroup* of G if and only if $(H, \circ)$ is a group.

Note that Definition 1 requires that the operation in any subgroup of G must be the one induced on H by the operation in G. Moreover, the induced operation must be associative and the set H must contain an identity and the inverse of each element in H. For example, $\mathbf{Z}$ and $\mathbf{Q}$ are both subgroups of $\mathbf{R}$ under addition. On the other hand, the set $\mathbf{R}^+$ of all positive real numbers is a group under multiplication but it is not a subgroup of $\mathbf{R}$ under addition.

2
Problem   a   Is $\{-1, 0, 1\}$ a subgroup of $\mathbf{Z}$ under addition?

b   Let H be a subgroup of $\mathbf{Z}$ under addition such that $3 \in H$. Find half a dozen other elements of H. Is H finite or infinite?

3
Problem   Prove that any subset of $\mathbf{Z}$ having the form $\{\underline{\hspace{3cm}}\}$ is a subgroup of $\mathbf{Z}$ under addition. (You may want to consider some examples first.)

4
Problem   Find all the subgroups of $\mathbf{Z}_6$ under addition.

5
Problem   Prove that any group $(G, \circ)$ with $G \neq \{e\}$ has at least two subgroups, namely $\{e\}$ and G.

Since the sets G and $\{e\}$ are always subgroups of the group G, we often are interested in finding subgroups which are distinct from these two. To such subgroups we give a special name.

6
Definition   A subgroup H of a group G is a *proper subgroup* if and only if $H \neq \{e\}$ and $H \neq G$. The subgroups G and $\{e\}$ are called improper subgroups.

In all the examples of subgroups that we have seen in this section, the identity of the group was also the identity of the subgroup. The next problem shows that this must always be true.

7

Problem   Prove that if H is a subgroup of a group G, then the identity
                       element e_H of H is the same as the identity element e of G.

8

Problem   Let H be a nonempty subset of a group G. Which of the
                       group axioms is (are) always true for H? Which axioms
                       must be verified for H if we are to prove that H is a subgroup
                       of G? (You may wish to consider the subsets $\{1, 2, 3, \ldots\}$,
                       $\{0, 1, 2, 3, \ldots\}$, and $\{-1, 0, 1\}$ of $\mathbf{Z}$.) Recall that H is not
                       necessarily closed under the operation of G. This closure
                       must be checked for any subset H of G.

Theorems 9 and 12 give us criteria for determining when a subset of a group is
in fact a subgroup. Each shows that just one condition must be checked.
Theorem 9 deals only with finite subsets of groups and is easy to apply since it
requires only that the subset be closed under the group operation.

9

Theorem   Let $(G, \circ)$ be a group and let H be a finite nonempty subset
                       of G. If H is closed under the operation $\circ$, then H is a sub-
                       group of G.

Leave the proof of this theorem for Exercise 2.2–4. Although the theorem can
be proved at this time, the proof is easier and neater when we can use the notation
developed in Section 2.2.

In Section 1.6 we noted that each of the symmetries of the square can be
represented as an element of the permutation group S_4. Thus D_4, the set of all
these symmetries, is a nonempty subset of S_4. A glance at the composition
table for D_4 shows us that D_4 is closed under the operation of S_4. Theorem 9
says that D_4 is a subgroup of S_4, that is, that $(D_4, \circ)$ is a group. (This result was
obtained before in a more laborious manner.) Thus D_4 gives us an example
using Theorem 9 to simplify the proof that a particular finite subset of a known
group is itself a group.

10
Problem

Use Theorem 9 to find all the subgroups of $\mathbf{Z}_n$ under addition for each $n \in \{4, 5, ..., 9\}$. Make a list of these subgroups for use in Section 2.3.

11
Problem

Show by example that if H is an infinite subset of a group and H is closed under the group operation, then H need not necessarily be a subgroup.

The following theorem states a criterion for any subset of a group to be a subgroup. If the set is infinite, it is no longer enough to know that the set is closed under the group operation. We must prove that it also contains inverses.

The group axioms tell us that if H is a subgroup of the group G under the operation $\circ$ and if $a, b \in H$, then $b' \in H$ and hence $a \circ b' \in H$. Theorem 12 gives a converse to this proposition. Note that Theorem 12 applies whether the set is finite or infinite.

12
Problem

Prove the following theorem:

Theorem

Let $(G, \circ)$ be a group and let H be a nonempty subset of G. If $a \circ b' \in H$ for every $a, b \in H$, then H is a subgroup of G. ▲

13
Problem

Restate Theorem 12 using the notation (a) of a multiplicative group and (b) of an additive group. This restatement is simple but it will be useful in later problems.

14
Problem

Use Theorem 12 to prove that if H and K are subgroups of a group G, then $H \cap K$ is a subgroup of G.

A lattice diagram can be used to give a picture of the relationship of the subgroups of a group. For example, if G is a group and H and K are subgroups of G,
then $H \cap K$ is a subgroup and $H \cap K \subseteq H$, $H \cap K \subseteq K$. To show this relationship we can draw a lattice diagram as in Figure 2.1.

Figure 2.1

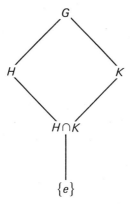

In the additive group $\mathbf{Z}$ the sets $2\mathbf{Z} = \{2n: n \in \mathbf{Z}\}$, $3\mathbf{Z} = \{3n: n \in \mathbf{Z}\}$, $4\mathbf{Z} =$
$\{4n: n \in \mathbf{Z}\}$, and $6\mathbf{Z} = \{6n: n \in \mathbf{Z}\}$ are all subgroups of $\mathbf{Z}$. In fact, these subgroups have the property that $4\mathbf{Z}$ is a subgroup of $2\mathbf{Z}$ and $6\mathbf{Z}$ is a subgroup of
both $2\mathbf{Z}$ and $3\mathbf{Z}$ (note that $6\mathbf{Z} = 2\mathbf{Z} \cap 3\mathbf{Z}$). We show this relationship in
Figure 2.2.

Figure 2.2

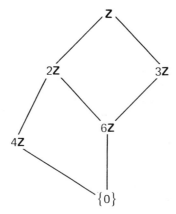

Note that in Figure 2.2 a group H_1 lies below a group H_2 and is connected to it by one or more line segments if and only if H_1 is a subgroup of H_2. A lattice diagram includes the group G at the top and the subgroup $\{e\}$ at the bottom.

15
Problem   Draw a lattice diagram for the subgroups of $\mathbf{Z}_6$.

EXERCISES   1   In S_4 find several subgroups with six elements.

    2   Define an operation $\circ$ for the set $H = \{-1, 0, 1\}$ by Table 2.1
    a   Show that $(H, \circ)$ is a group.
    b   Is $(H, \circ)$ a subgroup of $(\mathbf{Z}, +)$?

Table 2.1

$\circ$	0	1	-1
0	0	1	-1
1	1	-1	0
-1	-1	0	1

    3   If K is a subgroup of H and H is a subgroup of G, is K necessarily a subgroup of G? Why?

    4   Either prove the following statement or find a counterexample to it: If H and K are subgroups of G, then $H \cup K$ is a subgroup of G.

    5   The cartesian plane $\mathbf{R}^2 = \mathbf{R} \times \mathbf{R}$ is a group under the addition defined by $(a, b) + (c, d) = (a+c, b+d)$. Sketch each of the following sets in the plane. Determine whether or not each set is a subgroup. Justify your answers.
    a $\{(x, y): ax + b = y\}$, where $a, b \in \mathbf{R} - \{0\}$ are fixed
    b $\{(x, y): ax = y\}$, where $a \in \mathbf{R} - \{0\}$ is fixed
    c $\{(x, y): x, y \in \mathbf{Z}\}$
    d $\{(x, y): x = 0\}$
    e $\{(x, x): x \in \mathbf{Z}\}$

6   Let

$$\mathcal{D} = \left\{ \begin{pmatrix} a & 0 \\ 0 & d \end{pmatrix} : a, d \in \mathbf{R} \right\}$$

be the set of all diagonal 2×2 matrices. Use Theorem 12 to prove that $\mathcal{D}$ is a subgroup of $M_2(\mathbf{R})$ under addition. Is $(\mathcal{D}, +)$ a commutative group? Why?

7   Prove or disprove that the set

$$\mathcal{D}_1 = \left\{ \begin{pmatrix} a & 0 \\ 0 & d \end{pmatrix} : a, d \in \mathbf{R}, \ ad \neq 0 \right\}$$

is a subgroup of the multiplicative group $\mathcal{I}$ of nonsingular 2×2 matrices. Is multiplication commutative in $\mathcal{D}_1$?

8   Prove or disprove that the set

$$\mathcal{T} = \left\{ \begin{pmatrix} a & b \\ 0 & d \end{pmatrix} : a, b, d \in \mathbf{R} \right\}$$

of upper triangular matrices is a commutative subgroup of $M_2(\mathbf{R})$ under addition.

9   Prove or disprove that the set

$$\mathcal{T}_1 = \left\{ \begin{pmatrix} a & b \\ 0 & d \end{pmatrix} : a, b, d \in \mathbf{R}, \ ad \neq 0 \right\}$$

Is a subgroup of the multiplicative group $\mathcal{I}$ of nonsingular 2×2 matrices. Is multiplication commutative in $\mathcal{T}_1$?

10   Complete the following proposition and prove it: If $S \subseteq \mathbf{R}$, let

$$M_2(S) = \left\{ \begin{pmatrix} a & b \\ c & d \end{pmatrix} : a, b, c, d \in S \right\}$$

Then $M_2(S)$ is a subgroup of $M_2(\mathbf{R})$ under addition if and only if _____ .

*11 In Problem 3 you showed that any subset of $\mathbf{Z}$ having the form $\{nd: n \in \mathbf{Z}\}$, with d a fixed integer, is a subgroup of $\mathbf{Z}$ under addition. Prove that there are no other subgroups of $\mathbf{Z}$. Specifically, prove that if H is a subgroup of $\mathbf{Z}$ under addition and $H \neq \{0\}$, then there is an integer $d > 0$ such that $H = \{nd: n \in \mathbf{Z}\}$. ●

12a Draw a lattice diagram showing all the subgroups of the additive group $\mathbf{Z}_{24}$.
  b Draw a lattice diagram showing all the subgroups of the additive group $\mathbf{Z}_{30}$.

13 Draw a partial lattice diagram for the additive group $\mathbf{Z}$ containing all the subgroups $2\mathbf{Z}, 3\mathbf{Z}, \ldots, 12\mathbf{Z}$.

*14 Let m and n be positive integers. In the additive group $\mathbf{Z}$, $m\mathbf{Z} = \{mk: k \in \mathbf{Z}\}$ is a subgroup of $n\mathbf{Z} = \{nk: k \in \mathbf{Z}\}$ if and only if _____ . Complete the statement with a condition on m and n and then prove it.

15a In the additive group $\mathbf{Z}$, find $m\mathbf{Z} \cap n\mathbf{Z}$ for several different pairs of positive integers m and n.
  b If m and n are arbitrary positive integers, find the subgroup $m\mathbf{Z} \cap n\mathbf{Z}$ and prove that your answer is correct. Remember that it must be of the same form as $m\mathbf{Z}$ and $n\mathbf{Z}$. ●
  c Prove that the intersection of two proper subgroups of $\mathbf{Z}$ is a proper subgroup.

16 If $(G, +)$ is a commutative group with subgroups H and K, define $H+K$ to be the set

$$H + K = \{h+k: h \in H, k \in K\}$$

Then $H+K$ contains all possible sums $h+k$, where $h \in H$ and $k \in K$.
  a Prove that $H+K$ is a subgroup of G.
  b In the additive group $\mathbf{Z}$ find $m\mathbf{Z}+n\mathbf{Z}$ for several different pairs of positive integers m and n.

c If m and n are arbitrary positive integers, then $m\mathbf{Z}+n\mathbf{Z}=x\mathbf{Z}$ for some integer x. Find x in terms of m and n and prove that your answer is correct. ●

17 In the group $\mathbf{Z}$ the infinite sequence of subgroups

$$2\mathbf{Z} \supseteq 4\mathbf{Z} \supseteq 8\mathbf{Z} \supseteq 16\mathbf{Z} \supseteq \cdots$$

is called a descending chain. For any positive integer k find a descending chain in $\mathbf{Z}$ which includes the subgroup $k\mathbf{Z}$.

2.2 Orders of Elements

One natural way to start the construction of a subgroup is to choose a group element $a \neq e$ and include the element and all of its composites $a \circ a$, $(a \circ a) \circ a$, etc. In fact, you may already have used this technique in finding the subgroups of $\mathbf{Z}$ or of $\mathbf{Z}_n$ for $n = 4, 5, \ldots, 9$. In order to make this task more manageable, we need some notation and terminology.

16
Definition

In an additive group $(G, +)$ integral *multiples* of an element $a \in G$ are defined by setting

$$0 \cdot a = 0$$
$$1 \cdot a = a$$
$$na = (n-1)\,a + a \quad \text{for } n = 2, 3, \ldots$$
$$(-n)\,a = n(-a) \quad \text{for } n = 1, 2, 3, \ldots$$

Definition 16 tells us that $2a = a + a$, $3a = 2a + a = (a + a) + a$, and so on. Note that if G is a set of real numbers, then an integral multiple is just the usual multiplication of a real number by an integer.

As an extension of familiar properties of real numbers we have the following proposition:

17
Proposition

Let $(G, +)$ be a group. For every $a \in G$ and every pair $m, n \in \mathbf{Z}$,

$$ma + na = \underline{\hspace{2cm}}$$
$$m(na) = (mn)\,a$$

Leave the proof of this proposition for homework.

Just as integral multiples are defined for an additive group so integral powers are defined for a group such as $(\mathbf{R} - \{0\}, \cdot)$ or $(S_3, \circ)$ whose operation is not addition.

18
Definition   In a nonadditive group $(G, \circ)$ integral *powers* of an element $a \in G$ are defined by setting

$$a^0 = e$$
$$a^1 = a$$
$$a^n = a^{n-1} \circ a \qquad \text{for } n = 2, 3, \ldots$$
$$a^{-n} = (a')^n \qquad \text{for } n = 1, 2, 3, \ldots$$

As a consequence of Definition 18 we have $a^2 = a \circ a$, $a^3 = a^2 \circ a = (a \circ a) \circ a$, $a^{-3} = (a' \circ a') \circ a'$, etc. For example, in the multiplicative group $\mathbf{R} - \{0\}$, $2^{-3} = (\frac{1}{2})^3 = \frac{1}{8}$.

In order to facilitate our calculations with different powers of the same element, we need the following proposition:

19
Proposition   Let $(G, \circ)$ be a group. For every $a \in G$ and every pair $m, n \in \mathbf{Z}$,

$$a^m \circ a^n = a^{m+n}$$
$$(a^m)^n = a^{mn}$$

Leave the proof of this proposition for Exercise 3.

Perhaps you noticed in working with groups such as S_3, D_4 (the symmetries of the square), or $\mathbf{Z}_n$ that each element of the group has some power or multiple which is equal to the identity of the group. For example, in S_3 the permutation

$$f = \begin{pmatrix} 1 & 2 & 3 \\ 3 & 1 & 2 \end{pmatrix}$$

has the property that $f^3 = e = f^6 = f^9$, etc., but $f^1 \neq e$ and $f^2 \neq e$. Similarly, in $\mathbf{Z}_8$

$$4 \cdot 2_8 = 0_8 = 8 \cdot 2_8 = 12 \cdot 2_8, \text{ etc.}$$

but $1 \cdot 2_8$, $2 \cdot 2_8$, and $3 \cdot 2_8$ are all different from 0_8. The integers 3 for

$$f = \begin{pmatrix} 1 & 2 & 3 \\ 3 & 1 & 2 \end{pmatrix}$$

and 4 for 2_8 are given a special name, as indicated in the following definition.

20
Definition a Let $(G, +)$ be an additive group. The *order* of an element $a \in G$ is the smallest positive integer n such that $na = 0$; if $ma \neq 0$ for every positive integer m, then the element a has *infinite order*.

b Let $(G, \circ)$ be a (nonadditive) group. The *order* of an element $a \in G$ is the smallest positive integer n such that $a^n = e$; if $a^m \neq e$ for every positive integer m, then the element a has *infinite order*.

To obtain the order of an element such as 2_8 in the additive group $\mathbf{Z}_8$, compute consecutive multiples, $1 \cdot 2_8$, $2 \cdot 2_8$, $3 \cdot 2_8$, etc., until a multiple is found which is equal to 0_8. Since $4 \cdot 2_8 = 0_8$ while $1 \cdot 2_8$, $2 \cdot 2_8$, and $3 \cdot 2_8$ are all different from 0_8, the element 2_8 has order four.

Similarly, to find the order of μ_1 in D_4, compute the consecutive powers μ_1^1, μ_1^2, μ_1^3, etc. Since $\mu_1^2 = e$ and $\mu_1 \neq e$, the order of μ_1 is two.

21
Problem a Find the order of every element of $\mathbf{Z}_5$; of two nonzero elements of $\mathbf{Z}_6$.

b Find the order of every element of the group D_4 of symmetries of the square.

c Find the order of two nonzero elements of the additive group $\mathbf{Z}$.

In Section 2.1 you may have formed the subgroups of $\mathbf{Z}_6$ by choosing an element $a_6 \in \mathbf{Z}_6$ and considering all the multiples of this element: a_6, $2a_6$, $3a_6$, etc. We use a special symbol for this kind of set and give it a special name, as we see in the following definitions.

22
Definition   Let $(G, +)$ be an additive group. Let $a \in G$ have finite order n. We define $\langle a \rangle$ to be the set of all multiples ka $(k \in \mathbf{Z}^+)$ of a:

$$\langle a \rangle = \{ka : k \in \mathbf{Z}^+\} = \{1 \cdot a, 2 \cdot a, 3 \cdot a, \ldots\}$$

If $(G, \circ)$ is a nonadditive group, then $\langle a \rangle$ is the set of all powers a^k $(k \in \mathbf{Z}^+)$ of a:

$$\langle a \rangle = \{a^k : k \in \mathbf{Z}^+\} = \{a^1, a^2, a^3, \ldots\}$$

23
Problem   a   In D_4 find all the elements of $\langle \rho_1 \rangle$; of $\langle \mu_1 \rangle$.

          b   In the group $\mathbf{Z}_6$ find the sets $\langle 0_6 \rangle$, $\langle 1_6 \rangle$, $\langle 2_6 \rangle$, ..., $\langle 5_6 \rangle$.

24
Problem   a   Let $(G, \circ)$ be a group and $a \in G$. If the order of the element a is n, how many distinct elements are in $\langle a \rangle$? List these elements.

          b   Let $(G, \circ)$ be a group and $a \in G$ an element of finite order n. Prove that $\langle a \rangle$ is a commutative subgroup of G. Use Theorem 9 in your proof.

25
Definition   If $(G, \circ)$ is a group and $a \in G$ is an element of finite order, then $\langle a \rangle$ is called the *cyclic subgroup generated by* the element a.

EXERCISES 1   Find the order of every element of S_3.

          2   Let a_n be an element of the additive group $\mathbf{Z}_n$ and let k be a positive integer. We have seen that $ka_n = (ka)_n$. (See Exercise 1.8–3.)

          a   Use this fact to find the order of every element in $\mathbf{Z}_{20}$.

          b   Find the order of each of the following elements: $9_{102} \in \mathbf{Z}_{102}$, $7_{255} \in \mathbf{Z}_{255}$, $8_{320} \in \mathbf{Z}_{320}$.

3   Prove Proposition 19. What changes are necessary in order to have a proof of Proposition 17. ●

4   Prove Theorem 9. That is, prove that if $(G, \circ)$ is a group and H is a finite nonempty subset of G which is closed under the operation $\circ$, then H is a subgroup of G. You may want to choose an element a of the finite subset H and consider the powers $a, a^2, a^3, \ldots$. ●

5a   Write each of the subgroups of $\mathbf{Z}_8$ in the form $\langle a_8 \rangle$ for some $a_8 \in \mathbf{Z}_8$.

b   Choose a subgroup of order six in $\mathbf{Z}_{12}$. Write it in the form $\langle a_{12} \rangle$ for some $a_{12} \in \mathbf{Z}_{12}$. Find the order of each element ka_{12} in this subgroup. How is the order of ka_{12} related to the order of a_{12}?

6   Show that every finite noncommutative group has a commutative subgroup different from $\{e\}$.

★7   Let $(G, \circ)$ be a group and let $a, b \in G$.

a   Prove that the order of a is equal to the order of a'.

b   Prove that the order of $a \circ b$ is equal to the order of $b \circ a$.

★8   Let $(G, \circ)$ be a group and $a \in G$ an element of finite order n. Let k be an integer such that $a^k = e$. Show that n divides k.

★9   Let $(G, \circ)$ be a group and $a \in G$ an element of finite order n. Let k be an integer.

a   Show that if $1 \leq k < n$, then the inverse of a^k is equal to a positive power of a: $(a^k)' = a^x$ for some positive integer x. Similarly, in an additive group $-(ka)$ is equal to some positive multiple of a. (You may want to look at a few examples first.)

b   Using the division algorithm, show that if $k \geq n$, then $a^k = a^j$ for some $j \in \{0, 1, 2, \ldots, n-1\}$. Then show that the inverse of a^k is equal to a nonnegative power of a. Similarly, in an additive group $ka = ja$ for some $j \in \{0, 1, 2, \ldots, n-1\}$ and $-(ka)$ is equal to a nonnegative multiple of a.

c   Show that

$$\{a^k : k \in \mathbf{Z}\} = \langle a \rangle = \{a^k : k \in \mathbf{Z}^+\} \qquad \text{and}$$

$$\{a^k : k \in \mathbf{Z}^+\} = \{e, a, a^2, \ldots, a^{n-1}\}$$

Thus if a is an element of finite order n, the set of all powers of a is the same as the set of all positive powers of a. A similar result is true for additive groups.

10   Show by direct computation that every element $a_{12} \in \mathbf{Z}_{12}$ can be written as the sum of two elements b_{12} and c_{12} such that b_{12} has order dividing three and c_{12} has order dividing four. How are the orders of a_{12}, b_{12}, and c_{12} related?

*11a   Let $(G, \circ)$ be a commutative group and let b be an element of G with order mn. Show that if m and n are relatively prime (the greatest common divisor of m and n is 1), then there exist $b_1, b_2 \in G$ such that b_1 has order m, b_2 has order n, and $b_1 \circ b_2 = b$.   ●

b   Find an example in $\mathbf{Z}_{12}$ of an element b_{12} of order four which cannot be expressed as the sum of elements of order two.

c   Let G be a commutative group, $p_1, p_2, \ldots, p_r$ distinct primes, and $k_1, k_2, \ldots, k_r \in \mathbf{Z}^+$. Prove that if $b \in G$ has order $p_1^{k_1} p_2^{k_2} \cdots p_r^{k_r}$, then there exist $b_1, b_2, \ldots, b_r \in G$ such that $b = b_1 \circ b_2 \circ \cdots \circ b_r$ and b_j has order $p_j^{k_j}$.   ●

*12   Let G be a commutative group. Let p be a prime and let H_p be the collection of all elements of G whose orders are nonnegative powers of p.

a   In the additive group $\mathbf{Z}_{36}$ find all the elements of

$$H_2 = \{a_{36} : \text{order } a_{36} \text{ is } 2^k \text{ for some } k\} \qquad \text{and}$$

$$H_3 = \{a_{36} : \text{order } a_{36} \text{ is } 3^k \text{ for some } k\}$$

b   Show that if G is a commutative group, then H_p is a subgroup of G.   ●

13   *Challenge*. Let $(G, \circ)$ be a group and $a \in G$ an element of order n. Let $b \in \langle a \rangle$ with $b = a^s$ ($s \in \mathbf{Z}^+$).

a   Find the order of b. Justify your answer.   ●

b   Find necessary and sufficient conditions on s and n such that $\langle b \rangle = \langle a \rangle$, that is, so that a and b generate the same subgroup of G.   ●

2.3 Lagrange's Theorem and Cosets

We have seen that every group $G \neq \{e\}$ has at least two subgroups, the improper subgroups $\{e\}$ and G. We have also seen criteria that help us determine when a subset of a group is itself a group. Perhaps there are limitations on the size of a subgroup which might aid us further in eliminating certain sets as subgroups. For example, if a subset of S_3 has three elements, can it be a subgroup? Can a subset with five elements be a subgroup of S_3? The major theorem of this section, known as Lagrange's Theorem, will answer these questions.

26
Definition   The *order* of a group (or subgroup) G is the number of elements in G.

One of the fundamental results in group theory is the relationship between the order of a finite group and the order of each of its subgroups. The following problem will help you discover that relationship.

27
Problem   Refer to your list of subgroups of $\mathbf{Z}_n$ for $n = 4, 5, \ldots, 9$ (see Section 2.1). For each $n = 4, 5, \ldots, 9$ compare the order of the group $\mathbf{Z}_n$ with the order of each of its subgroups.

28
Problem   State a theorem relating the order of a finite group G to the order of an arbitrary subgroup of G.

Theorem   If H is a subgroup of the finite group G, then

_____ .

You probably have stated a result known as *Lagrange's Theorem*. Check it with your instructor. The following definition and problems lead to its proof.

29
Definition   Let $(G, \circ)$ be a group, H any subgroup of G, and $a \in G$. The *left coset* $a \circ H$ of the subgroup H in G is defined to

be the set

$$a \circ H = \{a \circ h : h \in H\}$$

Note that $a \circ H$ is the set of all elements $a \circ h$ with a fixed and h varying throughout the subgroup H.

In a multiplicative group $(G, \cdot)$ a left coset is written in the form

$$aH = \{ah : h \in H\}$$

In an additive group $(G, +)$ a left coset is written in the form

$$a + H = \{a + h : h \in H\}$$

Consider the subgroup $H = \{0_6, 3_6\}$ of the additive group $\mathbf{Z}_6$. The left coset $1_6 + H$ consists of all elements of the form $1_6 + h_6$, where $h_6 \in H$. Thus

$$1_6 + H = \{1_6 + 0_6, 1_6 + 3_6\} = \{1_6, 4_6\}$$

30
Problem

For every $a_6 \in \mathbf{Z}_6$ find all elements in the left coset $a_6 + H$, where $H = \{0_6, 3_6\}$. Do this systematically by first finding all elements in the coset $0_6 + H$, then finding all elements in the coset $1_6 + H$, etc. Then answer the following questions:

a   Is $a_6 + H$ a subgroup of $\mathbf{Z}_6$ for every $a_6 \in \mathbf{Z}_6$?

b   Is every element of $\mathbf{Z}_6$ in some left coset?

c   Can two different elements of $\mathbf{Z}_6$ determine the same left coset? In other words, is it possible that $a_6 \neq b_6$ in $\mathbf{Z}_6$ but $a_6 + H = b_6 + H$?

d   Do two different left cosets of H have any common elements?

e   How many different left cosets of H are there?

f   How many elements are in each left coset?

g   Find a relationship among the order of the group $\mathbf{Z}_6$, the order of the subgroup H, and the number of distinct left cosets of H.

The following lemma is true whether the group G is finite or infinite. Remember that in proving any statement in the lemma you may use a statement which precedes it.

31
Problem   Prove the following lemma:

Lemma   Let $(G, \circ)$ be a group and H a subgroup of G.

a   The subgroup H is a left coset of H (that is, there is an element $a \in G$ such that $a \circ H = H$).

b   Every $a \in G$ is an element of the left coset $a \circ H$. (This shows that every element a of G belongs to some left coset of H, namely $a \in a \circ H$.)

c   If $a \in b \circ H$, then $a \circ H = b \circ H$.   ▲

d   If $a \circ H \cap b \circ H \neq \varnothing$, then $a \circ H = b \circ H$.   ▲

e   If $a \circ H \neq b \circ H$, then $a \circ H \cap b \circ H = \varnothing$. (This result shows that two different left cosets of H can have no elements in common. Thus two left cosets of H are either equal or disjoint.)

f   The distinct left cosets of H form a partition of G. (A partition is a collection of mutually disjoint subsets of G whose union is equal to G.)

g   If H is a finite subgroup with k elements, then the number of elements in any left coset of H is _____ .

Now we are ready to prove Lagrange's Theorem.

32

Problem   Prove Lagrange's Theorem using Lemma 31. In your proof
                        let n denote the order of the finite group G, k the order of
                        the subgroup H, and i the number of distinct left cosets of
                        H in G.

33

Definition   The number of distinct left cosets of a subgroup H in a
                        group G is called the *index* of H in G.

34

Problem   Write a formula expressing the index of a subgroup H in
                        terms of the order of G and the order of H. (See Problem 32.)

Caution   Lagrange's Theorem does not guarantee that a finite group
                        of order n actually has a subgroup with a specified order.
                        In Exercise 14 there is an example of a group of order twelve
                        which has no subgroup of order six. Thus the converse of
                        Lagrange's Theorem is not true.

In Section 2.2 we defined the order of an element and looked at the subgroup
generated by an element with finite order. The following theorem shows how
the order of an element is related to the order of the subgroup it generates.

35

Problem   Prove the following theorem:

Theorem   In a finite group the order of any element a is the same as
                        the order of the subgroup $\langle a \rangle$ generated by it, and the
                        order of a divides the order of the group.   ▲

In our proof of Lagrange's Theorem we used only the left cosets of a subgroup.
Now let us consider briefly the right cosets of a subgroup.

36
Definition

Let $(G, \circ)$ be a group, let H be a subgroup of G, and let $a \in G$. The *right coset* $H \circ a$ of H in G is the set

$$H \circ a = \{h \circ a : h \in H\}$$

A corresponding form of all the statements of Lemma 31 can also be proved for the collection of right cosets of the subgroup H. If H is a subgroup of a group G and H has finite index in G, then the number of left cosets of H is equal to the number of right cosets of H. This fact is proved in Exercise 7.

37
Problem

In the group D_4 of the symmetries of the square, let H be the subgroup $\{e, \mu_2\}$. Find an element $a \in D_4$ such that $a \circ H \neq H \circ a$. This example shows that the left cosets of a subgroup H are not necessarily the same as the right cosets of H.

38
Problem

Prove the proposition: If H is a subgroup of the group G and if G is commutative, then $a \circ H = H \circ a$ for every $a \in G$.

EXERCISES 1 Show that a group of prime order has no proper subgroups.

2 Find all the subgroups of the group D_4 of symmetries of the square. There are ten of these subgroups. Some of them are not generated by one element; they are built up from at least two elements (and their powers). Construct a lattice diagram for these subgroups.

★3 In future work we need the coset decompositions for several subgroups of the group D_4 of symmetries of the square.
a Compute all the left cosets and all the right cosets of the subgroup $\{e, \mu_2\}$ and record your results in Table 2.2. The entry given in the table is the left coset $\delta_1 \circ \{e, \mu_2\} = \{\delta_1 \circ e, \delta_1 \circ \mu_2\}$.

Table 2.2

	e	ρ_1	ρ_2	ρ_3	μ_1	μ_2	δ_1	δ_2
left cosets of $\{e,\mu_2\}$							$\{\delta_1,\rho_3\}$	
right cosets of $\{e,\mu_2\}$								

b   Make a table of all the cosets of the subgroup $\{e,\rho_2\}$.

c   Make a table of all the cosets of the subgroup $\{e,\delta_1\}$.

4   Find all the subgroups of S_3 and display them in a lattice diagram.

5a   Choose a subgroup H of order two in S_3 and determine the right and left cosets of H.

b   Repeat part a with a subgroup of order three in S_3.

*6   Let G be a group, H a subgroup of G, and $a, b \in H$.

a   Show that $a \in b \circ H$ if and only if $b' \circ a \in H$. Thus $a \circ H = b \circ H$ if and only if $b' \circ a \in H$. Why?

b   Show that $a \in H \circ b$ if and only if $a \circ b' \in H$. Thus $H \circ a = H \circ b$ if and only if $a \circ b' \in H$. Why?

c   Show that $a \circ H = b \circ H$ if and only if $H \circ a' = H \circ b'$.

7   Let G be a group (either finite or infinite) and let H be a subgroup of finite index k in G. Thus H is a subgroup of G with k distinct left cosets in G. Use Exercise 6 to prove that there are exactly k distinct right cosets of H in G. In particular, this proves that if the index of a subgroup is finite (e.g., in a subgroup of a finite group), then the number of left cosets is equal to the number of right cosets of the subgroup.

*8   Let $(G, \circ)$ be a finite commutative group. Let $a, b \in G$ have orders m and n, respectively. Show that if m and n are relatively prime (the greatest common divisor of m and n is 1), then $a \circ b$ has order mn. ●

9   Let G be a group and H a subgroup of G. Define a relation on G by stating that $x \sim y$ if and only if $y' \circ x \in H$.

a   Prove that $\sim$ is an equivalence relation on G.

b   Let $a \in G$. Prove that the equivalence class

$$[a]_H = \{x: x \in G \text{ and } x \sim a\}$$

is equal to the left coset $a \circ H$ of H.

c   Let G be the additive group $\mathbf{Z}$ and let $H = n\mathbf{Z} = \{nk: k \in \mathbf{Z}\}$. Then the condition $y' \circ x \in H$ is exactly the condition $x - y = nk$ for some $k \in \mathbf{Z}$. Show that $x \sim y$ for $x, y \in \mathbf{Z}$ if and only if $x \equiv y \pmod{n}$. Then show that the equivalence class $[a]_H$ is the class

$$a_n = \{x: x \in \mathbf{Z}, x \equiv a \pmod{n}\}$$

Hence the collection of (distinct) left cosets of $n\mathbf{Z}$ in $\mathbf{Z}$ is the group $\mathbf{Z}_n$. Illustrate this result with $n = 5$.

10   In transformation geometry one studies mappings called translations. A translation $\phi_a: \mathbf{Z} \to \mathbf{Z}$ is defined by setting $\phi_a(x) = x + a$ for every $x \in \mathbf{Z}$, where a is a fixed integer. The translation ϕ_a moves the set a units to the right or left. Let H be the subgroup $n\mathbf{Z}$ of $\mathbf{Z}$.

a   Prove that the left coset $a + H$ is equal to the translated set $\phi_a(H) = \{a + x: x \in H\}$.

b   Illustrate geometrically the fact that if $a \in H$, then the left coset (or translate) $a + H$ is equal to H.

c   In $\mathbf{R}^2$ a translation $\phi_{hk}: \mathbf{R}^2 \to \mathbf{R}^2$ is defined by setting

$$\phi_{hk}(x, y) = (x + h, y + k)$$

for all $(x, y) \in \mathbf{R}^2$ where $h, k \in \mathbf{R}$ are fixed. Let

$$H = \{(x, y): ax = y\}$$

where $a \in \mathbf{R}$ is fixed. Then H is a subgroup of $\mathbf{R}^2$ under addition. Sketch the set $\phi_{hk}(H)$ for several values of $h, k \in \mathbf{R}$. Describe geometrically the cosets (translates) $(h, k) + H$.

*11   Let n and k be positive integers such that k divides n. Construct a subgroup of $\mathbf{Z}_n$ of order k. This proves that if k is a factor of n, then $\mathbf{Z}_n$ has a subgroup of order k. Note that this result does *not* follow from Lagrange's Theorem.

12   Prove by construction that the dihedral group $(D_n, \circ)$ has a subgroup of order n. (For the construction of D_n see Exercise 1.6–5.)

*13   *Challenge.* Let G be a group of order six. Either G has an element of order six (as in the group $\mathbf{Z}_6$) or there exist elements a, b_1, b_2, b_3 such that a has order three, b_1, b_2, b_3 all have order two, and $G = \{e, a, a^2, b_1, b_2, b_3\}$ (as in the group S_3). Prove this statement by doing the following problems:

a   Show that G contains an element of order three or order six. In order to do so assume that every element $a \neq e$ of G has order two. Then show that G is commutative and G has a subgroup of order four. (Is this possible?)   ●

b   Assume that G is a group of order six and that no element of G has order six. Let $a \in G$ be an element of order three and let

$$H = \{e, a, a^2\} = \langle a \rangle$$

Prove that if $y \notin H$, then y has order two. To do so rule out the possibilities $y^2 = y \circ a^k$ for $k = 0, 1, 2$, $y^2 = a$, $y^2 = a^2$.

c   Complete the proof of the proposition.

*14   *Challenge.* The group S_4 of permutations on $\{1, 2, 3, 4\}$ contains many elements of the form

$$\begin{pmatrix} a & b & c & d \\ b & a & c & d \end{pmatrix}$$

in which two integers are left fixed. The permutation

$$\begin{pmatrix} 1 & 4 & 2 & 3 \\ 4 & 1 & 2 & 3 \end{pmatrix}$$

is such an element. These elements are called transpositions.

a Find all the transpositions in S_4.

Let A_4 be the collection of elements of S_4 which are the composite of an *even* number of transpositions (not necessarily all different). Thus elements of A_4 are of the form

$$\begin{pmatrix} a & b & c & d \\ b & a & c & d \end{pmatrix} \circ \begin{pmatrix} e & f & g & h \\ f & e & g & h \end{pmatrix}$$

or composites of these elements. We shall make the assumption, which is not justified until Section 4.2, that no transposition can belong to the set A_4.

b Use Theorem 9 to prove that A_4 is a subgroup of S_4. The set A_4 is a proper subgroup since we have assumed that no transposition belongs to A_4. What are the possible values for the order of A_4?

c Make a list of the elements of A_4 and find the order of A_4.

d Find the order of every element of A_4.

e Show that A_4 does not have a subgroup of order six. ●

2.4 Homomorphisms

In this section we consider some special functions which map a group G into a group $\overline{G}$. We are not interested at present in all of the functions from one group into another but only in those functions which in some sense "preserve the group operations" of G and $\overline{G}$.

Logarithms provide a familiar example of such functions. We know that $(\mathbf{R}, +)$ and $(\mathbf{R}^+, \cdot)$ are both groups. The logarithm has the property that if x and y are positive real numbers, then

$$\log_{10}(xy) = \log_{10}x + \log_{10}y$$

Thus the logarithm maps a product in $\mathbf{R}^+$ onto a sum in $\mathbf{R}$.

**39
Definition**

Let $(G, \circ)$ and $(\overline{G}, *)$ be groups. A *homomorphism* from G into $\overline{G}$ is a function $\phi: G \to \overline{G}$ such that

$$\phi(a \circ b) = \phi(a) * \phi(b)$$

for every $a, b \in G$.

Under a homomorphism the image of a product (or sum) is the product or sum of the images. We can show this as in Figure 2.3.

Figure 2.3

$$\phi: G \longrightarrow \overline{G}$$
$$a \longrightarrow \phi(a)$$
$$b \longrightarrow \phi(b)$$
$$a \circ b \longrightarrow \phi(a \circ b) = \phi(a) * \phi(b)$$

**40
Problem**

In each part of this problem determine whether or not the given function $\phi: G \to \overline{G}$ is a homomorphism and justify your answers.

a ϕ from $(\mathbf{R}-\{0\}, \cdot)$ into itself defined by $\phi(x) = x^n$, where n is a fixed positive integer

b ϕ from $(\mathbf{R}^+, \cdot)$ into itself defined by $\phi(x) = x+1$

c ϕ from $(\mathbf{R}-\{0\}, \cdot)$ into $(\mathbf{R}^+, \cdot)$ defined by $\phi(x) = |x|$

d ϕ from $(\mathbf{Z}, +)$ into $(2\mathbf{Z}, +)$ defined by $\phi(a) = 2a$ for every $a \in \mathbf{Z}$

Every group must contain an identity and inverses of its elements. Since the identity and inverses are defined by means of the group operation and a homomorphism "preserves the operation," we might hope to determine their images under a homomorphism. That is the purpose of the following theorem.

41
Problem

Prove the following theorem:

Theorem

Let ϕ be a homomorphism from a group $(G, \circ)$ into a group $(\overline{G}, *)$. Let e denote the identity element of G and $\bar{e}$ the identity element of $\overline{G}$. Then $\phi(e) = \bar{e}$ and $\phi(a') = [\phi(a)]'$ for every $a \in G$.

State the result of Theorem 41 in words. Under a homomorphism $\phi: G \to \overline{G}$ the image of the identity element in G is _____ and the image of the inverse of an element is _____.

42
Problem

For each function in Problem 40 which is a homomorphism, use Theorem 41 to compute explicitly $\phi(e)$ and $\phi(a')$, where $a \in G$.

43
Problem

Prove that if ϕ is a homomorphism from a group $(G, \circ)$ into a group $(\overline{G}, *)$, n is a positive integer, and $a \in G$, then

$$\phi(a \circ a \circ \cdots \circ a) = \phi(a) * \phi(a) * \cdots * \phi(a)$$

where there are n terms in each expression. Use the definitions of multiples and powers to write this result when $(G, +)$ and $(\overline{G}, +)$ are both additive groups and when $(G, \cdot)$ and $(\overline{G}, \cdot)$ are both multiplicative groups.

There is a natural correspondence $a \rightarrow a_n$ from **Z** into $\mathbf{Z}_n$. In the following problem this correspondence is shown to be a homomorphism.

44

Problem

Let n be a fixed positive integer. Define a function $\phi : \mathbf{Z} \rightarrow \mathbf{Z}_n$ by setting $\phi(a) = a_n$ for every $a \in \mathbf{Z}$.

a   Prove that ϕ is a homomorphism from $(\mathbf{Z}, +)$ into $(\mathbf{Z}_n, +)$.

b   Does ϕ map **Z** onto $\mathbf{Z}_n$?

c   Is ϕ a one-to-one function?

Associated with any homomorphism $\phi : G \rightarrow \overline{G}$ are two important sets, the kernel and the image set, which we now begin to study.

45

Definition

Let $(G, \circ)$ and $(\overline{G}, *)$ be groups. The *kernel* of a homomorphism $\phi : G \rightarrow \overline{G}$ is the set of all elements in G which are mapped onto the identity element $\overline{e}$ of $\overline{G}$. The kernel of ϕ is denoted $\ker(\phi)$. Thus

$$\ker(\phi) = \{x : x \in G \text{ and } \phi(x) = \overline{e}\}$$

(See Figure 2.4.)

Figure 2.4

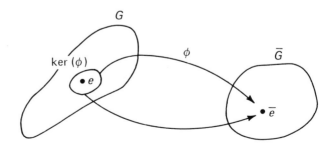

46

Problem

Find ker(ϕ) for the homomorphism of Problem 44. Is it a subgroup of **Z**?

47

Problem

Define a function $\phi: M_2(\mathbf{R}) \to \mathbf{R}$ by setting

$$\phi\left(\begin{pmatrix} a & b \\ c & d \end{pmatrix}\right) = a + d$$

The image $\phi(A)$ of a matrix A is called the trace of A.

a   Is ϕ a homomorphism from $(M_2(\mathbf{R}), +)$ into $(\mathbf{R}, +)$? Justify your answer.

b   Find the kernel of ϕ. Is it a subgroup of $M_2(\mathbf{R})$?

c   Find the image set $\{\phi(A): A \in M_2(\mathbf{R})\}$.

Both the kernel and the image set of a homomorphism provide us with useful subgroups. The fact that these sets are subgroups of their respective groups is the content of Theorems 48 and 51. In Section 2.9 we show that the kernel of a homomorphism ϕ from a group G onto a group $\overline{G}$ plays a very important role in describing $\overline{G}$.

48

Problem

Prove the following theorem:

Theorem

Let $(G, \circ)$ and $(\overline{G}, *)$ be groups. If $\phi: G \to \overline{G}$ is a homomorphism, then ker(ϕ) is a subgroup of G.

49

Problem

Prove the following theorem:

Theorem

Let $(G, \circ)$ and $(\overline{G}, *)$ be groups. A homomorphism $\phi: G \to \overline{G}$ is a one-to-one function if and only if the kernel of ϕ

consists solely of the identity element in G. Stated more briefly, a homomorphism ϕ is one-to-one if and only if $\ker(\phi) = \{e\}$. ▲

Theorem 49 allows us to determine whether or not a homomorphism is one-to-one by finding the kernel of the homomorphism. If the kernel consists of just the single point e, then the homomorphism is one-to-one; if the kernel contains even one point besides e, then the homomorphism fails to be one-to-one.

Note that for a given homomorphism we can prove or disprove the global property of being one-to-one simply by testing this property at a single point in the image set, namely the point $\bar{e} = \phi(e)$. Thus the homomorphism ϕ is one-to-one if and only if for every $x \in G$, $\phi(x) = \bar{e}$ implies $x = e$.

50

Problem

Let ϕ be the homomorphism from $(\mathbf{R}^+, \cdot)$ into $(\mathbf{R}, +)$ defined by $\phi(x) = \log_{10} x$. Use Theorem 49 to prove that ϕ is one-to-one.

Leave the proof of the following theorem for Exercise 9.

51

Theorem

If ϕ is a homomorphism from the group $(G, \circ)$ into the group $(\bar{G}, *)$, then the image set $\phi(G)$ is a subgroup of $\bar{G}$. (Recall that $\phi(G) = \{\phi(x): x \in G\}$.)

EXERCISES 1

Define a function ϕ from the multiplicative group $\mathscr{I}$ of non-singular 2×2 matrices into $(\mathbf{R} - \{0\}, \cdot)$ by setting

$$\phi\left(\begin{pmatrix} a & b \\ c & d \end{pmatrix}\right) = ad - bc$$

for every

$$\begin{pmatrix} a & b \\ c & d \end{pmatrix} \in \mathscr{I}$$

For every $A \in \mathscr{I}$, $\phi(A)$ is the determinant of A.

a Prove that ϕ is a homomorphism from $(\mathscr{I}, \cdot)$ into $(\mathbf{R} - \{0\}, \cdot)$.

b Find the kernel of ϕ.

c Let $A \in \mathscr{I}$. Use the fact that ϕ is a homomorphism to find $\phi(A^{-1})$.

2 Define a function $\phi: M_2(\mathbf{R}) \to \mathbf{R}$ by setting

$$\phi\left(\begin{pmatrix} a & b \\ c & d \end{pmatrix}\right) = a + b + c + d$$

for every

$$\begin{pmatrix} a & b \\ c & d \end{pmatrix} \in M_2(\mathbf{R})$$

a Is ϕ a homomorphism from $(M_2(\mathbf{R}), +)$ into $(\mathbf{R}, +)$? Justify your answer.

b Find the kernel of ϕ and the image of $M_2(\mathbf{R})$ under ϕ.

3 Find a homomorphism from $(\mathbf{R} - \{0\}, \cdot)$ onto $(\{-1, 1\}, \cdot)$.

4 Determine all the homomorphisms from $(\mathbf{Z}, +)$ into $(\mathbf{Z}, +)$. Justify your answer.

5 Find a homomorphism from $(\mathbf{Z}_8, +)$ onto $(\mathbf{Z}_4, +)$. Don't forget to prove that your function is a homomorphism.

6 Let $\phi: S_3 \to \mathbf{Z}_2$ be defined by setting

$$\phi(\alpha) = \begin{cases} 0_2 & \text{if } \alpha = \begin{pmatrix} 1 & 2 & 3 \\ 1 & 2 & 3 \end{pmatrix}, \begin{pmatrix} 1 & 2 & 3 \\ 2 & 3 & 1 \end{pmatrix}, \begin{pmatrix} 1 & 2 & 3 \\ 3 & 1 & 2 \end{pmatrix} \\ 1_2 & \text{otherwise} \end{cases}$$

Show that ϕ is a homomorphism. This shows that a non-commutative group can be mapped onto a commutative group by a homomorphism.

7 Let $(G, \circ)$ and $(\overline{G}, *)$ be groups and let $\overline{g} \in \overline{G}$. Define a function $\phi: G \to \overline{G}$ by setting $\phi(a) = \overline{g}$ for every $a \in G$. Find all the elements $\overline{g} \in \overline{G}$ such that ϕ is a homomorphism.

8   Define $\phi: \mathbf{Z}_n \to \mathbf{Z}_k$ by setting $\phi(a_n) = a_k$ for every $a \in Z$.

a   If $n = 6$ and $k = 5$, find $\phi(0_6)$, $\phi(3_6)$, $\phi(5_6)$, and $\phi(6_6)$. Is $\phi: \mathbf{Z}_6 \to \mathbf{Z}_5$ a function? If $n = 6$ and $k = 3$, find $\phi(0_6)$, $\phi(3_6)$, $\phi(5_6)$, and $\phi(6_6)$. Is $\phi: \mathbf{Z}_6 \to \mathbf{Z}_3$ a function?

b   Prove that ϕ is a properly defined function if and only if $k \mid n$. ●

c   Prove that if $k \mid n$, then the function $\phi: \mathbf{Z}_n \to \mathbf{Z}_k$ is a homomorphism.

d   If $k \mid n$, find explicitly $\ker(\phi)$ and $\phi(\mathbf{Z}_n)$.

9   Prove Theorem 51.

10   Either prove the following statement or else find a counterexample to it: If ϕ is a homomorphism from a commutative group $(G, \circ)$ onto a group $(\bar{G}, *)$, then $\bar{G}$ is a commutative group.

11   Consider the possible effects of a homomorphism $\phi: G \to \bar{G}$ upon the order of an element $x \in G$:

order of x	order of $\phi(x)$
finite	finite
finite	infinite
infinite	finite
infinite	infinite

In each case either prove that the given combination of orders cannot occur or give an example in which it does occur.

12   Prove that if ϕ is a homomorphism from the group $(G, \circ)$ onto the group $(\bar{G}, *)$ and if $G = \langle a \rangle$ for some $a \in G$ of finite order, then there exists $\bar{a} \in \bar{G}$ such that $\langle \bar{a} \rangle = \bar{G}$.

★13   Let $\phi: G \to \bar{G}$ be a homomorphism from the group $(G, \circ)$ into the group $(\bar{G}, *)$ and let $a \in G$ be an element of finite order. Prove that the order of $\phi(a)$ is a divisor of the order of a.

★14   Let ϕ be a homomorphism from the group $(G, \circ)$ into the group $(\bar{G}, *)$ and let H be a subset of $\bar{G}$. Define the *inverse* *image* of $\bar{H}$ to be the set

$$\phi^{-1}(\bar{H}) = \{x: x \in G \text{ and } \phi(x) \in \bar{H}\}$$

a Define $\phi: \mathbf{Z} \to \mathbf{Z}_4$ by setting $\phi(a) = a_4$ for every $a \in \mathbf{Z}$. Let $\bar{H}$ be the subgroup $\{0_4, 2_4\}$ in $\mathbf{Z}_4$. Find $\phi^{-1}(\bar{H})$ and show that in this case $\phi^{-1}(\bar{H})$ is a subgroup of $\mathbf{Z}$. What is $\ker(\phi)$? Is $\ker(\phi)$ a subgroup of $\phi^{-1}(\bar{H})$?

b Let $(G, \circ)$ and $(\bar{G}, *)$ be groups and $\phi: G \to \bar{G}$ a homomorphism. Prove that if $\bar{H}$ is a subgroup of $\bar{G}$, then $\phi^{-1}(\bar{H})$ is a subgroup of G and that $\ker(\phi) \subseteq \phi^{-1}(\bar{H})$.

2.5 Isomorphisms

Among our many examples of groups some are quite different from others; for example, the groups $\mathbf{Z}$ and D_4 appear to have little in common. However, other groups such as $\mathbf{Z}_4$ and the subgroup $\{e, \rho_1, \rho_2, \rho_3\}$ of D_4 have at least their orders in common. Thus the question arises as to how we can compare or classify groups to determine whether two groups have basically the same structure. One way to do this requires that there be a one-to-one correspondence between the two groups which also preserves the group operations and, in the case of finite groups, "matches up" the two tables.

52

Problem   a   In the operation tables for the additive group $\mathbf{Z}_4$ and the subgroup $H = \{e, \rho_1, \rho_2, \rho_3\}$ of D_4, compare the placement of the identity elements in the two tables. Then compare the placement of 1_4 and ρ_1 in their respective tables. What similarities do you observe?

         b   We formalize the correspondence between the two groups by defining a function ϕ from $\mathbf{Z}_4$ into H, where $\phi(a_4) = \rho_1^a$ for $a = 0, 1, 2, 3$. (Recall that $\rho_1^0 = e$ and $\rho_1^a = \rho_a$ for $a = 1, 2, 3$.) Prove that ϕ is a homomorphism which is one-to-one and maps $\mathbf{Z}_4$ onto $\{e, \rho_1, \rho_2, \rho_3\}$.

53

Definition   An *isomorphism* between the groups $(G, \circ)$ and $(\overline{G}, *)$ is a homomorphism from G into $\overline{G}$ which is both one-to-one and onto. Two groups $(G, \circ)$ and $(\overline{G}, *)$ are *isomorphic* if and only if there exists an isomorphism ϕ from G onto $\overline{G}$.

54

Problem   Find an isomorphism between $(\mathbf{Z}, +)$ and the additive group $3\mathbf{Z} = \{3n : n \in \mathbf{Z}\}$.

We have seen that if $\phi: G \to \overline{G}$ is a homomorphism, then the kernel of ϕ and the image set $\phi(G)$ can be used to determine whether ϕ is one-to-one and/or onto. These results can be used to decide when ϕ is an isomorphism.

55
Problem

Prove the following theorem:

Theorem

Let $(G, \circ)$ and $(\overline{G}, *)$ be groups and $\phi: G \to \overline{G}$ a homomorphism. Then ϕ is an isomorphism if and only if $\ker(\phi) = \{e\}$, where e is the identity of G, and $\phi(G) = \overline{G}$.

One consequence of Theorem 55 is that we need check only two sets, namely the kernel and the image set, to determine whether or not a given homomorphism is an isomorphism. In particular, if there exists $a \neq e$ such that $a \in \ker(\phi)$, then ϕ is not an isomorphism. Similarly, if there exists $\overline{a} \in \overline{G}$ such that $\overline{a} \notin \phi(G)$, then ϕ is not an isomorphism.

56
Problem

Determine whether or not each of the following functions is an isomorphism from $(\mathbf{R} - \{0\} \cdot)$ into itself:

a $\phi(x) = x^2$ for $x \in \mathbf{R} - \{0\}$
b $\phi(x) = x^3$ for $x \in \mathbf{R} - \{0\}$

One way of deciding whether two finite groups $(G, \circ)$ and $(\overline{G}, *)$ can be isomorphic is to compare their operation tables. If a proposed function $\phi: G \to \overline{G}$ is to be an isomorphism, then the image of the identity of G is _____, while the image of the inverse of an element $a \in G$ is _____. We also know that for every $a \in G$

$$\phi(a \circ a \circ \cdots \circ a) = \phi(a) * \phi(a) * \cdots * \phi(a)$$

where there are n terms in each composite.

For example, consider the subgroup $H = \{e, \mu_1, \mu_2, \rho_2\}$ of D_4 and the group $\mathbf{Z}_4$. If a proposed function $\phi: \mathbf{Z}_4 \to H$ is to be an isomorphism, then $\phi(2_4) = \phi(1_4 + 1_4) = \phi(1_4) \circ \phi(1_4)$ and $\phi(2_4) \neq e$. Is this compatible with the operation table for H?

57
Problem

Let $(G, \circ)$ and $(\overline{G}, *)$ be two finite groups, each of order n. Suppose the elements of the two groups can be arranged in some order so that the one-to-one correspondence

$$a_1 \to \bar{a}_1, \; a_2 \to \bar{a}_2, \; ..., \; a_n \to \bar{a}_n$$

has the following property: Whenever a_k appears in the ith row and the jth column of the operation table for G, then $\bar{a}_k$ appears in the corresponding position of the operation table for $\bar{G}$. Thus by relabeling the elements of one group we can make the two tables (Tables 2.3 and 2.4) "match up."

Show that under these conditions G and $\bar{G}$ are isomorphic. To do so define a suitable function $\phi \colon G \to \bar{G}$ and use Tables 2.3 and 2.4 to prove that ϕ is an isomorphism.

58
Problem

Compare the operation tables for the subgroup $\{e, \mu_1, \mu_2, \rho_2\}$ of D_4 and the group $\{a, b, c, d\}$ given in Exercise 1.2–9. Use Problem 57 to determine whether or not the two groups are isomorphic.

Perhaps you have noticed in every operation table we have studied that each row contains all the elements of the group and that no two rows of the table are the same. For example, in the table (Table 2.5) for $(\mathbf{Z}_3, +)$ the first row contains the elements $0_3 + a_3$ with a_3 ranging through $\mathbf{Z}_3$. The correspondence $a_3 \to 0_3 + a_3$ gives us the permutation

$$\tau_0 = \begin{pmatrix} 0_3 & 1_3 & 2_3 \\ 0_3 & 1_3 & 2_3 \end{pmatrix}$$

The second row of the table contains all the elements $1_3 + a_3$, where a_3 ranges through $\mathbf{Z}_3$. This correspondence $a_3 \to 1_3 + a_3$ gives us the permutation

$$\tau_1 = \begin{pmatrix} 0_3 & 1_3 & 2_3 \\ 1_3 & 2_3 & 0_3 \end{pmatrix}$$

Finally, the third row contains all the elements $2_3 + a_3$ for $a_3 \in \mathbf{Z}_3$. This row gives us the permutation

$$\tau_2 = \begin{pmatrix} 0_3 & 1_3 & 2_3 \\ 2_3 & 0_3 & 1_3 \end{pmatrix}$$

Table 2.3

$\circ$	a_1	a_2	$\cdots$	a_j	$\cdots$	a_n
a_1						
a_2						
$\vdots$						
a_i				$a_i \circ a_j = a_k$		
$\vdots$						
a_n						

Table 2.4

$*$	$\bar{a}_1$	$\bar{a}_2$	$\cdots$	$\bar{a}_j$	$\cdots$	$\bar{a}_n$
$\bar{a}_1$						
$\bar{a}_2$						
$\vdots$						
$\bar{a}_i$				$\bar{a}_i \circ \bar{a}_j = \bar{a}_k$		
$\vdots$						
$\bar{a}_n$						

Table 2.5

$+$	0_3	1_3	2_3
0_3	0_3	1_3	2_3
1_3	1_3	2_3	0_3
2_3	2_3	0_3	1_3

59

Problem   a   Write down the composition table for the permutations τ_0, τ_1, τ_2 defined above. Let $\Omega = \{\tau_0, \tau_1, \tau_2\}$. Is Ω a group? (Remember that Ω is a finite subset of $S(\{0_3, 1_3, 2_3\})$, the group of permutations on $\{0_3, 1_3, 2_3\}$.)

            b   Show by matching tables that the correspondence $0_3 \to \tau_0$, $1_3 \to \tau_1$, and $2_3 \to \tau_2$ defines an isomorphism from $\mathbf{Z}_3$ onto the group $\Omega = \{\tau_0, \tau_1, \tau_2\}$.

The correspondence defined in Problem 59 proves that $\mathbf{Z}_3$ is isomorphic to the subgroup Ω of the group of permutations on $\mathbf{Z}_3$. A generalization of this result to an arbitrary group is based on this same technique of forming permutations. This generalization, which is named after the English mathematician Arthur Cayley, is one of the most striking results in group theory.

Recall that for any nonempty set G the set $S(G)$ consisting of all permutations of G is a group with the operation of composition of functions.

60

Theorem   *Cayley's Theorem.* Every group G is isomorphic to a subgroup of a permutation group. In particular, G is isomorphic to a subgroup of $S(G)$.

Prove the theorem by means of the following problem:

61

Problem   a   Let $a \in G$. Define a function $\tau_a \colon G \to G$ by setting $\tau_a(x) = a \circ x$ for every $x \in G$. Show that τ_a is a permutation of G (that is, a one-to-one function from G onto G).

            b   Complete the statement $\tau_a \circ \tau_b = $ _____. To do so compute $(\tau_a \circ \tau_b)(x)$, where $x \in G$.

            c   Show that the set $\Omega = \{\tau_a \colon a \in G\}$ is a subgroup of $S(G)$ under the operation of composition.

            d   Define a function $\phi \colon G \to \Omega$ by setting $\phi(a) = \tau_a$ for every $a \in G$. Prove that ϕ is an isomorphism between G and Ω.

(Don't forget to prove that (i) ϕ is a homomorphism, (ii) ϕ is one-to-one, and (iii) ϕ is onto.)

Cayley's Theorem (Theorem 60) tells us that if we want to find all groups of a certain order we need only look at the subgroups of permutation groups. While this does restrict our attention, it does not actually describe all the desired groups. In fact, this problem of finding all groups of order n, where n is an arbitrary positive integer, is one of the great unsolved problems of group theory; the subgroups of the permutation groups are not all known.

EXERCISES 1   Let $(G, \circ)$ and $(\overline{G}, *)$ be isomorphic groups. Prove that $(G, \circ)$ is commutative if and only if $(\overline{G}, *)$ is commutative.

2   Display an isomorphism between $(\mathbf{Z}_3, +)$ and a suitable subgroup of S_3 under composition.

3   In each part of this exercise prove or disprove the existence of an isomorphism between the given pair of groups.
   a $(\mathbf{Z}_8, +)$ and the group $(D_4, \circ)$ of symmetries of the square
   b $(\mathbf{Z}_6, +)$ and $(S_3, \circ)$
   c $(S_3, \circ)$ and the group D_3 of symmetries of an equilateral triangle with the operation of composition
   d   The subgroups $\{e, \mu_1, \mu_2, \rho_2\}$ and $\{e, \rho_1, \rho_2, \rho_3\}$ of D_4 with the operation of composition

4   Determine all values of the integer n for which the following function is an isomorphism: ϕ_n from $(\mathbf{R} - \{0\}, \cdot)$ into itself defined by $\phi_n(x) = x^n$.

5   Prove that if H is a subgroup of the additive group $\mathbf{Z}$ and $H \neq \{0\}$, then H is isomorphic to $\mathbf{Z}$.

6   Prove or disprove the existence of an isomorphism between $(\mathbf{Z}, +)$ and $(\mathbf{Q}, +)$.   •

7   Prove or disprove the existence of an isomorphism between $(\mathbf{Z}, +)$ and the additive group

$$\left\{ \begin{pmatrix} a & 0 \\ 0 & d \end{pmatrix} : a, d \in \mathbf{Z} \right\}$$

8   Prove or disprove the existence of an isomorphism between $(\mathbf{R}, +)$ and $(\mathbf{R} - \{0\}, \cdot)$.

9   Let k and n be positive integers. Complete the following statement and prove it: The group $(\mathbf{Z}_k, +)$ is isomorphic to a subgroup of the additive group $\mathbf{Z}_n$ if and only if_____

_____ .

10   Let $\phi: \mathbf{R}^+ \to \mathbf{R}$ be defined by $\phi(x) = \log_{10} x$ for every $x \in \mathbf{R}^+$ and let $\alpha: \mathbf{R} \to \mathbf{R}^+$ be defined by $\alpha(y) = 10^y$ for every $y \in \mathbf{R}$.
   a Prove that $\alpha = \phi^{-1}$, the inverse function of ϕ.
   b Prove that α is an isomorphism between $(\mathbf{R}, +)$ and $(\mathbf{R}^+, \cdot)$.
   c Prove that ϕ is an isomorphism between $(\mathbf{R}^+, \cdot)$ and $(\mathbf{R}, +)$. (See Problem 50.)

*11 Prove that if ϕ is an isomorphism from a group $(G, \circ)$ onto a group $(\overline{G}, *)$, then ϕ^{-1} is an isomorphism from $(\overline{G}, *)$ onto $(G, \circ)$.

12   The statement "G is isomorphic to $\overline{G}$" defines a relation on the collection of all groups. Prove that this relation is an equivalence relation (i.e., that it is reflexive, symmetric, and transitive). (See Exercise 11.)

13   Illustrate Cayley's Theorem (Theorem 60) with the subgroup $H = \{e, \mu_1, \mu_2, \rho_2\}$ in D_4. For each element $a \in H$ write the corresponding function τ_a in permutation notation. Make a composition table for the group $\Omega = \{\tau_a : a \in H\}$. Show directly (without using the conclusion of Cayley's Theorem) that H is isomorphic to Ω.

14a Let $G = \{e, a\}$ be a group of order two. Construct an operation table for G and prove that G is isomorphic to the additive group $\mathbf{Z}_2$.
   b Let $G = \{e, a, b\}$ be a group of order three. Construct an operation table for G and prove that G is isomorphic to the additive group $\mathbf{Z}_3$.

15   Let $G = \{e, a, b, c\}$ be a group of order four. What are the possible orders of the elements of G?

a Suppose that G has an element, say a, of order four. Construct an operation table for G and prove that G is isomorphic to the additive group $\mathbf{Z}_4$.

b Suppose that G has no element of order four. Then every element of G except the identity has order _____. Make an operation table for G and show that G is isomorphic to the subgroup $\{e, \mu_1, \mu_2, \rho_2\}$ of D_4.

Exercise 15 shows that any group of order four is isomorphic to either $\mathbf{Z}_4$ or the subgroup $V = \{e, \mu_1, \mu_2, \rho_2\}$ of D_4. Note that $\mathbf{Z}_4$ and V are not isomorphic groups. (Why?) Thus we say that we have determined all the nonisomorphic groups of order four. In Exercise 14 we determined all the nonisomorphic groups of orders two and three.

16 Determine all the nonisomorphic groups of order five. To do so let G be a group of order five. Let $a \in G$ with $a \neq e$. Then a has order _____ . Construct an operation table for G and prove that G is isomorphic to the additive group $\mathbf{Z}_5$.

Exercises 14 through 16 show that any group of order two, three, four, or five must be commutative.

17 Prove that every group of order six is isomorphic to the additive group $\mathbf{Z}_6$ or to the group of permutations S_3. (See Exercise 2.3–13.) Thus $\mathbf{Z}_6$ and S_3 are the nonisomorphic groups of order six.

18 Let ϕ be an isomorphism between the groups $(G, \circ)$ and $(\overline{G}, *)$. Prove that for every $a \in G$ the order of $\phi(a)$ in $\overline{G}$ is the same as the order of a in G.

2.6 Cyclic Groups

We have seen several examples of a group which is generated by using powers (or multiples) of a single element. These examples include the additive group $\mathbf{Z}$ and the subgroups of $\mathbf{Z}_n$ under addition. In this section we see that any group which consists solely of the powers or multiples of a single element is isomorphic to some familiar group.

Recall that if $(G, \circ)$ is a group and $a \in G$ is an element of finite order n, then the set

$$\langle a \rangle = \{a^k : k \in \mathbf{Z}^+\}$$

is a commutative subgroup of G. (In an additive group $\langle a \rangle = \{ka : k \in \mathbf{Z}^+\}$.) However, if the element a has infinite order, then the set $\{a^k : k \in \mathbf{Z}^+\}$ (or $\{ka : k \in \mathbf{Z}^+\}$) is not a subgroup. For example, in the additive group $\mathbf{Z}$, the set

$$\{k \cdot 2 : k \in \mathbf{Z}^+\} = \{2, 4, 6, \dots\}$$

certainly is not a group. For such cases we have the following definition:

62
Definition

If $(G, +)$ is an additive group and $a \in G$ has infinite order, define $\langle a \rangle$ to be the set

$$\langle a \rangle = \{ka : k \in \mathbf{Z}\}$$
$$= \{\cdots, (-2) \cdot a, (-1) \cdot a, 0 \cdot a, 1 \cdot a, 2 \cdot a, \dots\}$$

If G is a nonadditive group and $a \in G$ has infinite order, define $\langle a \rangle$ to be the set

$$\langle a \rangle = \{a^k : k \in \mathbf{Z}\}$$
$$= \{\cdots, a^{-2}, a^{-1}, a^0, a^1, a^2, \dots\}$$

63
Problem

a   In the additive group $\mathbf{Z}$ describe all the elements of the set $\langle 2 \rangle$.

b   In the multiplicative group $\mathbf{R} - \{0\}$ describe all the elements of the set $\langle \frac{1}{3} \rangle$.

64

Problem

In the group D_4 find the element ρ_1^{-17} and express it as a positive power of ρ_1. Also express the element μ_2^{-21} as a positive power of μ_2.

If $(G, \circ)$ is a group and $a \in G$ has finite order n, then

$$\{a^k : k \in \mathbf{Z}\} = \{a^k : k \in \mathbf{Z}^+\}$$

The proof of this result follows immediately from Exercise 2.2–9. This shows that we can define $\langle a \rangle$ to be the set $\{a^k : k \in \mathbf{Z}\}$ for every $a \in G$, regardless of the order of a. Thus this new definition agrees with the earlier one in the case of an element of finite order. Naturally, in an additive group G if a has finite order,

$$\{ka : k \in \mathbf{Z}\} = \{ka : k \in \mathbf{Z}^+\}$$

65

Problem

Prove that if G is a group and $a \in G$, then $\langle a \rangle$ is a commutative subgroup of G. (We already know this result if $a \in G$ has finite order.)

The set $\langle a \rangle$ is called the cyclic subgroup generated by a. At times there may be an element $a \in G$ such that the cyclic subgroup generated by a is all of G. This case is considered in the following definition.

66

Definition

A group $(G, \circ)$ is a *cyclic group* if and only if there is an element $a \in G$ such that $G = \langle a \rangle$. The element a is said to *generate G*.

Note that every cyclic group is commutative since for any $a \in G$, $\langle a \rangle$ is a commutative group. Now let us look at the familiar groups $(\mathbf{Z}, +)$ and $(\mathbf{Z}_n, +)$ for $n \geq 2$.

67
Problem   Show that $(\mathbf{Z}, +)$ is a cyclic group. Is there more than one
                      element which can (by itself) generate $\mathbf{Z}$?

68
Problem   Show that $(\mathbf{Z}_5, +)$ is a cyclic group. Is there more than
                      one element which can (by itself) generate $\mathbf{Z}_5$?

69
Problem   Let $n \geq 2$ be a fixed integer. Prove that $(\mathbf{Z}_n, +)$ is a cyclic
                      group.

70
Problem   Let $(G, \circ)$ be a cyclic group generated by an element of
                      order three. How many distinct elements are in G? Make
                      an operation table for G and show that G is isomorphic to
                      the familiar group ____ . (Pay careful attention to the defi-
                      nition of the order of an element.)

The following theorem shows that all finite cyclic groups of the same order
are isomorphic and that all of them resemble some familiar groups.

71
Problem   Complete the statement and prove the following theorem:

Theorem   If $(G, \circ)$ is a cyclic group generated by an element of finite
                      order n, then G is isomorphic to the group ____ . ▲

72
Problem   Complete the statement and prove the following theorem:

Theorem   If $(G, \circ)$ is a cyclic group generated by an element of in-
                      finite order, then G is isomorphic to the group ____ .

Theorems 71 and 72 complete the characterization of all cyclic groups. Any finite cyclic group of order n is isomorphic to _____ and any infinite cyclic group is isomorphic to _____ .

73
Theorem   Every subgroup of a cyclic group is cyclic.

Leave the proof of this theorem for Exercise 3.

In the case of a group whose order is a prime number, we can actually strengthen Theorem 71 to obtain the following very important theorem.

74
Problem   Complete the statement and prove the following theorem:

Theorem   Any group of prime order is cyclic. Specifically, if p is a
                        prime, then any group of order p is cyclic and is isomorphic
                        to the group _____ .

EXERCISES 1   Determine whether or not each of the following groups is
                        cyclic. Justify your answers.
             a $(S_3, \circ)$
             b $(D_4, \circ)$
             c   The subgroup $\{e, \rho_1, \rho_2, \rho_3\}$ of D_4.
             d   The subgroup $\{e, \mu_1, \mu_2, \rho_2\}$ of D_4.

          2   Prove that a finite group $(G, \circ)$ is a cyclic group if and only
                        if there exists an element $a \in G$ whose order is the same as
                        the order of G.

          3   Prove Theorem 73. ●

          4   Prove or disprove that $(\mathbf{Q}, +)$ is a cyclic group.

          5   Prove that every noncommutative group (finite or infinite)
                        contains commutative subgroups different from $\{e\}$.

6   Let G be a group of prime order p. Describe all possible generators of G (that is, all elements $a \in G$ such that $G = \langle a \rangle$). Justify your answer.

7   Let G be a finite cyclic group of order n. Determine all possible subgroups of G.

8   Let G be an infinite cyclic group. Determine all possible subgroups of G.

2.7 Normal Subgroups

When we encountered left cosets and right cosets of a subgroup in Section 2.3 we saw that they need not be the same for a given element. However, when a subgroup H has the property that $a \circ H = H \circ a$ for every $a \in G$, it is possible to form a new type of group using H. As a first step to the construction of this type of group, we consider in this section properties of the special subgroups for which the left cosets and the right cosets are the same.

To begin this work with subgroups it is useful to recall some properties of cosets. Carefully review the results of Lemma 31.

75
Problem

In the group $(D_4, \circ)$ of symmetries of the square let K be the subgroup $\{e, \mu_1, \mu_2, \rho_2\}$.

a   Determine the elements of the left coset $\rho_1 \circ K$.

b   Determine the elements of the left coset $\rho_3 \circ K$. Do this *without computation* by using the following property of cosets: If two left cosets have even one element in common, then they are the same.

c   Calculate the index of K in D_4.

d   Without any computing determine the remaining left cosets of K in D_4. (Naturally, the same techniques can be used to find right cosets.)

76
Definition

Let $(G, \circ)$ be a group and K a subgroup of G. Then K is a *normal subgroup* of G if and only if for every $a \in G$ the left coset $a \circ K$ is equal to the right coset $K \circ a$, that is, if and only if *for every $a \in G$*,

$$\{k \circ a : k \in K\} = K \circ a = a \circ K = \{a \circ k : k \in K\}$$

Caution

To show that a given subgroup K of a group G is normal in G, one must prove that $K \circ a = a \circ K$ for every element a in the (whole) group G. It is not enough to use only those elements in the subgroup K. In fact, if $a \in K$, then $K \circ a = K = a \circ K$.

77
Problem

In the group $(D_4, \circ)$ of the symmetries of the square determine whether or not each of the following subgroups is normal. Justify your answers. You may want to compute the index of each subgroup and refer to Table 2.2 of Exercise 2.3–3.

a $\{e, \mu_2\}$
b $\{e, \rho_2\}$
c $\{e, \mu_1, \mu_2, \rho_2\}$

78
Problem

It follows immediately from Problem 38 that if a group is commutative, then every subgroup is normal. Some people erroneously believe a partial converse to this fact. They think that if K is a normal subgroup of a group G, then $k \circ a = a \circ k$ for every $k \in K$ and $a \in G$. Choose a normal subgroup of D_4 (for example, see Problem 77) and find an element k in the subgroup and an element $a \in D_4$ such that $a \circ k \neq k \circ a$.

Although the definition of a normal subgroup is given in terms of the equality of sets, it is often more convenient to work with statements involving elements of the sets. As a first step in proving some useful equivalent forms of the definition, we have the following lemma.

79
Problem

Prove the following lemma:

Lemma

Let $(G, \circ)$ be a group. A subgroup K of G is a normal subgroup if and only if for every $k \in K$ and every $a \in G$ there are elements $k_1, k_2 \in K$ such that

$$k \circ a = a \circ k_1 \qquad \text{and} \qquad a \circ k = k_2 \circ a \quad \blacktriangle$$

The following theorem gives several conditions, all equivalent, for a subgroup to be a normal subgroup. Use Lemma 79 to prove the equivalence of statements a and b of the theorem (i.e., prove that statement a implies statement b and vice versa). Leave the rest of the proof for Exercise 7.

80
Theorem   Let $(G, \circ)$ be a group and let K be a subgroup of G. Then the following statements are equivalent:

a K is a normal subgroup of G.

b   For every $a \in G$ and $k \in K$,

$a' \circ k \circ a \in K$

c   For every $a \in G$,

$a' \circ K \circ a \subseteq K$

where $a' \circ K \circ a = \{a' \circ k \circ a : k \in K\}$.

d   For every $a \in K$,

$a' \circ K \circ a = K$

In Section 2.4 we defined the kernel of a homomorphism $\phi: G \to \overline{G}$ and showed that the kernel is a subgroup of G. We can extend this result as follows:

81
Problem   Prove the following theorem:

Theorem   If $(G, \circ)$ and $(\overline{G}, *)$ are groups and $\phi: G \to \overline{G}$ is a homomorphism, then the kernel of ϕ, $\ker(\phi)$, is a normal subgroup of G. ▲

We have seen that if H and K are subgroups of a group $(G, \circ)$, then $H \cap K$ is a subgroup. Proposition 82 extends this result.

82
Proposition   Let $(G, \circ)$ be a group. If H and K are normal subgroups of G, then $H \cap K$ is a normal subgroup of G.

The proof of this proposition is left for Exercise 1.

83
Problem   Let $(G, \circ)$ be a group and K a subgroup of G. We have already stated that if $a \in K$, then $a \circ K = K = K \circ a$. It is useful to note what happens when $a \notin K$. Let $k \in K$ and $a \in G - K$.

       a   Decide whether $k \circ a \in K$ or $k \circ a \in G - K$. ▲

       b   Decide whether $a \circ k \in K$ or $a \circ k \in G - K$.

84
Problem   Prove the following theorem:

Theorem   If $(G, \circ)$ is a finite group of even order $2n$ and K is a subgroup of G of order n, then K is normal in G. ▲

For applications of Theorem 84 see Exercises 2 through 4.

If we recall that the index of a subgroup K in G is the number of distinct left cosets of K, then we can restate Theorem 84 as follows:

84′
Theorem   If $(G, \circ)$ is a finite group and K is a subgroup of index two in G, then K is normal in G.

For a generalization of this form of the theorem see Exercise 5.

85
Problem   Use Theorem 84 to find a proper normal subgroup of the group S_3.

We have seen that for any subgroup H of a group G the cosets of H behave like the classes of an equivalence relation (e.g., two cosets of H are either disjoint or equal). In the next section we study the collection of all cosets of a normal subgroup (just as we studied the set of all equivalence classes for the relation on **Z** of congruence modulo n). We show that for a normal subgroup it is possible to define a binary operation on this collection of cosets.

EXERCISES 1   Prove Proposition 82.

2   Find all the normal subgroups of D_4. ●

3   Prove that for every integer $n \geq 3$ the dihedral group D_n (defined in Exercise 1.6–5) has a normal subgroup of order n.

4   Find all the normal subgroups of S_3.

5   Prove the following theorem, which is an extension of Theorem 84'. In doing so you may want to refer to Exercise 2.3–7.

   Theorem   Let $(G, \circ)$ be a group (either finite or infinite). If K is a subgroup of index two in G, then K is normal in G.

6   Find a homomorphism from S_3 onto S_2. Don't forget that the kernel of the homomorphism must be a normal subgroup of S_3.

7   Complete the proof of Theorem 80. You might want to prove the chain of implications $b \Rightarrow c \Rightarrow d \Rightarrow b$ since you already have proved $a \Leftrightarrow b$.

*8   Let $(G, \circ)$ and $(\overline{G}, *)$ be groups and let $\phi: G \rightarrow \overline{G}$ be a homomorphism.
   a   Prove that if ϕ maps G onto $\overline{G}$ and if H is a normal subgroup of G, then the image set $\phi(H)$ is a normal subgroup of $\overline{G}$.
   b   Prove that if $\overline{H}$ is a normal subgroup of $\overline{G}$, then the inverse image $\phi^{-1}(\overline{H})$ is a normal subgroup of G. See Exercise 2.4–14 for the definition of $\phi^{-1}(\overline{H})$.

*9   **Definition**   If $(G, \circ)$ is a group, the *center* of G, denoted by $Z(G)$, is the set

$$Z(G) = \{x: x \in G \text{ and } x \circ g = g \circ x \text{ for all } g \in G\}$$

   Thus an element x belongs to the center of G if and only if x commutes with *every* element of G.

   a   Find the center of the group $(S_3, \circ)$.
   b   Find the center of the group $(D_4, \circ)$.

*10   Let $(G, \circ)$ be a group. Prove the following statements about $Z(G)$:
    a $Z(G)$ is a subgroup of G.
    b $Z(G)$ is a commutative subgroup of G.
    c $Z(G)$ is a normal subgroup of G.
    d $Z(G) = G$ if and only if G is commutative.

11   Find the center of the multiplicative group $\mathscr{I}$ of nonsingular 2×2 matrices. Be careful: $Z(\mathscr{I})$ is not just the identity matrix.

*12   In a group $(G, \circ)$ a *commutator* is any element of the form $x' \circ y' \circ x \circ y$, where $x, y \in G$. One example of a commutator in D_4 is the element $\rho_1' \circ \mu_1' \circ \rho_1 \circ \mu_1$.

Let C be the set of all finite products of commutators in G. Specifically, if $x_i, y_i \in G$ for $i = 1, 2, \ldots, n$, where n is any positive integer, then the definition of C says that the composite

$$(x_1' \circ y_1' \circ x_1 \circ y_1) \circ \cdots \circ (x_n' \circ y_n' \circ x_n \circ y_n)$$

is an element of C.
    a   Prove that C is a subgroup of G. This set C is called the *commutator subgroup* of G.
    b   Prove that C is a normal subgroup of G. ●
    c   Find the commutator subgroup of D_4. Begin by finding commutators in D_4 and then compare with the normal subgroups of D_4.
    d   If the group $(G, \circ)$ is commutative, then the commutator subgroup of G is equal to _____. Is the converse true? Justify your answers.

13   Prove that if K is a subgroup of G and $a \in G$, then $a' \circ K \circ a$ is a subgroup of G. Thus the set $a' \circ K \circ a$ is of interest even if K is not a normal subgroup of G. In fact, the set $a' \circ K \circ a$ can be different from K only if K is not a normal subgroup.

*14   Let $(G, \circ)$ be a group and H and K normal subgroups of G such that $H \cap K = \{e\}$. Prove that $h \circ k = k \circ h$ for every $h \in H$ and $k \in K$. ●

15 Let H and K be subgroups of a group G. We define the composite of the subgroups H and K to be the set

$$H \circ K = \{h \circ k \colon h \in H,\ k \in K\}$$

a In the group D_4 let $H = \{e, \rho_2\}$ and $K = \{e, \mu_1\}$. Note that H is normal in D_4. Find $H \circ K$ and decide whether or not it is a subgroup of D_4.

b Give an example in S_3 to show that the composite of two subgroups is not necessarily a subgroup.

*16 Let $(G, \circ)$ be a group and let H and K be subgroups of G. Prove the following statements.

a If H is normal in G or K is normal in G, then $H \circ K$ is a subgroup of G. ●

b If H is normal in G and K is normal in G, then $H \circ K$ is a normal subgroup of G.

2.8 Quotient Groups

In Section 2.7 we focused on properties of a normal subgroup of a group G (that is, a subgroup K for which every left coset $a \circ K$ is equal to the corresponding right coset $K \circ a$). With these properties in hand we can now construct a new group whose elements are the cosets of the normal subgroup K of G. This group of cosets plays an important role in the theory of groups. Surprisingly, the notion of the group of cosets allows us to determine all the images of a group G under homomorphisms.

We begin by studying the additive group $\mathbf{Z}$ and the normal subgroup $n\mathbf{Z} = \{nk: k \in \mathbf{Z}\}$.

86

Problem   a   Let $n = 5$. List the distinct cosets of the subgroup $5\mathbf{Z}$ in the additive group $\mathbf{Z}$: $0 + 5\mathbf{Z}$, _____ .
State a relationship between these cosets and the equivalence classes 0_5, 1_5, etc., in $\mathbf{Z}_5$.

          b   For a fixed positive integer n show that for every $a \in \mathbf{Z}$ the coset $a + n\mathbf{Z}$ is equal to the equivalence class a_n.

          c   If $a, b \in \mathbf{Z}$, find the coset $x + n\mathbf{Z}$ corresponding to the sum $a_n + b_n$ in the group $\mathbf{Z}_n$. Written in terms of cosets,

$$(a + n\mathbf{Z}) + (b + n\mathbf{Z}) = \underline{\hspace{2cm}}$$

Thus we see that for the group $\mathbf{Z}$ and the normal subgroup $n\mathbf{Z}$ the collection of cosets $\{a + n\mathbf{Z}: a \in \mathbf{Z}\}$ forms a group, the group $\mathbf{Z}_n$, with addition of cosets defined by

$$(a + n\mathbf{Z}) + (b + n\mathbf{Z}) = \underline{\hspace{2cm}} + n\mathbf{Z}$$

Let us use $\mathbf{Z}_n$ as a model for the construction of a group from a given group G and a normal subgroup K.

87

Definition   For a group G and a normal subgroup K let G/K be the collection of all distinct left cosets of K in G. Thus

$$G/K = \{a \circ K: a \in G\}$$

The symbol G/K is often read "G mod K."

We want to define an operation on the cosets of K which will make G/K a group. Following the example of Problem 86, we define $(a \circ K) \circ (b \circ K)$ to be the coset $(a \circ b) \circ K$ for every $a, b \in G$. Thus for every $a, b \in G$,

$$(a \circ K) \circ (b \circ K) = (a \circ b) \circ K$$

88

Problem

Let $G = D_4$, the group of symmetries of the square. Let K be the normal subgroup $\{e, \rho_2\}$.

a   Find the index of K in D_4 and list the distinct elements of G/K (that is, the distinct cosets of K in G).

b   Compute $(\mu_1 \circ K) \circ (\delta_1 \circ K)$ as defined above.

c   Show that $\mu_1 \circ K = \mu_2 \circ K$, $\delta_1 \circ K = \delta_2 \circ K$, and

$$(\mu_1 \circ K) \circ (\delta_1 \circ K) = (\mu_2 \circ K) \circ (\delta_2 \circ K)$$

This shows that the operation is properly defined for at least these particular cosets.

d   Make an operation table for the set G/K using the definition above for $(a \circ K) \circ (b \circ K)$. Remember to use only the distinct cosets of K in your table.

e   Find an identity element and the inverse of every element in D_4/K.

Now let us return to the general problem. Let G be a group, K a normal subgroup, and G/K the collection of distinct cosets of K in G. We have defined an operation $\circ$ on G/K by setting

$$(a \circ K) \circ (b \circ K) = (a \circ b) \circ K$$

for every $a, b \in G$. If the correspondence

$$(a \circ K, b \circ K) \rightarrow (a \circ b) \circ K$$

is to be a properly defined binary operation on G/K, then it must assign to every pair of cosets in G/K exactly one coset in G/K and this assignment must not depend on the particular choice of representation for the cosets. The fact that the operation is properly defined is established in the following problem.

89

Problem   Let K be a normal subgroup of the group G and let $a_1, a_2, b_1, b_2 \in G$. Show that if $a_1 \circ K = a_2 \circ K$ and $b_1 \circ K = b_2 \circ K$, then

$$(a_1 \circ b_1) \circ K = (a_2 \circ b_2) \circ K$$

and hence that

$$(a_1 \circ K) \circ (b_1 \circ K) = (a_2 \circ K) \circ (b_2 \circ K) \quad \blacktriangle$$

Now that we know that there is a properly defined binary operation on G/K if K is a normal subgroup, we can prove that G/K is a group with this operation

90

Problem   Prove the following theorem:

Theorem   If $(G, \circ)$ is a group and K is a normal subgroup of G, then $(G/K, \circ)$ is a group.

The group G/K, which consists of all the distinct cosets of K in G, is called the *quotient group* or factor group of G by K.

If $(G, +)$ is an additive group, the sum of two cosets $a+K$ and $b+K$ is written

$$(a+K) + (b+K) = (a+b) + K$$

If $(G, \cdot)$ is a multiplicative group, the coset $a \cdot K$ is often written aK and the product of two cosets aK and bK in G/K is written in the form

$$(aK) \cdot (bK) = (ab) K$$

91

Problem   a   Choose a subgroup K of order four in the additive group $\mathbf{Z}_{12}$. List the distinct cosets of K in $\mathbf{Z}_{12}$ and make an addition table for the quotient group $\mathbf{Z}_{12}/K$. In your table use the symbols $0_{12}+K$, etc., for the elements of the quotient group $\mathbf{Z}_{12}/K$.

b   Prove that $(\mathbf{Z}_{12}/K, +)$ is isomorphic to the familiar group
_____ .

If $(G, \circ)$ is a finite group and K a normal subgroup of G, then there is an important relationship among the orders of the group G, the normal subgroup K, and the quotient group G/K.

92
Problem   Let G be a finite group and K a normal subgroup of G.
               Express the order of the quotient group G/K in terms of the
               order of G and the order of K.

There is a close relationship between the operation of the group G and the operation of the quotient group G/K of G by the normal subgroup K. In fact, there is a natural mapping $a \rightarrow a \circ K$ $(a \in G)$ from the group G into the quotient group G/K which assigns to every element $a \in G$ the coset $a \circ K$ to which a belongs.

As an example of this mapping let us consider the additive group $\mathbf{Z}_n = \mathbf{Z}/n\mathbf{Z}$. Define $\pi : \mathbf{Z} \rightarrow \mathbf{Z}/n\mathbf{Z}$ by setting

$$\pi(a) = a + n\mathbf{Z} \ (= a_n)$$

for every $a \in \mathbf{Z}$. We have already seen that π is a homomorphism which maps $\mathbf{Z}$ onto $\mathbf{Z}/n\mathbf{Z} = \mathbf{Z}_n$ and that $\ker(\pi) = $ _____ . (See Problems 44 and 46.)

93
Problem   As a second example let us consider the group D_4 of the
               symmetries of the square and the normal subgroup $K =$
               $\{e, \mu_1, \mu_2, \rho_2\}$. Define $\pi : D_4 \rightarrow D_4/K$ by setting $\pi(a) = a \circ K$
               for every $a \in D_4$.

        a   Describe π by finding $\pi(a)$ explicitly for every $a \in D_4$.

        b   Does π map D_4 onto D_4/K?

        c   Find $\ker(\pi)$.

Now let us state the general theorem.

94

Problem   Prove the following theorem:

Theorem   Let K be a normal subgroup of the group G. Define
                   $\pi: G \to G/K$ by setting $\pi(a) = a \circ K$ for every $a \in G$. Then

                   a π is a homomorphism,
                   b π maps G onto G/K,
                   c   the kernel of π is the normal subgroup K. ▲

The homomorphism $\pi: G \to G/K$ defined in Theorem 94 is called the *canonical homomorphism*. The quotient group G/K is said to be a *homomorphic image* of G because there is a homomorphism from G onto G/K. In the next section we continue our study of groups which can be homomorphic images of G (that is, the groups $\overline{G}$ for which there exists a homomorphism mapping G onto $\overline{G}$).

EXERCISES 1   In the group $(S_3, \circ)$ choose a normal subgroup K of order three.
                   a   Make an operation table for the quotient group S_3/K.
                   b   Prove that S_3/K is isomorphic to the familiar group _____.

          2   Choose a normal subgroup K of order three in the additive group $\mathbf{Z}_{18}$.
                   a   Make an addition table for the quotient group $\mathbf{Z}_{18}/K$.
                   b   Prove that $\mathbf{Z}_{18}/K$ is isomorphic to the familiar group _____.

          3   Let $(G, \circ)$ be a group.
                   a   Prove that the quotient group $G/\{e\}$ is isomorphic to G.
                   b   Describe the distinct elements of the quotient group G/G.

         *4   Let G and $\overline{G}$ be groups, ϕ a homomorphism from G *onto* $\overline{G}$, K a normal subgroup of G, and $\overline{K} = \{\phi(k): k \in K\}$. Then $\overline{K}$ is a normal subgroup of $\overline{G}$ (Exercise 2.7–8). Define $\overline{\phi}: G/K \to \overline{G}/\overline{K}$ by setting $\overline{\phi}(a \circ K) = \phi(a) \circ \overline{K}$. Show that
                   a $\overline{\phi}$ is a properly defined function,
                   b $\overline{\phi}$ is a homomorphism,
                   c $\overline{\phi}$ maps G/K onto $\overline{G}/\overline{K}$.

5   Let $(G, \circ)$ be a group and let C be the commutator sub-
     group of G (see Exercise 2.7–12). Prove that the quotient
     group G/C is commutative. ●

6   Let $(G, \circ)$ be a group and let K be a normal subgroup of G.
     Prove that if G/K is commutative, then K contains the com-
     mutator subgroup of G.

7   A natural question to ask in the study of quotient groups is
     the following: If cosets are defined for any subgroup, why
     is the quotient group defined only for normal subgroups?
     A subgroup of D_4 helps answer this question by showing
     that the proposed operation in the set G/K is not properly
     defined if K is not normal. Let $K = \{e, \mu_1\}$.
a   Is K normal in D_4?
b   Show that $\rho_1 \circ K = \delta_1 \circ K$ and $\rho_3 \circ K = \delta_2 \circ K$.
c   Show that the cosets $(\rho_1 \circ \rho_3) \circ K$ and $(\delta_1 \circ \delta_2) \circ K$ are not
     equal.
d   Is $(\rho_1 \circ K) \circ (\rho_3 \circ K) = (\delta_1 \circ K) \circ (\delta_2 \circ K)$?

8   Let G be a group, K a subgroup of G, and G/K the collection
     of distinct left cosets of K in G. We have seen that if K is a
     normal subgroup of G, then the correspondence

     $$(a \circ K, b \circ K) \rightarrow (a \circ b) \circ K$$

     is a properly defined binary operation on G/K. Prove the
     converse: If the correspondence is a properly defined binary
     operation on G/K, then K is a normal subgroup of G. ●

9   Another natural question that arises in the study of quotient
     groups is the following: If K is a normal subgroup of a
     group G, what properties of G are inherited by G/K? Deter-
     mine whether each of the following statements is true or
     false. If it is true, prove it; if it is false, give a counterexample.
     Let K be a normal subgroup of $(G, \circ)$.
a   If G is commutative, then G/K is commutative.
b   If G is cyclic, then G/K is cyclic. ●
c   If G is infinite, then G/K is infinite.

*10   Let $(G, \circ)$ be a group, K a normal subgroup of G, and $a \in G$.

   a   Show that the order of $a \circ K$ in G/K divides the order of a in G.

   b   Show that if p is a prime, $a \notin K$, and $(a \circ K)^p = K$ in G/K, then there exists an element $b \in G$ such that b has order p.

*11   Prove Cauchy's Theorem for Abelian Groups: If $(G, \circ)$ is a commutative finite group and if the prime p divides the order of G, then there exists $a \in G - \{e\}$ such that $a^p = e$.   ●

2.9 Homomorphic Images and Quotient Groups

In the preceding section we saw that the natural mapping $a \to a \circ K$ of an element a of a group G onto its coset $a \circ K$ of a normal subgroup K was a homomorphism from G onto G/K, the quotient group. In general, if ϕ is a homomorphism from a group G onto a group $\overline{G}$, then $\ker(\phi)$ is a normal subgroup of G. Thus this homomorphism determines a normal subgroup K of G and a quotient group G/K. In this section we want to compare the quotient group G/K with the image group $\overline{G}$.

95
Definition

A group $(\overline{G}, *)$ is a *homomorphic image* of a group $(G, \circ)$ if and only if there is a homomorphism from G onto $\overline{G}$ (that is, a homomorphism $\phi: G \to \overline{G}$ such that $\phi(G) = \overline{G}$).

96
Problem

Define a function ϕ from $(\mathbf{Z}_{12}, +)$ onto $(\mathbf{Z}_3, +)$ by setting $\phi(a_{12}) = a_3$ for every $a \in \mathbf{Z}$.

a   Prove that ϕ is a homomorphism from $\mathbf{Z}_{12}$ onto $\mathbf{Z}_3$. Thus $\mathbf{Z}_3$ is a homomorphic image of $\mathbf{Z}_{12}$.

b   Find the elements in $K = \ker(\phi)$.

c   Show that for every element $b_{12} \in 2_{12} + K$, $\phi(b_{12}) = \phi(2_{12})$.

d   Prove that $\mathbf{Z}_{12}/K$ is isomorphic to $\mathbf{Z}_3$. See Problem 91 for the addition table for $\mathbf{Z}_{12}/K$.

The following lemma for homomorphisms is useful not only in proving Theorem 101 below but also in solving linear equations (see Exercise 2). Leave the proof of Lemma 97 and Corollary 98 to Exercise 1.

97
Lemma

Let $(G, \circ)$ and $(\overline{G}, *)$ be groups and let $\phi: G \to \overline{G}$ be a homomorphism. Let $a, b \in G$. Then $\phi(a) = \phi(b)$ if and only if $b = a \circ k$ for some $k \in \ker(\phi)$.

98
Corollary

Let $\phi: G \to \overline{G}$ be a homomorphism from a group $(G, \circ)$ into a group $(\overline{G}, *)$. Let $K = \ker(\phi)$. Then $\phi(a) = \phi(b)$ for $a, b \in G$ if and only if $b \in a \circ K$ or, equivalently, $a \circ K = b \circ K$.

99
Problem

Let us examine the homomorphism $\pi: \mathbf{Z} \to \mathbf{Z}_n$ defined by setting $\pi(a) = a_n$ for every $a \in \mathbf{Z}$. Fix $a \in \mathbf{Z}$. Use Lemma 97 and Corollary 98 to show that $\pi(b) = a_n$ if and only if $b = a + k$ for some $k \in n\mathbf{Z}$. Moreover, $\pi(b) = \pi(a)$ if and only if $a + n\mathbf{Z} = b + n\mathbf{Z}$.

We saw in Problem 96 that if $\phi: \mathbf{Z}_{12} \to \mathbf{Z}_3$ is defined by setting $\phi(a_{12}) = a_3$ for every $a \in \mathbf{Z}$ and $K = \ker(\phi)$, then $\mathbf{Z}_{12}/K$ is isomorphic to $\mathbf{Z}_3$. In proving the existence of an isomorphism, you may have used the correspondence $a_{12} + K \to a_3$. Let us study this correspondence.

100
Problem

Define $\overline{\phi}: \mathbf{Z}_{12}/K \to \mathbf{Z}_3$ by setting

$$\overline{\phi}(a_{12} + K) = a_3 = \phi(a_{12})$$

a   Evaluate $\overline{\phi}(a_{12} + K)$ for every distinct coset $a_{12} + K$ in $\mathbf{Z}_{12}/K$. Use Lemma 97 to show that $\overline{\phi}$ is a properly defined function (i.e., if $a_{12} + K = b_{12} + K$, then $\overline{\phi}(a_{12} + K) = \overline{\phi}(b_{12} + K)$). (See Figure 2.5.)

Figure 2.5

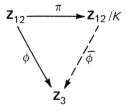

b   Show that $\overline{\phi}$ is a homomorphism.

c   Find $\ker(\overline{\phi})$.

d   Show that $\overline{\phi}$ is an isomorphism from $\mathbf{Z}_{12}/K$ onto $\mathbf{Z}_3$.

Let $(G, \circ)$ and $(\overline{G}, *)$ be groups, ϕ a homomorphism from G onto $\overline{G}$, and $K = \ker(\phi)$. Lemma 97 and Corollary 98 tell us that every element of the coset $a \circ K$ $(a \in G)$ is mapped onto $\phi(a)$ and that if $a \circ K \neq b \circ K$, then $\phi(a) \neq \phi(b)$. Thus an element $a \circ K$ of the quotient group G/K corresponds to the element $\phi(a)$ of $\overline{G}$. We want to show that this mapping $a \circ K \to \phi(a)$ from G/K into $\overline{G}$ is a function which is, in fact, an isomorphism. (See Figure 2.6.)

Figure 2.6

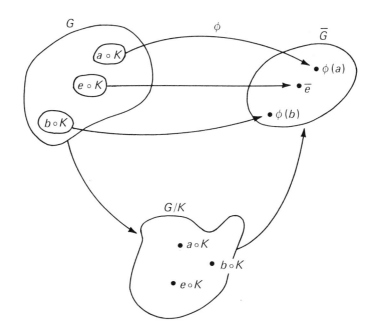

101
Theorem

First Isomorphism Theorem for Groups. Let ϕ be a homomorphism from a group $(G, \circ)$ *onto* a group $(\overline{G}, *)$ and let K denote the kernel of ϕ. Then $\overline{G}$ is isomorphic to the quotient group G/K.

Prove the theorem by working the following problem:

102
Problem

Let $(G, \circ)$ and $(\overline{G}, *)$ be groups and let $\phi: G \to \overline{G}$ be a homomorphism from G *onto* $\overline{G}$. Let $K = \ker(\phi)$. Define $\overline{\phi}: G/K \to \overline{G}$ by setting $\overline{\phi}(a \circ K) = \phi(a)$ for every $a \in G$. (See Figure 2.7.)

a   Show that $\bar{\phi}$ is a properly defined function (i.e., if $a \circ K = b \circ K$, then $\bar{\phi}(a \circ K) = \bar{\phi}(b \circ K)$).

b   Prove that $\bar{\phi}$ is a homomorphism.

c   Find $\ker(\bar{\phi})$ (that is, find all the elements $x \in G$ such that $\bar{\phi}(x \circ K) = \bar{e}$).

d   Show that $\bar{\phi}$ is one-to-one.

e   Show that $\bar{\phi}$ maps G/K onto $\bar{G}$.

Figure 2.7

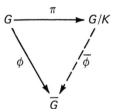

103
Problem

Prove that if $\bar{\phi}: G/K \to \bar{G}$ is the isomorphism defined in Problem 102 and if $\pi: G \to G/K$ is the homomorphism defined by $\pi(a) = a \circ K$ for every $a \in G$, then $\bar{\phi} \circ \pi = \phi$.

It now follows quickly that the isomorphism $\bar{\phi}: G/K \to \bar{G}$ defined in Problem 102 is the only isomorphism from G/K onto $\bar{G}$ for which $\bar{\phi} \circ \pi = \phi$. If $\bar{\phi}_1$ is any function from G/K into $\bar{G}$ such that $\bar{\phi}_1 \circ \pi = \phi$, then

$$\bar{\phi}_1(a \circ K) = \bar{\phi}_1\big(\pi(a)\big) = \phi(a)$$

for every $a \in G$. Thus $\bar{\phi}_1 = \bar{\phi}$.

Using the definition of the homomorphic image of a group, we can restate the First Isomorphism Theorem as follows:

101'
Theorem

For every homomorphic image $\bar{G}$ of G there is a normal subgroup K in G such that $\bar{G}$ is isomorphic to G/K.

Combining the First Isomorphism Theorem with Theorem 94, we have the following characterization of the homomorphic images of a group G.

Suppose we want to find all those groups which are homomorphic images of a given group G and yet are not isomorphic to one another. The First Isomorphism Theorem says that we do not have to look farther than the quotient groups of G. Certainly every normal subgroup K of the group G determines a homomorphic image of G, namely the quotient group G/K. Moreover, if $\overline{G}$ is a homomorphic image of G, then $\overline{G}$ is isomorphic to one of these quotient groups. Thus, in order to find the collection of all nonisomorphic groups which are homomorphic images of G, we need only choose those quotient groups which are not isomorphic to one another.

In the following problems we consider examples of this characterization.

104

Problem   a   Choose a proper subgroup K in $\mathbf{Z}_{12}$ of order $k \neq 4$. List the elements of $\mathbf{Z}_{12}/K$, make the addition table for $\mathbf{Z}_{12}/K$, and find a familiar group which is isomorphic to $\mathbf{Z}_{12}/K$.

            b   Find all the nonisomorphic groups which are homomorphic images of the group $(\mathbf{Z}_{12}, +)$.

105

Problem   a   Let the group $(\overline{G}, *)$ be a homomorphic image of a finite group $(G, \circ)$. Find a relationship between the order of $\overline{G}$ and the order of G.

            b   Use the relationship of part a to determine which of the groups $(\mathbf{Z}_m, +)$ can be homomorphic images of $(\mathbf{Z}_{15}, +)$.

EXERCISES   1   Prove Lemma 97 and Corollary 98.

            2   Define $\phi: M_2(\mathbf{R}) \to M_2(\mathbf{R})$ by setting $\phi(X) = AX$ for a fixed matrix $A \in M_2(\mathbf{R})$.

            a   Show that ϕ is a homomorphism from $\big(M_2(\mathbf{R}), +\big)$ into itself.

b   Let

$$A = \begin{pmatrix} 2 & -1 \\ -2 & 1 \end{pmatrix}$$

With this choice for A find $\ker(\phi)$.

c   Show that

$$\begin{pmatrix} 2 & 3 \\ -1 & 2 \end{pmatrix}$$

is one solution of the equation

$$\phi(X) = \begin{pmatrix} 5 & 4 \\ -5 & -4 \end{pmatrix}$$

for the choice of A given in part b. Use Lemma 97 to show that

$$\phi(X) = \begin{pmatrix} 5 & 4 \\ -5 & -4 \end{pmatrix}$$

if and only if

$$X = \begin{pmatrix} 2+\alpha & 3+\beta \\ -1+2\alpha & 2+2\beta \end{pmatrix}$$

for $\alpha, \beta \in \mathbf{R}$. Thus the system of equations

$$
\begin{aligned}
2x - z &= 5 \\
2y - w &= 4 \\
-2x + z &= -5 \\
-2y + w &= -4
\end{aligned}
$$

or

$$\begin{pmatrix} 2 & -1 \\ -2 & 1 \end{pmatrix}\begin{pmatrix} x & y \\ z & w \end{pmatrix} = \begin{pmatrix} 5 & 4 \\ -5 & -4 \end{pmatrix}$$

has the solution $x = 2+\alpha$, $y = 3+\beta$, $z = -1+2\alpha$, and $w = 2+2\beta$ for every $\alpha, \beta \in \mathbf{R}$.

This technique is not really necessary in the case of 2×2 matrices but it is quite useful with larger systems of linear equations and with differential equations.

3   Let $(G, \circ)$ be a group of finite order p, where p is a prime. Let $(\overline{G}, *)$ be a homomorphic image of G. Show that either $\overline{G} = \{\overline{e}\}$ or $\overline{G}$ is isomorphic to G. Give two different proofs of this proposition, one using the First Isomorphism Theorem (Theorem 101).

4   In a group G there may be two (or more) normal subgroups H and K such that G/H is isomorphic to G/K. Give an example of this phenomenon in D_4.

5   Let $\mathbf{R}^2 = \mathbf{R} \times \mathbf{R}$ with addition defined by

$$(a, b) + (c, d) = (a+c, b+d)$$

for every $(a, b), (c, d) \in \mathbf{R}^2$.

   a   Let $K = \{(x, y) : x = 0\}$. Then K is a normal subgroup of $\mathbf{R}^2$ and one can represent $\mathbf{R}^2/K$ as the set of lines $x = k$, where $k \in \mathbf{R}$. Show that $\mathbf{R}^2/K$ is isomorphic to the group $\overline{G} = \{(x, y) : y = 0\}$. To do so find a homomorphism ϕ from $\mathbf{R}^2$ onto $\overline{G}$ such that $\ker(\phi)$ is the given subgroup K and use the First Isomorphism Theorem.

   b   Fix $a \in \mathbf{R} - \{0\}$. Define $\phi : \mathbf{R}^2 \to \mathbf{R}$ by setting $\phi(x, y) = ax - y$. Show that ϕ is a homomorphism and that ϕ maps $\mathbf{R}^2$ onto $\mathbf{R}$. Find $\ker(\phi)$ and describe $\ker(\phi)$ geometrically.

   c   Fix $a \in \mathbf{R} - \{0\}$. Let $K = \{(x, y) : ax = y\}$. Show that $\mathbf{R}^2/K$ is isomorphic to $\mathbf{R}$.

6   Let G be the additive group $M_2(\mathbf{R})$ and let K be the subgroup consisting of all diagonal matrices:

$$K = \left\{ \begin{pmatrix} a & 0 \\ 0 & d \end{pmatrix} : a, d \in \mathbf{R} \right\}$$

Let $\overline{G}$ be the additive group

$$\overline{G} = \left\{ \begin{pmatrix} 0 & b \\ c & 0 \end{pmatrix} : b, c \in \mathbf{R} \right\}$$

a Prove that G/K is isomorphic to $\overline{G}$. To do so find a homomorphism ϕ from G onto $\overline{G}$ such that $\ker(\phi)$ is the given subgroup K and use the First Isomorphism Theorem.

b Describe the isomorphism $\overline{\phi}: G/K \to \overline{G}$ defined in Problem 102. To do so let

$$A_1 = \begin{pmatrix} a_1 & b_1 \\ c_1 & d_1 \end{pmatrix}$$

and evaluate $\overline{\phi}(A_1 + K)$.

c Let A_2 be any element of the coset $A_1 + K$. Express A_2 in terms of A_1 and then evaluate $\overline{\phi}(A_2 + K)$.

7 The set

$$T = \left\{ \begin{pmatrix} a & b \\ 0 & d \end{pmatrix} : a, b, d \in \mathbf{R} \right\}$$

of all upper triangular matrices is a subgroup of the additive group $M_2(\mathbf{R})$. Find a suitable subgroup $\overline{G}$ of $M_2(\mathbf{R})$ and prove that $M_2(\mathbf{R})/T$ is isomorphic to $\overline{G}$. (If in doubt about how to proceed, see Exercise 6.)

8 Let G, K, $\overline{G}$ be the following subsets of $M_2(\mathbf{R})$:

$$G = \left\{ \begin{pmatrix} a & b \\ c & d \end{pmatrix} : a, b, c, d \in \mathbf{R} \text{ and } ad - bc > 0 \right\}$$

$$K = \left\{ \begin{pmatrix} a & 0 \\ 0 & a \end{pmatrix} : a \in \mathbf{R} \text{ and } a > 0 \right\}$$

$$\overline{G} = \left\{ \begin{pmatrix} a & b \\ c & d \end{pmatrix} : a, b, c, d \in \mathbf{R} \text{ and } ad - bc = 1 \right\}$$

a Prove that G is a subgroup of the multiplicative group $\mathscr{I}$ of all nonsingular 2×2 matrices.

b Prove that K is a normal subgroup of G.

c Prove that $(\overline{G}, \cdot)$ is a group.

9   Let G, K, and $\overline{G}$ be the multiplicative groups defined in Exercise 8.

a   Define a function $\phi\colon G \to \overline{G}$ by setting

$$\phi\begin{pmatrix} a & b \\ c & d \end{pmatrix} = \begin{pmatrix} ax & bx \\ cx & dx \end{pmatrix}$$

for a suitable number x which depends on the matrix

$$\begin{pmatrix} a & b \\ c & d \end{pmatrix} \in G$$

Choose the number x so that

$$\phi\begin{pmatrix} a & b \\ c & d \end{pmatrix} \in \overline{G}$$

b   Prove that with the proper choice of the real number x for every matrix $A \in G$ the function ϕ is a homomorphism from G onto $\overline{G}$.

c   Prove that G/K is isomorphic to $\overline{G}$.

10a   Find a homomorphism which maps $(\mathbf{Z}_{15}, +)$ onto $(\mathbf{Z}_3, +)$.

  b   Prove or disprove the existence of a homomorphism from $(\mathbf{Z}_{10}, +)$ onto $(\mathbf{Z}_4, +)$.

11a   Let n be a fixed positive integer. Determine all the non-isomorphic groups which are homomorphic images of the group $(\mathbf{Z}_n, +)$. Be explicit. Let $k_1, k_2, ..., k_r$ be all the distinct factors of n with $k_i > 1$. Use these integers in describing the homomorphic images of $\mathbf{Z}_n$.

  b   Complete the following statement and then prove it: Let m and n be positive integers with $m \le n$. Then $(\mathbf{Z}_m, +)$ is a homomorphic image of $(\mathbf{Z}_n, +)$ if and only if _____ .

12   Determine all the nonisomorphic groups which are homomorphic images of the group $(S_3, \circ)$.

13 Let $(G, +)$ be a commutative group and X a nonempty set. Let $F(X, G)$ be the collection of all functions $f: X \to G$. The sum $f + g$ of $f, g \in F(X, G)$ is defined by setting

$$(f + g)(x) = f(x) + g(x)$$

for every $x \in X$. Then $(F(X, G), +)$ is a group. (See Exercise 1.5–10.)

a For a fixed element $a \in X$ let

$$K_a = \{f: f \in F(X, G) \text{ and } f(a) = 0\}$$

Show that K_a is a normal subgroup of $F(X, G)$.

b Let $a \in X$ be fixed. Define a function $\phi_a: F(X, G) \to G$ by setting $\phi_a(f) = f(a)$ for every $f \in F(X, G)$. Prove that ϕ_a is a homomorphism from $F(X, G)$ *onto* G and find the kernel of ϕ_a.

c Show that $F(X, G)/K_a$ is isomorphic to G.

14 Let H and K be normal subgroups of a group $(G, \circ)$. Then the set

$$H \circ K = \{h \circ k: h \in H, k \in K\}$$

is a normal subgroup of G (Exercise 2.7–16). We want to prove that $(H \circ K)/K$ is isomorphic to $H/(H \cap K)$. This result is known as the Second Isomorphism Theorem for Groups.

a Prove that K is a normal subgroup of $H \circ K$ and that $H \cap K$ is a normal subgroup of H.

b Define $\phi: H \to (H \circ K)/K$ by setting $\phi(h) = h \circ K$. Prove that ϕ is a homomorphism which maps H onto $(H \circ K)/K$. Find the kernel of ϕ.

c Prove that $(H \circ K)/K$ is isomorphic to $H/(H \cap K)$.

d Prove that if $H \cap K = \{e\}$, then $(H \circ K)/K$ is isomorphic to H.

e In $M_2(\mathbf{R})$ let

$$H = \left\{ \begin{pmatrix} a & 0 \\ 0 & d \end{pmatrix} : a, d \in \mathbf{R} \right\} \quad \text{and}$$

$$K = \left\{ \begin{pmatrix} 0 & b \\ c & 0 \end{pmatrix} : b, c \in \mathbf{R} \right\}$$

Then H and K are normal subgroups. Use the Second Isomorphism Theorem (part c above) to prove that $M_2(\mathbf{R})/K$ is isomorphic to H.

f   In $M_2(\mathbf{R})$ let

$$H = \left\{ \begin{pmatrix} a & b \\ 0 & d \end{pmatrix} : a, b, d \in \mathbf{R} \right\} \qquad \text{and}$$

$$K = \left\{ \begin{pmatrix} e & 0 \\ f & g \end{pmatrix} : e, f, g \in \mathbf{R} \right\}$$

Prove that $M_2(\mathbf{R})/K$ is isomorphic to H/H_1, where

$$H_1 = \left\{ \begin{pmatrix} a & 0 \\ 0 & d \end{pmatrix} : a, d \in \mathbf{R} \right\}$$

Then prove that $M_2(\mathbf{R})/K$ is isomorphic to the subgroup

$$\left\{ \begin{pmatrix} 0 & b \\ 0 & 0 \end{pmatrix} : b \in \mathbf{R} \right\}$$

2.10 A Bit of History

In high school algebra one learns that for any (real) numbers a, b, c with $a \neq 0$ the equation $ax^2 + bx + c = 0$ has solutions in the form

$$x = \frac{-b \pm \sqrt{b^2 - 4ac}}{2a}$$

This formula is true for any of these equations. All that must be done to find a solution to a particular quadratic equation (for example, $3x^2 - x + 5 = 0$) is to substitute the numbers for the appropriate letters in the formula. This quadratic formula was known to the Hindus and transmitted to the Western world by the Arabs. In fact, the term "algebra" comes from the title of a book by an Arabian astronomer in which solutions are set forth for the linear equation $(ax + b = 0)$ and for the quadratic equations. The original title, *Al-jabr w'al muqâbala*, was translated in the twelfth century as *Ludus algebrae et almuc-grabalaeque* (among other titles). This was eventually shortened to "algebra." The Arabic word *al-jabr* originally meant "restoring," in this case restoring the balance of an equation by transposing terms from one side of the equation to the other. The word *muqâbala* meant "simplification" such as occurs when one combines terms in an equation.

Although linear and quadratic formulas were already known by the Hindus and Arabs, mathematicians sought for centuries to find a formula which would give the solutions to the general polynomial equation

$$\text{A} \qquad x^n + a_{n-1}x^{n-1} + \cdots + a_1 x + a_0 = 0$$

or

$$a_n x^n + a_{n-1}x^{n-1} + \cdots + a_1 x + a_0 = 0 \qquad (a_n \neq 0)$$

where $a_0, a_1, \ldots, a_n$ are arbitrary, but fixed, rational numbers. They wanted this formula to involve only algebraic methods: addition, subtraction, multiplication, division, and radicals (that is, kth roots). As we noted in the introduction to Chapter 1, the third-degree equation was solved by Niccolò Tartaglia (1499?–1557) and described in a letter to Jerome Cardan, who published the solution (without Tartaglia's permission). In 1545 the solution to the fourth-degree equation was given by Lodovico Ferrari (1522–1565), a student of Cardan. It was not until the early nineteenth century, however, that it was determined whether or not the general polynomial equation of degree $n \geq 5$ has a solution in terms of algebraic formulas. Of course, solutions were known for certain types of polynomial equations (for example, $x^n = 1$), but it took the work of Niels Henrik Abel (1802–1829) and Évariste Galois (1811–1832) to show that there is no formula involving only algebraic methods that would work for all sets $a_0, a_1, \ldots, a_{n-1}$ of rational coefficients in equation A.

A major step toward an answer to this problem and the development of abstract algebra was taken by Joseph Louis Lagrange (1736–1813) in a paper published in the 1770s. He noted that there is a relationship between the roots of the polynomial equation (equation A) and the coefficients $a_0, a_1, \ldots, a_{n-1}$. In particular, if $\alpha_1, \alpha_2, \ldots, \alpha_n$ are the roots of the equation, then

$$x^n + a_{n-1}x^{n-1} + \cdots + a_1 x + a_0 = (x - \alpha_1)(x - \alpha_2) \cdots (x - \alpha_n)$$

and

$$a_{n-1} = \alpha_1 + \alpha_2 + \cdots + \alpha_n$$
$$a_{n-2} = \alpha_1 \alpha_2 + \alpha_1 \alpha_3 + \cdots + \alpha_{n-1} \alpha_n$$
$$\vdots$$
$$a_0 = \alpha_1 \alpha_2 \cdots \alpha_n$$

These functions of the roots which give the coefficients of the equation remain unchanged if the roots are rearranged. As a result they are called symmetric functions.

From these relationships between the roots and the coefficients, Lagrange devised a technique for solving the third- and fourth-degree equations by first finding a related equation whose degree was smaller than the degree of the original equation. However, when this technique was applied to the fifth-degree equation, Lagrange obtained a related equation which was a sixth-degree equation. From this Lagrange finally concluded that the solution of the general fifth-degree equation might be impossible by purely algebraic methods.

Finally in 1824 Abel proved that the general equation of degree greater than four is unsolvable by algebraic methods. However, this first paper contained an error which was later corrected by Abel himself. (He eventually gave two correct proofs.) This still left unanswered the question of which classes of polynomial equations could be solved by algebraic methods.

It took the work of the young Frenchman Galois to determine those classes of polynomials for which it is possible to find a solution by algebraic methods. His work involved the radical notions of normal subgroup and "extension field." His results were not widely known until 1870, almost forty years after he was killed at the age of 21 in a political duel.

Niels Henrik Abel

Évariste Galois

Galois used normal subgroups and the index of a subgroup in the determination of the classes of equations which could be solved. One interesting fact is that Galois's work not only gave a method for determining whether or not equations have a solution (written in terms of radicals) but it also proved impossible such geometric constructions as the trisecting of an angle or the construction of a square with the same area as a given circle ("squaring a circle") using only a straightedge and compass.

The first definition of a group was given by Augustin-Louis Cauchy (1789–1857). His set of memoirs formed the first careful study of finite substitution groups, which we have called permutation groups in this book. These memoirs were published in the 1840s and it was not until 1853 that the Englishman Arthur Cayley (1821–1895) stated the definition of an abstract group. The work of Cayley was not immediately recognized by other mathematicians, partly because matrices and quaternions (see Exercise 3.7–10) were not widely known at that time.

The word "matrix" was first used in 1850 by the English mathematician James Sylvester (1814–1897) (who was later transplanted to the Johns Hopkins

Arthur Cayley

James Sylvester

University in Baltimore). He used the word "matrix" to distinguish a rectangular array such as

$$\begin{pmatrix} a & b \\ c & d \end{pmatrix} \quad \text{or} \quad \begin{pmatrix} a_{11} & a_{12} & \cdots & a_{1n} \\ a_{21} & a_{22} & \cdots & a_{2n} \\ \vdots & \vdots & & \vdots \\ a_{m1} & a_{m2} & \cdots & a_{mn} \end{pmatrix}$$

from the determinant such as

$$\begin{vmatrix} a & b \\ c & d \end{vmatrix} = ad - bc$$

which was simply a real number. Since determinants had been studied for several years before 1850, many of the properties of matrices had been explored although they were not stated as such. However, Cayley was the first to publish papers on the theory of matrices distinct from that of determinants and consequently he is often credited with inventing matrices.

The notion of congruence modulo n for integers appears in the works of Leonhard Euler (1707–1783), Lagrange, Adrien-Marie Legendre (1752–1833), and Karl Friedrich Gauss (1777–1855). It was Gauss who introduced the notation which we use in abbreviated form (perhaps following Cauchy): $a \equiv b$ modulo n. This notation appeared in Gauss's *Disquisitiones Arithmeticae*, which appeared in 1801. It was in this volume that Gauss proved Fermat's Minor Theorem in terms of congruences, namely $a^{p-1} \equiv 1 \pmod{p}$ for every $a \in \mathbf{Z}$ which is not a multiple of the prime p. (See Problem 64 in Chapter 3 for the proof.)

REVIEW

Important Phrases	operation induced on a subset subgroup proper subgroup left coset of a subgroup right coset of a subgroup normal subgroup lattice diagram multiples of an element powers of an element order of an element order of a group index of a subgroup quotient group cyclic subgroup generated by an element a cyclic group	homomorphism isomorphism kernel of a homomorphism canonical homomorphism homomorphic image inverse image center of a group commutator commutator subgroup

Symbols $a^n, n \cdot a$ $\qquad$ $\ker(\phi)$

$\langle a \rangle$ $\qquad$ $\phi(G)$

$a \circ H, H \circ a$ $\qquad$ G/K

Questions

1 What is the identity element of a subgroup?

2a State a special criterion for showing that a finite nonempty subset of a group G is a subgroup. Does this criterion work for an infinite set?

b State a special criterion for showing that a subset (finite or infinite) of a group is a subgroup.

3 Let H and K be subgroups of a group G. Is either of the sets $H \cap K$ or $H \cup K$ a subgroup of G? If H and K are normal subgroups of G, is either $H \cap K$ or $H \cup K$ a normal subgroup?

4 Let G be a finite group and $a \in G$. How is the order of a related to the order of G? How is the order of the element a related to the order of the cyclic subgroup generated by a?

5   What are the subgroups of **Z**?

6   State Lagrange's Theorem. Is the converse of Lagrange's Theorem necessarily true?

7   How is the index of a subgroup of a finite group related to the order of the group and the order of the subgroup? How is the index of a normal subgroup related to the order of the quotient group G/K?

8   Under what conditions either on the subgroup or on the group is a subgroup necessarily a normal subgroup?

9   If G and $\bar{G}$ are groups and $\phi: G \to \bar{G}$ is a homomorphism, what are the images of the identity element of G and the inverse of an element $a \in G$?

10   Associated with a homomorphism ϕ from a group G into a group $\bar{G}$ are two sets, the kernel and the image set. Are these sets subgroups of their respective groups? Are they normal subgroups? Under what conditions on these sets will the homomorphism be an isomorphism?

11   What is a technique for showing that two (small) finite groups are isomorphic?

12   State Cayley's Theorem.

13   What are the nonisomorphic cyclic groups? Every cyclic group is isomorphic to a familiar group. If the order of the given cyclic group is n, to what group is it isomorphic? If the given group has infinite order, to what group is it isomorphic?

14   If a group has prime order, to what group is it isomorphic? What are the subgroups of a group of prime order? What is the order of any element in a group of prime order?

15   Give at least four equivalent conditions for a subgroup to be normal in a group.

16 For which subgroups K of a group G can a binary operation be properly defined on the collection of cosets G/K? How is this operation defined?

17 What is the canonical homomorphism from G into a quotient group G/K?

18 State the First Isomorphism Theorem for Groups. Explain what it means.

19 How would you "determine all nonisomorphic groups which are homomorphic images of a group G"?

The following questions are answered in the exercises:

20 Describe all nonisomorphic groups with orders two, three, four, five, and six, respectively.

21 Let G and $\bar{G}$ be groups and let $\phi: G \to \bar{G}$ be a homomorphism. Which of the following properties of G are inherited by $\bar{G}$ if $\ker(\phi) \neq \{e\}$ and ϕ maps G into $\bar{G}$? Which are inherited if ϕ maps G onto $\bar{G}$ and $\ker(\phi) \neq \{e\}$? Which are inherited if ϕ is an isomorphism?
 a G is a commutative group.
 b G contains a proper subgroup H.
 c G contains a proper normal subgroup K.

22 When is a group $(\mathbf{Z}_m, +)$ a homomorphic image of the group $(\mathbf{Z}_n, +)$?

23 What are the subgroups of the additive group $\mathbf{Z}_n$?

Chapter 3   Rings, Integral Domains, And Fields

There are many familiar sets, such as **Z**, **Q**, **R**, and $M_2(\mathbf{R})$, which have two binary operations—addition and multiplication—although the set is a group only with the operation of addition. These sets, **Z**, **Q**, **R**, and $M_2(\mathbf{R})$, with their operations of multiplication have quite different characteristics. The sets $\mathbf{R} - \{0\}$ and $\mathbf{Q} - \{0\}$ are both groups under multiplication while $\mathbf{Z} - \{0\}$ is not. Yet the cancellation laws hold for the set $\mathbf{Z} - \{0\}$ with the operation of multiplication. On the other hand, in the set $M_2(\mathbf{R})$ it is possible to find two non-zero matrices whose product is zero; for example,

$$\begin{pmatrix} 0 & 0 \\ 1 & 0 \end{pmatrix}\begin{pmatrix} 0 & 0 \\ 1 & 0 \end{pmatrix} = \begin{pmatrix} 0 & 0 \\ 0 & 0 \end{pmatrix}$$

Moreover, multiplication is not commutative in $M_2(\mathbf{R})$.

The sets **Z**, **Q**, **R**, and $M_2(\mathbf{R})$ serve as our prototypes for different kinds of algebraic systems in this chapter. We start by considering sets which have two associative operations related by a distributive property. As we add more requirements for the multiplication, we progress from the "rings" such as $M_2(\mathbf{R})$ to the "integral domains" such as **Z** to the "fields" such as **Q** and **R**.

3.1 Rings: Definition and Examples

We begin immediately with a definition.

1
Definition   A *ring* $(R, +, \cdot)$ is a nonempty set R with two binary operations, usually denoted by $+$ (addition) and $\cdot$ (multiplica-
tion), which satisfy the following axioms:

a   Addition is associative: for every $a, b, c \in R$,

$$(a+b) + c = a + (b+c)$$

b   Addition is commutative: for every $a, b \in R$,

$$a + b = b + a$$

c R has an additive identity: there exists an element, denoted
by 0, in R such that $a+0 = a$ for every $a \in R$.

d   There exist additive inverses: for every $a \in R$ there exists an
element, denoted by $-a$, in R such that $a+(-a) = 0$.

e   Multiplication is associative: for every $a, b, c \in R$,

$$(a \cdot b) \cdot c = a \cdot (b \cdot c)$$

f   Multiplication is left and right distributive over addition: for
every $a, b, c \in R$,

$$a \cdot (b+c) = (a \cdot b) + (a \cdot c) \qquad \text{and}$$
$$(b+c) \cdot a = (b \cdot a) + (c \cdot a)$$

To show that a particular system $(R, +, \cdot)$ is a ring, one must first be certain
that addition and multiplication are binary operations on R. Hence one must
prove that R is closed under both addition and multiplication (i.e., for every
$a, b \in R$, $a+b \in R$ and $a \cdot b \in R$).

Note that axioms a through d in Definition 1 say that $(R, +)$ is a commutative
group. Thus we can state the definition of a ring as follows:

1'
Definition   A ring $(R, +, \cdot)$ is a set R with two binary operations, $+$ and $\cdot$, such that

a $(R, +)$ is a commutative group,
b   multiplication is associative,
c   multiplication is left and right distributive over addition.

When working with real numbers we often omit the multiplication symbol and denote multiplication of a and b by juxtaposition; thus we write ab for the product of a and b. Following this example, it is common practice to denote multiplication in a ring $(R, +, \cdot)$ by juxtaposition; thus $a \cdot b = ab$. In an expression such as $ab + ac$ it is assumed that the multiplication is performed first (that is, $ab + ac = (a \cdot b) + (a \cdot c)$).

2
Definition   A ring $(R, +, \cdot)$ is a *ring with identity* (or unity) if and only if there exists an element, denoted by 1, in R such that $a \cdot 1 = 1 \cdot a = a$ for every $a \in R$. The element 1 is called a *multiplicative identity*.

When we studied groups we singled out those with a commutative operation and gave them a special name. Similarly, we single out rings which have a commutative multiplication. As we shall see later, these rings often have other special properties.

3
Definition   A ring $(R, +, \cdot)$ is a *commutative ring* if and only if multiplication is a commutative operation on R: $ab = ba$ for every $a, b \in R$.

4
Problem   Determine whether or not each of the following systems is a ring, a ring with identity, a commutative ring, or a commutative ring with identity. Justify your answers. Feel free to use previous results about groups. See Appendix 3 for properties of the real numbers and Sections 1.1 and 1.2 for results on $M_2(\mathbf{R})$.

a $(\mathbf{R}, +, \cdot)$
b $(\mathbf{Q}, +, \cdot)$
c $(\mathbf{Z}, +, \cdot)$
d $(M_2(\mathbf{R}), +, \cdot)$
e $2\mathbf{Z} = \{2k : k \in \mathbf{Z}\}$ with the usual addition and multiplication of numbers
f $\{x : x \text{ is irrational}\} = \mathbf{R} - \mathbf{Q}$ with the usual addition and multiplication of numbers

In our study of groups we worked with the additive group $\mathbf{Z}_n$ of integers modulo n. We now wish to define a multiplication on $\mathbf{Z}_n$ and prove that the system $(\mathbf{Z}_n, +, \cdot)$ is a ring. To help us in this task we have available the following result on multiplication of integers congruent modulo n: If $a, b, c, d \in \mathbf{Z}$ with $a \equiv c \pmod{n}$ and $b \equiv d \pmod{n}$, then $ab \equiv cd \pmod{n}$.

5
Problem   Let n be a fixed positive integer. Define a product $a_n \cdot b_n$ for elements a_n and b_n of $\mathbf{Z}_n$ by setting

$$a_n \cdot b_n = (ab)_n$$

a Give several examples of this definition.

b Prove that the correspondence

$$(a_n, b_n) \rightarrow a_n \cdot b_n$$

is a properly defined binary operation on $\mathbf{Z}_n$. (To do so prove that if $a_n = c_n$ and $b_n = d_n$, then $a_n b_n = c_n d_n$ or, equivalently, $(ab)_n = (cd)_n$.) This operation is called multiplication on $\mathbf{Z}_n$.

c Construct the multiplication tables for $\mathbf{Z}_5$ and $\mathbf{Z}_6$.

d Prove that $(\mathbf{Z}_n, +, \cdot)$ is a ring.

EXERCISES 1   Determine which of the following sets, with the usual addition and multiplication of numbers, is a ring or a ring with identity. Justify your answers.

a $\{3n: n \in \mathbf{Z}\}$

b $\{m/7^n: m \in \mathbf{Z}, n \in \mathbf{Z}^+\}$

c $\{a+b\sqrt{p}: a, b \in \mathbf{Q}\}$, where p is a prime so that $\sqrt{p}$ is irrational

2 Construct a multiplication table for $\mathbf{Z}_4$.

3 Let S be a nonempty set. Let R be the collection of *all* subsets of S. Define two binary operations, $\oplus$ and $\odot$ on R as follows:

$$A \oplus B = (A-B) \cup (B-A) \quad \text{and}$$

$$A \odot B = A \cap B$$

for every $A, B \in R$. Prove that $(R, \oplus, \odot)$ is a commutative ring with identity. ●

4 Is the set

$$\left\{ \begin{pmatrix} a & b \\ 0 & a \end{pmatrix} : a, b \in \mathbf{R} \right\}$$

with the usual addition and multiplication for matrices a ring? a commutative ring? a ring with identity?

5 Let $(G, +)$ be a commutative group. Show that there exists a multiplication for G such that the system $(G, +, \cdot)$ is a commutative ring. Thus any commutative group can be made into a commutative ring. ●

*6 Let $(R, +, \cdot)$ be a ring and X a nonempty set. Let $F(X, R)$ be the set of all functions from X into R. We define the sum $f+g$ of two functions $f, g \in F(X, R)$ by setting

$$(f+g)(x) = f(x) + g(x)$$

for every $x \in X$ (the pointwise sum). We define the product fg of $f, g \in F(X, R)$ by setting

$$(fg)(x) = f(x) \cdot g(x)$$

for every $x \in X$ (the pointwise product). We have seen that $(F(X,R), +)$ is a group (Exercise 1.5–10).

a   Give several examples of elements of $F(\mathbf{Z}_4, \mathbf{Z}_4)$.

b   Let X be the interval $[0,1]$. In $F(X, \mathbf{R})$ let $f(x) = x^2$ and $g(x) = 2x+1$ for every $x \in X$. Find $f+g$ and fg.

c   In $F(\mathbf{Z}_4, \mathbf{Z}_4)$ let $f(a_4) = 3a_4$ and let $g(a_4) = a_4^2$ for every $a_4 \in \mathbf{Z}_4$. Find $(f+g)(a_4)$ and $(fg)(a_4)$ for every $a_4 \in \mathbf{Z}_4$.

d   Let $(R, +, \cdot)$ be a ring and X a nonempty set. Show that $(F(X,R), +, \cdot)$ is a ring.

e   Show that multiplication is commutative in $F(X,R)$ if and only if R is a commutative ring.   ●

f   Show that $F(X,R)$ has a multiplicative identity function if and only if R has a multiplicative identity.   ●

★7   We say that a function $f: \mathbf{R}^2 \to \mathbf{R}^2$ is a linear function if and only if there exist $a, b, c, d \in \mathbf{R}$ such that

$$f(x, y) = (ax+by,\ cx+dy)$$

for every $(x, y) \in \mathbf{R}^2$. Let $L(\mathbf{R}^2)$ be the set of all linear functions $f: \mathbf{R}^2 \to \mathbf{R}^2$. We define the sum $f+g$ of $f, g \in L(\mathbf{R}^2)$ by setting

$$(f+g)(x, y) = f(x, y) + g(x, y)$$

Note that $L(\mathbf{R}^2)$ is a subset of $F(\mathbf{R}^2, \mathbf{R}^2)$ and that the operation of addition is the same for both sets.

a   Prove that $(L(\mathbf{R}^2), +)$ is a commutative group.

b   Prove that $L(\mathbf{R}^2)$ is closed under composition of functions: If $f, g \in L(\mathbf{R}^2)$, then $f \circ g \in L(\mathbf{R}^2)$. Thus composition is an associative binary operation on $L(\mathbf{R}^2)$.

c   Prove that composition is distributive over addition in $L(\mathbf{R}^2)$.

d   Prove that $L(\mathbf{R}^2)$ is a ring with identity.

★8   Let $(G, +)$ be a commutative group. Let hom(G) be the set of all (group) homomorphisms from G into G. Thus a function $\phi: G \to G$ is in hom(G) if and only if $\phi(a+b) = \phi(a) + \phi(b)$ for every $a, b \in G$. Define the sum $\phi_1 + \phi_2$ of two functions $\phi_1, \phi_2 \in$ hom(G) by setting

$$(\phi_1 + \phi_2)(a) = \phi_1(a) + \phi_2(a)$$

for every $a \in G$.

a   Give several examples of elements of hom($\mathbf{Z}$).

b   In hom($\mathbf{Z}$) find $\phi_1 + \phi_2$ if $\phi_1(a) = 3a$ and $\phi_2(a) = -7a$ for every $a \in \mathbf{Z}$.

c   Show that if $\phi_1, \phi_2 \in$ hom(G), then $\phi_1 + \phi_2 \in$ hom(G).

d   Show that $($hom$(G), +)$ is a commutative group.

*9   Let $(G, +)$ be a commutative group. For every pair of homomorphisms $\phi_1, \phi_2 \in$ hom(G) the composite $\phi_1 \circ \phi_2$ is defined as usual by setting

$$(\phi_1 \circ \phi_2)(a) = \phi_1(\phi_2(a))$$

for every $a \in G$.

a   In hom($\mathbf{Z}$) find $\phi_1 \circ \phi_2$ for the homomorphisms defined by $\phi_1(a) = 3a$ and $\phi_2(a) = -7a$ for every $a \in \mathbf{Z}$.

b   In hom($\mathbf{Z}_4$) find $\phi_1 \circ \phi_2$ for the homomorphisms ϕ_1 and ϕ_2 defined by $\phi_1(a_4) = 2a_4$ and $\phi_2(a_4) = -a_4$ for every $a_4 \in \mathbf{Z}_4$.

c   Let $(G, +)$ be a commutative group and $\phi_1, \phi_2 \in$ hom(G). Show that $\phi_1 \circ \phi_2 \in$ hom(G).

d   Prove that $($hom$(G), +, \circ)$ is a ring if G is a commutative group.

e   Let $a, b, c, d \in \mathbf{R}$. Define $\phi: \mathbf{R}^2 \to \mathbf{R}^2$ by setting

$$\phi(x, y) = (ax + by, cx + dy)$$

for all $(x, y) \in \mathbf{R}^2$. Show that ϕ is a homomorphism from $\mathbf{R}^2$ into itself. (Recall that addition is defined on $\mathbf{R}^2$ by $(x, y) + (z, w) = (x+z, y+w)$.) Find two homomorphisms $\phi_1, \phi_2 \in$ hom($\mathbf{R}^2$) such that $\phi_1 \circ \phi_2 \neq \phi_2 \circ \phi_1$. This shows that hom($G$) is not necessarily commutative with the operation of composition.

3.2 Elementary Properties of a Ring

Axioms a through d in Definition 1 assure us that for any ring R, $(R, +)$ is a commutative group. This immediately gives the following properties of a ring $(R, +, \cdot)$.

6
Proposition a   If $a, b, c \in R$ and $a + b = a + c$, then $b = c$ (cancellation for addition).

b   If $z \in R$ and $z + a = a$ for *some* $a \in R$, then $z = 0$ (uniqueness of the additive identity).

c   If $a, b \in R$ and $a + b = 0$, then $b = -a$ (uniqueness of the additive inverse).

d   For every $a, b \in R$ there exists exactly one $x \in R$ such that $a + x = b$. In fact, $x = b + (-a)$, and x is often denoted by $b - a$. (This defines the operation of subtraction in a ring.)

e   For every $a \in R$, $-(-a) = a$.

There are other properties of a ring resulting from the existence of multiplication and from the distributive property. Prove these properties in the following problem.

7
Problem   a   For every $a \in R$, $a \cdot 0 = 0 \cdot a = 0$. ▲

b   For every $a, b \in R$, $a(-b) = -(ab)$ and $(-a)b = -(ab)$. (Prove only the first of these.)

c   For every $a, b \in R$, $(-a)(-b) = ab$.

d   If $(R, +, \cdot)$ is a ring with identity 1 and if there is an element $u \in R$ such that $ua = au = a$ for *every* $a \in R$, then $u = 1$ (uniqueness of the multiplicative identity when it exists).

e   If $(R, +, \cdot)$ is a ring with identity 1 and if there exist a, a^{-1}, and b in R such that $a^{-1}a = aa^{-1} = 1$ and $ab = ba = 1$, then $a^{-1} = b$ (uniqueness of the multiplicative inverse when it exists).

f   For every $a, b, c \in R$, $a(b-c) = ab - ac$ and $(b-c)a = ba - ca$.

EXERCISES   1   Prove that if R is a ring with identity 1 and $R \neq \{0\}$, then $1 \neq 0$.

In the following exercises let $(R, +, \cdot)$ be a ring. In Exercises 2 through 8 correctly complete the statement if necessary. Then prove the result.

2   $-(a+b) =$ _____
    $-(a-b) =$ _____

3   $(a-b) - c = a$ ____ $(b$ ____ $c)$
    $a - (b-c) = (a$ ____ $b)$ ____ c

4   $a + [b + (c+d)] = ($__$+$__$) + ($__$+$__$)$
    $\qquad\qquad = [(a+b) + $__$] + $__

5   $(a+b) \cdot (c+d) = (ac+bc) + ($_____ $+$ _____$)$
    $(a-b) \cdot (c-d) = (ac+$_____$) - ($_____$)$

6   $(a-b) + (c-d) = (a+$____$) - ($____$+$____$)$
    $(a+b) - (c+d) = (a-$____$) + ($_____$)$

7   $-0 = 0$
    $(-1)a = -a$ if R has a multiplicative identity 1

8   $a - b = c - d$ if and only if $a +$ ____ $=$ ____$+c$

9   The statement of the uniqueness of the additive identity is that if $a + z = a$ for *some* $a \in R$, then $z = 0$. On the other hand, the statement for the uniqueness of the multiplicative identity is that if $ua = au = a$ for *every* $a \in R$, then $u = 1$. Show that the latter statement cannot be altered to read "if $ua = au = a$ for *some* $a \in R$, then $u = 1$." Do this by finding an element $U \in M_2(\mathbf{R})$ different from the identity

matrix and a nonzero matrix $A \in M_2(\mathbf{R})$ such that $UA = A = AU$.

10 Show by contradiction that if a and b are nonzero elements of R and $ab = 0$, then a cannot have a multiplicative inverse.

11 In a ring R any element a such that $a^2 = a$ is called an idempotent element. It may be surprising to find that a ring R with identity may have idempotent elements a with $a \neq 0$ and $a \neq 1$.

a Find all the idempotent elements in $\mathbf{Z}_6$; $\mathbf{Z}_{12}$; $\mathbf{Z}_7$.

b Show that if k is odd, then the element $(k)_{2k}$ is an idempotent element of $\mathbf{Z}_{2k}$.

c Find several idempotent elements of $M_2(\mathbf{R})$.

d Determine all values of x for which the matrix

$$\begin{pmatrix} x & x \\ x & x \end{pmatrix}$$

is an idempotent element of $M_2(\mathbf{R})$.

e Find a relationship between x and y such that the matrix

$$\begin{pmatrix} x & -x \\ y & -y \end{pmatrix}$$

is an idempotent element of $M_2(\mathbf{R})$.

3.3 Subrings and Ideals

In our study of groups we saw that if a set H was contained in a known group G, then we only had to check one special criterion ($a \circ b' \in H$ for every $a, b \in H$) to see whether H was itself a group with the operation of G. Following the example of groups, we consider "subrings" and look for some minimal criteria for a set to be a subring of a ring.

8
Definition   Let $(R, +, \cdot)$ be a ring. A subset S of R is a *subring* of R if and only if $(S, +, \cdot)$ is a ring (that is, S is a ring with the operations induced from R).

To determine whether or not a given subset S of a ring R is actually a subring, we must first decide whether or not S is a subgroup of R under addition. Recall that S is a subgroup of the additive group R if and only if S is closed under subtraction: $a + (-b) = a - b \in S$ for every $a, b \in S$. (See Theorem 12 in Chapter 2.) What other properties must be checked to show that S is a ring?

9
Problem   Determine whether or not each of the following subsets S of a ring R is a subring of R. If S is a subring, is it a commutative ring? a ring with identity? Justify your answers.

a $R = M_2(\mathbf{R})$,

$$S = \left\{ \begin{pmatrix} 0 & 0 \\ 0 & d \end{pmatrix} : d \in \mathbf{R} \right\}$$

b $R = \mathbf{Z}$,

$$S = n\mathbf{Z} = \{nk : k \in \mathbf{Z}\}$$

where $n \in \mathbf{Z}$ is fixed.

Any ring $R \neq \{0\}$ has at least two subrings, $\{0\}$ and R. (Why?) As we did with groups, we wish to give a special name to subrings other than $\{0\}$ and R.

10
Definition   A subring of R is a *proper subring* if and only if it is different from $\{0\}$ and from R.

11
Problem   For which values of $n \in \mathbf{Z}^+$ is the set $n\mathbf{Z}$ a proper subring of $\mathbf{Z}$?

In order to simplify the work of deciding whether or not a subset S of a ring R is a subring, let us find a condition similar to the one for subgroups of a group.

12
Problem   Let $(R, +, \cdot)$ be a ring and S a subset of R. Using the subgroup criterion above, find a (minimal) necessary and sufficient condition for the subset S to be a subring of R. State this condition in the form of a theorem as follows:

13
Theorem   Let $(R, +, \cdot)$ be a ring. A subset S of R is a subring of R if and only if _____ .

Check this result with your instructor.

How can we form subrings? Certainly it is not enough to consider the set $\langle a \rangle$ of multiples of an element (or of powers). For example, in $\mathbf{Q}$ the set

$$\langle \tfrac{1}{2} \rangle = \{k \cdot \tfrac{1}{2} \colon k \in \mathbf{Z}\}$$

is not a subring since $\tfrac{1}{2} \cdot \tfrac{1}{2} = \tfrac{1}{4}$ is not an element. In the following problem we explore one method for finding subrings.

14
Problem   a   Use Theorem 13 to prove that if $(R, +, \cdot)$ is a ring and $a \in R$ is fixed, then the sets

$$aR = \{ax \colon x \in R\}$$

and

$$Ra = \{xa: x \in R\}$$

are subrings of R.

b   Find each of the subrings $1_6\mathbf{Z}_6, 2_6\mathbf{Z}_6, ..., 5_6\mathbf{Z}_6$ in $\mathbf{Z}_6$.

Note that we could have used Problem 14a to prove that each of the sets $n\mathbf{Z} = \{nk: k \in \mathbf{Z}\}$ $(n \in \mathbf{Z}^+)$ is a subring of $\mathbf{Z}$.

15
Problem

Show that the set $n\mathbf{Z}$, where n is a fixed positive integer, has the following property: For every $s \in n\mathbf{Z}$ and $r \in \mathbf{Z}$ the product sr (or rs) is in $n\mathbf{Z}$.

Many of the subrings of a given ring may have this special "closure" property. Such subrings are given a special name, as defined below.

16
Definition

Let $(R, +, \cdot)$ be a ring. A subring S of R is a *left ideal* in R if and only if for every $s \in S$ and $r \in R$, $rs \in S$. Equivalently, a subring S of R is a left ideal in R if and only if for every $r \in R$, $rS \subseteq S$.

A subring S of R is a *right ideal* in R if and only if for every $s \in S$ and $r \in R$, $sr \in S$. Equivalently, a subring S of R is a right ideal in R if and only if for every $r \in R$, $Sr \subseteq S$.

A subring S of R is an *ideal* (or a two-sided ideal) if and only if it is both a left ideal and a right ideal. Equivalently, a subring S of R is an ideal in R if and only if for every $r \in R$, $rS \subseteq S$ and $Sr \subseteq S$.

Caution

When proving that a particular set is an ideal, don't forget to prove that it is a subring.

17

Problem   Is the set

$$S = \left\{ \begin{pmatrix} a & b \\ 0 & 0 \end{pmatrix} : a, b \in \mathbf{R} \right\}$$

a left ideal in $M_2(\mathbf{R})$? a right ideal in $M_2(\mathbf{R})$? a two-sided ideal? Justify your answers.

In Problem 14 we defined subsets aR and Ra in a ring R and showed that these subsets are subrings. Now we can say more about these subrings.

18

Problem   Show that if $(R, +, \cdot)$ is a ring and $a \in R$ is fixed, then the subring $S_1 = aR$ is a right ideal in R while the subring $S_2 = Ra$ is a left ideal.

We have seen that the concept of a group arose from a desire to find a solution to polynomial equations. Similarly, the concept of ideals has its roots in an attempt to solve a famous problem, one which is still unsolved today.

One of the most famous unsolved problems in mathematics is to find a proof to Fermat's Last Theorem, which states that if $n > 2$ is an integer, then there are *no* integers x, y, and z, all different from zero, such that $x^n + y^n = z^n$. The attempts to prove Fermat's Last Theorem in general (in particular for all primes $p > 2$) have led to the invention of ideals in ring theory, among other concepts.

Ernst Eduard Kummer (1810–1893), a German mathematician who began as a student of theology, believed in 1843 that he had proved Fermat's Last Theorem. He let p be a prime and considered the number α which is the solution to the polynomial equation

$$\alpha^{p-1} + \alpha^{p-2} + \cdots + \alpha + 1 = 0$$

Thus α is a pth root of unity since

$$\alpha^p - 1 = (\alpha - 1)(\alpha^{p-1} + \alpha^{p-2} + \cdots + \alpha + 1) = 0$$

Kummer then constructed the set of all numbers of the form

$$a_0 + a_1\alpha + \cdots + a_{p-2}\alpha^{p-2}$$

where $a_0, a_1, \ldots, a_{p-2}$ are integers. For this set he defined such concepts as "integers," "prime integers," and "divisibility." He then assumed a unique factorization theorem similar to the Fundamental Theorem of Arithmetic (see Theorem 14 in Appendix 6). At this point his proof failed since the unique factorization holds only for certain "primes." In the hopes of retrieving unique factorization, Kummer then devised the notion of ideal numbers and with these proved that Fermat's Last Theorem is true for many prime numbers n.

The ideal numbers were not well defined, however. The concept of ideal number was generalized by Richard Dedekind (1831–1916), who used ideals to attack the problem of unique factorization for the so-called algebraic numbers (numbers which are solutions of polynomial equations with integral coefficients). For example, he generalized the notion of prime number by considering the prime ideal (an ideal S such that if $st \in S$, then either $s \in S$ or $t \in S$), which is studied in Chapter 5. Dedekind stated not only axioms defining ideals but also those for rings and fields (see Section 3.7). These definitions and many of Dedekind's results in algebraic number theory appeared in a supplement to Dirichlet's *Zahlentheorie* (Number Theory) which Dedekind, a teacher for fifty years in a German technical high school, edited in 1871.

EXERCISES   1   Determine whether or not each of the following sets S is a subring of $M_2(\mathbf{R})$. If S is a subring, is it a commutative ring? a ring with identity? Justify your answers.

a $S = \left\{ \begin{pmatrix} a & 0 \\ 0 & d \end{pmatrix} : a, d \in \mathbf{R} \right\}$ (the set of diagonal matrices)

b $S = \left\{ \begin{pmatrix} a & b \\ 0 & d \end{pmatrix} : a, b, d \in \mathbf{R} \right\}$ (the set of upper triangular matrices)

*2   Let S be a subset of a ring R. Prove that S is a left ideal in R if S is a subgroup of R under addition and for every $s \in S$ and $r \in R$, $rs \in S$. This result can be used to simplify slightly the proof that a particular subset of a ring is actually a left ideal. A similar result is true for right ideals.

*3   Let R be a ring with identity.
a   Prove that if S is a proper ideal in R, then $1 \notin S$. (Do a proof by contraposition.)
b   Prove that if S is a proper ideal and a has a multiplicative inverse in R, then $a \notin S$. (Do a proof by contraposition.)

4   Find all the ideals of the following sets. Justify your answers.

a $\mathbf{Z}_6$ c $\mathbf{Q}$
b $\mathbf{Z}$ d $\mathbf{R}$

5   Let n be a fixed positive integer. Determine all the subrings and all the ideals of the ring $\mathbf{Z}_n$.

*6   Let $\mathbf{Q}[\sqrt{2}] = \{a+b\sqrt{2}\colon a, b \in \mathbf{Q}\}$. Prove that $\mathbf{Q}[\sqrt{2}]$ is a subring of $\mathbf{R}$. Prove or disprove that $\mathbf{Q}[\sqrt{2}]$ is an ideal in $\mathbf{R}$ (See Exercises 1.2–5 and 1.2–6.)

7   Find an element $A \in M_2(\mathbf{R})$ such that

$$A(M_2(\mathbf{R})) = \left\{ \begin{pmatrix} 0 & 0 \\ c & d \end{pmatrix}\colon c, d \in \mathbf{R} \right\}$$

This proves that this set is a subring of $M_2(\mathbf{R})$ and a right ideal. Show that $A(M_2(\mathbf{R}))$ is not a left ideal.

8a   Let

$$A = \begin{pmatrix} 2 & -2 \\ 1 & -1 \end{pmatrix}$$

Find the subring $A(M_2(\mathbf{R}))$ of $M_2(\mathbf{R})$. Show that for every $X \in A(M_2(\mathbf{R}))$, $AX = X$. Thus A is a left identity for the subring. Is A an identity for this subring? Justify your answer.

b   Let a be an idempotent element in a ring R (that is, an element such that $a^2 = a$). Prove that a is a left identity element for the subring aR.

*9   Show that $M_2(\mathbf{R})$ has no proper two-sided ideals. To do so suppose that $S \subseteq M_2(\mathbf{R})$ is an ideal and $S \neq \{0\}$. You must prove that $S = M_2(\mathbf{R})$. Begin by considering the products XY and YX, where $Y \in S$ and X is one of the matrices

$$\begin{pmatrix} 1 & 0 \\ 0 & 0 \end{pmatrix}, \quad \begin{pmatrix} 0 & 1 \\ 0 & 0 \end{pmatrix}, \quad \begin{pmatrix} 0 & 0 \\ 1 & 0 \end{pmatrix}, \quad \begin{pmatrix} 0 & 0 \\ 0 & 1 \end{pmatrix}$$

10a Prove that if S_1 and S_2 are subrings of a ring R, then $S_1 \cap S_2$ is a subring of R.

b Prove that if S_1 and S_2 are both left ideals in R, then $S_1 \cap S_2$ is a left ideal in R. Naturally, similar propositions are true for right and two-sided ideals.

11a Prove that if S_1 and S_2 are ideals in a ring R and

$$S_1 + S_2 = \{a + b : a \in S_1 \text{ and } b \in S_2\}$$

then $S_1 + S_2$ is an ideal in R which contains both S_1 and S_2.
b Find $S_1 + S_2$ explicitly when $R = \mathbf{Z}$, $S_1 = 21\mathbf{Z}$, and $S_2 = 12\mathbf{Z}$.

12 Let $(R, +, \cdot)$ be a commutative ring and X a nonempty set. We have seen in Exercise 3.1–6 that the set $F(X, R)$ of all functions $f : X \to R$ is a ring with the operations of addition and multiplication defined for $f, g \in F(X, R)$ as follows:

$$(f + g)(x) = f(x) + g(x)$$

$$(fg)(x) = f(x) \cdot g(x)$$

for every $x \in X$. Which of the following subsets of $F(X, R)$ are subrings of $F(X, R)$? Which are ideals in $F(X, R)$? Justify your answers.
a $\{f : f \in F(X, R) \text{ and } f(x_0) = 0\}$, where $x_0 \in X$ is fixed
b $\{f : f \in F(X, R) \text{ and } f(x_0) = a\}$, where $x_0 \in X$ and $a \in R$ are fixed
c $\{af : f \subset F(X, R)\}$, where $a \in R$ is fixed and af is the function defined by setting $(af)(x) = a(f(x))$ for every $x \in X$

13 Let $(G, +)$ be a commutative group. Then the set $\hom(G)$ of all the (group) homomorphisms from G into itself is a ring with the sum and composite of two homomorphisms $\phi_1, \phi_2 \in \hom(G)$ defined by setting

$$(\phi_1 + \phi_2)(x) = \phi_1(x) + \phi_2(x) \qquad \text{and}$$

$$(\phi_1 \circ \phi_2)(x) = \phi_1(\phi_2(x))$$

for every $x \in G$. (See Exercises 3.1–8 and 3.1–9.) Which of the following sets are subrings of $\hom(G)$? Which are left ideals? Justify your answers.
a $\{\phi : \phi \in \hom(G) \text{ and } \phi \text{ maps } G \text{ onto } G\}$
b $\{\phi : \phi \in \hom(G) \text{ and } \phi \text{ is an isomorphism}\}$
c $\{\phi : \phi \in \hom(G) \text{ and } \phi(x_0) = 0\}$, where $x_0 \in G - \{0\}$ is fixed
d $\{\phi_0 \circ \phi : \phi \in \hom(G)\}$, where $\phi_0 \in \hom(G)$ is fixed

3.4 Homomorphisms

If R and $\bar{R}$ are rings, then they are additive groups. Hence we can consider a (group) homomorphism or isomorphism ϕ from $(R, +)$ into $(\bar{R}, +)$. This function ϕ may or may not preserve the second operation of multiplication in the two rings. In this section we examine functions from R into $\bar{R}$ called ring homomorphisms which preserve both addition and multiplication.

19
Definition
Let $(R, +, \cdot)$ and $(\bar{R}, +, \cdot)$ be rings. A function $\phi: R \to \bar{R}$ is a (ring) *homomorphism* if and only if for every $a, b \in R$,

$$\phi(a+b) = \phi(a) + \phi(b) \qquad \text{and}$$
$$\phi(ab) = \phi(a) \cdot \phi(b)$$

A function $\phi: R \to \bar{R}$ is a (ring) *isomorphism* from R onto $\bar{R}$ if and only if ϕ is a (ring) homomorphism and ϕ is both one-to-one and onto. Two rings R and $\bar{R}$ are said to be *isomorphic* if and only if there exists an isomorphism from R onto $\bar{R}$.

20
Problem
Let n be a fixed positive integer. Define a function ϕ from the ring $\mathbf{Z}$ into the ring $\mathbf{Z}_n$ by setting $\phi(a) = a_n$ for every $a \in \mathbf{Z}$. Prove that ϕ is a ring homomorphism.

The word "homomorphism" is used both for a group homomorphism and for a ring homomorphism. Usually, there should be no confusion. It is understood that if $\phi: S \to \bar{S}$ is a homomorphism and S and $\bar{S}$ are both groups (but not both rings), then ϕ is a group homomorphism, while if S and $\bar{S}$ are both rings, then ϕ is a ring homomorphism. Of course, it is possible for a function from a ring R into a ring $\bar{R}$ to be a group homomorphism but not a ring homomorphism (i.e., it preserves addition but not multiplication). For example, the function $\phi: \mathbf{Z} \to n\mathbf{Z}$ defined by setting $\phi(a) = na$ for every $a \in \mathbf{Z}$ is a group homomorphism which does not preserve the ring multiplication. In such a case it is necessary to specify that the function is a group homomorphism.

Note that if ϕ is a (ring) homomorphism from a ring R into a ring $\bar{R}$, then ϕ is also a (group) homomorphism from $(R, +)$ into $(\bar{R}, +)$. Thus we can speak of the kernel of ϕ (that is, the set

$$\ker(\phi) = \{r: r \in R \text{ and } \phi(r) = 0\})$$

and the image of R under ϕ (that is, the set

$$\phi(R) = \{\phi(r): r \in R\})$$

21
Problem

Define a function $\phi: \mathbf{R} \to M_2(\mathbf{R})$ by setting

$$\phi(a) = \begin{pmatrix} a & 0 \\ 0 & a \end{pmatrix}$$

for every $a \in \mathbf{R}$.

a   Is ϕ a (ring) homomorphism? Justify your answer.

b   Is the kernel of ϕ a subring of $\mathbf{R}$?

c   Is the image of $\mathbf{R}$ under ϕ a subring of $M_2(\mathbf{R})$? an ideal in $M_2(\mathbf{R})$?

22
Problem

Let C be a matrix with a multiplicative inverse. Define a function $\phi_c: M_2(\mathbf{R}) \to M_2(\mathbf{R})$ by setting

$$\phi_c(X) = C \cdot X \cdot C^{-1}$$

for every $X \in M_2(\mathbf{R})$. For one example of this function, let

$$C = \begin{pmatrix} 1 & 1 \\ 1 & 0 \end{pmatrix}$$

so that

$$C^{-1} = \begin{pmatrix} 0 & 1 \\ 1 & -1 \end{pmatrix}$$

a   Prove that ϕ_c is a homomorphism.

b   Find the kernel of ϕ_c.

c   Prove that ϕ_c maps $M_2(\mathbf{R})$ onto itself.

d   Is ϕ_c an isomorphism?

When we studied group homomorphisms we showed that the kernel of a homomorphism is a (normal) subgroup of the domain. Ideals occupy a place in ring theory similar to that of normal subgroups in group theory. Thus we might expect the kernel of a ring homomorphism to be a subring which is also an ideal.

23
Problem   Let $(R, +, \cdot)$ and $(\bar{R}, +, \cdot)$ be rings and $\phi \colon R \to \bar{R}$ be a homomorphism. Prove the following statements:

a   The image of R under ϕ is a subring of $\bar{R}$. (See Theorem 51 in Chapter 2.)

b   The kernel of ϕ is an ideal in R. (See Theorem 48 in Chapter 2.)

24
Proposition   Let $(R, +, \cdot)$ and $(\bar{R}, +, \cdot)$ be rings and let ϕ be a homomorphism from R into $\bar{R}$. Then ϕ is an isomorphism if and only if $\ker(\phi) = \{0\}$ and $\phi(R) = \bar{R}$.

Leave the proof of this proposition for Exercise 2.

The following problem provides an example of the role that ideals play in the study of homomorphisms of a particular ring.

25
Problem   Let R be a ring with no proper ideals and let ϕ be a homomorphism from R into a ring $\bar{R}$. Prove that if $\phi(r) \neq 0$ for some $r \in R$, then $\phi(x) \neq 0$ for every nonzero $x \in R$. Thus the only homomorphisms on R are the "zero" homomorphism (that is, $\phi(r) = 0$ for every $r \in R$) and those that are one-to-one. (Why?)

EXERCISES 1 Which of the following functions are (ring) homomorphisms? Justify your answers. If a function is a homomorphism, find $\ker(\phi)$ and verify that it is an ideal in the domain of the function.

a $\phi: \mathbf{Z}_6 \to \mathbf{Z}_2$ defined by $\phi(a_6) = a_2$ for every $a \in \mathbf{Z}$

b $\phi: \mathbf{R} \to \left\{ \begin{pmatrix} 0 & 0 \\ c & d \end{pmatrix} : c, d \in \mathbf{R} \right\}$

defined by

$$\phi(r) = \begin{pmatrix} 0 & 0 \\ 0 & r \end{pmatrix}$$

for every $r \in \mathbf{R}$

c $\phi: M_2(\mathbf{R}) \to \mathbf{R}$ defined by

$$\phi \begin{pmatrix} a & b \\ c & d \end{pmatrix} = a + d$$

d $\phi: \mathbf{R} \to M_2(\mathbf{R})$ defined by

$$\phi(r) = \begin{pmatrix} -r & 2r \\ r & 2r \end{pmatrix}$$

for every $r \in \mathbf{R}$

2 Prove Proposition 24.

3 Find a homomorphism $\phi: \mathbf{Z} \to \mathbf{Z}_n$ such that

$$\ker(\phi) = n\mathbf{Z} = \{nk: k \in \mathbf{Z}\}$$

Prove that the function you have defined is a ring homomorphism.

4 Let $(R, +, \cdot)$ be a ring with identity and X a nonempty set. Let $F(X, R)$ be the ring of all functions from X into R with the operations of pointwise addition and multiplication (see Exercise 3.1–6). Determine whether or not each of the

following functions with domain $F(X,R)$ is a homomorphism. If ϕ is a homomorphism, find the kernel of ϕ and the image of $F(X,R)$ under ϕ.

a $\phi_a: F(X,R) \to R$ defined by $\phi_a(f) = f(a)$ for every $f \in F(X,R)$, where $a \in X$ is fixed

b $\phi: F(X,R) \to F(X,R)$ defined by $\phi(f) = f^2$ for every $f \in F(X,R)$

c   Let $f_0 \in F(X,R)$ be a function with multiplicative inverse $1/f_0$. Define $\phi: F(X,R) \to F(X,R)$ by setting $\phi(f) = f_0 \cdot f \cdot (1/f_0)$ for every $f \in F(X,R)$.

5   Let $L(\mathbf{R}^2)$ be the set of all linear functions $f: \mathbf{R}^2 \to \mathbf{R}^2$ (where $f \in L(\mathbf{R}^2)$ is defined by

$$f(x,y) = (ax+by, cx+dy)$$

for some fixed real numbers a, b, c, d). Then with the operations of pointwise addition and composition of functions, $L(\mathbf{R}^2)$ is a ring with identity (see Exercise 3.1–7). Prove that $L(\mathbf{R}^2)$ is (ring) isomorphic to the ring $M_2(\mathbf{R})$.   •

6   Prove that if R is a ring and $\phi: M_2(\mathbf{R}) \to R$ is a homomorphism with $\phi(A) \neq 0$ for some $A \in M_2(\mathbf{R})$, then $\phi(X) \neq 0$ for every $X \in M_2(\mathbf{R})$.   •

7   Let R be a ring with identity 1, let $\bar{R}$ be a ring, and let $\phi: R \to \bar{R}$ be a homomorphism. Prove that if $\phi(1) = 0$, then $\ker(\phi) = R$ (that is, $\phi(r) = 0$ for every $r \in R$).

8   Let R and $\bar{R}$ be rings and let $\phi: R \to \bar{R}$ be a homomorphism. Prove the following statements:

a   If ϕ maps R onto $\bar{R}$ and if R is commutative, then $\bar{R}$ is commutative. (For a counterexample to the statement if the "onto" condition is omitted see Problem 21.)

b   If ϕ is one-to-one (but not necessarily onto) and $\bar{R}$ is commutative, then R is commutative.

c   Show by example that if ϕ is not one-to-one, then $\bar{R}$ may be commutative while R is not commutative.

9   Let $(R, +, \cdot)$ be a ring with identity 1 and let $(\bar{R}, +, \cdot)$ be a ring. Let ϕ be a homomorphism from R onto $\bar{R}$. Prove the following statements:

a The ring $\bar{R}$ has a multiplicative identity $\bar{e} = \phi(1)$.
b If r has a multiplicative inverse in R, then $\phi(r)$ has a multiplicative inverse in $\bar{R}$. What is the inverse of $\phi(r)$?

10 Let ϕ be a homomorphism from a ring R into a ring $\bar{R}$. Prove the following statements:
   a If $\bar{S}$ is an ideal in $\bar{R}$, then the inverse image

   $$\phi^{-1}(\bar{S}) = \{r: r \in R \text{ and } \phi(r) \in \bar{S}\}$$

   is an ideal in R. (See Exercise 2.4–14.)
   b If ϕ maps R onto $\bar{R}$ and S is an ideal in R, then the image set $\phi(S)$ is an ideal in $\bar{R}$. Similar statements may be made for left ideals or right ideals.

3.5 Polynomial Rings

Are there ways of beginning with a ring R with identity and building other rings which contain R? As an illustration of a solution to this question, let us consider the ring $\mathbf{Q}$ and any irrational number α. Both $\mathbf{Q}$ and α are contained in the ring $\mathbf{R}$. Let us find a smallest subring $\mathbf{Q}[\alpha]$ containing both $\mathbf{Q}$ and α. By "smallest subring" we mean that every subring of $\mathbf{R}$ which contains $\mathbf{Q}$ and α also contains $\mathbf{Q}[\alpha]$.

26
Problem   Let S be any subring of $\mathbf{R}$ which contains both $\mathbf{Q}$ and α.

a   Explain why all the following elements must be in S: α; α^2; α^3; α^k, where k is any positive integer; 3α; $-\alpha^4$; and

$$2\alpha^4 + (-\tfrac{4}{5})\alpha^3 + 4\alpha^2 - \tfrac{3}{7}$$

b   Show that S must contain all possible expressions of the form

$$a_n \alpha^n + a_{n-1} \alpha^{n-1} + \cdots + a_1 \alpha + a_0$$

where n is any nonnegative integer and $a_0, a_1, \ldots, a_n \in \mathbf{Q}$. Give several specific examples of elements of this form.

c   Let $\mathbf{Q}[\alpha]$ be the set of all expressions with the above form, that is,

$$\mathbf{Q}[\alpha] = \left\{ \sum_{j=0}^{n} a_j \alpha^j : n \in \mathbf{Z}^+ \cup \{0\}, \ a_j \in \mathbf{Q}, \ 0 \leq j \leq n \right\}$$

Examples of particular elements of $\mathbf{Q}[\alpha]$ are given in parts a and b. Verify that $\mathbf{Q}[\alpha]$ is a subring of $\mathbf{R}$ and hence the smallest subring containing both $\mathbf{Q}$ and α.

Now let us look at some specific examples of this subring.

27
Problem   Let $\alpha = \sqrt{2}$. In this case we can obtain an explicit description of $\mathbf{Q}[\sqrt{2}]$. Show that

$$\mathbf{Q}[\sqrt{2}] = \{a + b\sqrt{2}: a, b \in \mathbf{Q}\}$$

(See Exercises 1.2–5 and 1.2–6.) Note that in $\mathbf{Q}[\sqrt{2}]$,

$$a + b\sqrt{2} = c + d\sqrt{2}$$

if and only if $a = c$ and $b = d$.

28

Problem

As a second illustration of the ring $\mathbf{Q}[\alpha]$, let $\alpha = \sqrt[4]{2}$. Then $\mathbf{Q}[\sqrt[4]{2}]$ is the smallest subring of $\mathbf{R}$ which contains both $\mathbf{Q}$ and $\sqrt[4]{2}$. Show that

$$\mathbf{Q}[\sqrt[4]{2}] = \{a_0 + a_1\sqrt{2} + a_2\sqrt[4]{2} + a_3\sqrt[4]{8}: \\ a_j \in \mathbf{Q}, \ j = 0, 1, 2, 3\}$$

and that $\mathbf{Q}[\sqrt{2}] \subseteq \mathbf{Q}[\sqrt[4]{2}]$.

In Problems 27 and 28 we saw that each of the numbers $\sqrt{2}$ and $\sqrt[4]{2}$ has the property that some power is an element of the ring $\mathbf{Q}$. This is not the case with the number π. Moreover, number theory tells us that for every positive integer n and every set $\{a_0, a_1, ..., a_n\} \subseteq \mathbf{Q}$ with $a_n \neq 0$, the number

$$a_n\pi^n + a_{n-1}\pi^{n-1} + \cdots + a_1\pi + a_0$$

is irrational. With this in mind let us consider the ring $\mathbf{Q}[\pi]$. Note that

$$\mathbf{Q}[\pi] = \left\{\sum_{j=0}^{n} a_j\pi^j: n \in \mathbf{Z}^+ \cup \{0\}, \ a_j \in \mathbf{Q} \text{ for } 0 \leq j \leq n\right\}$$

In the ring $\mathbf{Q}[\pi]$ two elements $\sum_{j=0}^{n} a_j\pi^j$ and $\sum_{k=0}^{m} b_k\pi^k$ are equal if and only if the coefficients of like powers of π are equal. Thus, with coefficients in $\mathbf{Q}$,

$$\sum_{j=0}^{n} a_j\pi^j = \sum_{k=0}^{m} b_k\pi^k$$

if and only if $n = m$ and $a_j = b_j$ for $j = 0, 1, ..., n$. Leave the proof of this fact for Exercise 2. This type of equality, term by term, is not true for the rings $\mathbf{Q}[\sqrt{2}]$ or $\mathbf{Q}[\sqrt[4]{2}]$.

29

Problem   Give an example of two expressions $\sum_{j=0}^{n} a_j (\sqrt{2})^j$ and $\sum_{k=0}^{m} b_k (\sqrt{2})^k$ which are equal in $\mathbf{Q}[\sqrt{2}]$ but have $a_j \neq b_j$ for some j.

30

Problem   a   Since $\mathbf{Q}[\pi]$ is a subring of $\mathbf{R}$, we have at hand the properties of associativity and commutativity of addition. Using these properties, find the coefficient of π^k in the sum

$$\sum_{j=0}^{n} a_j \pi^j + \sum_{i=0}^{m} b_i \pi^i$$

where $m \leq n$.

   b   In multiplying two elements of $\mathbf{Q}[\pi]$ we can use the distributive law to obtain the following expression:

$$\left(\sum_{j=0}^{n} a_j \pi^j \right) \left(\sum_{k=0}^{m} b_k \pi^k \right) = \left(\sum_{j=0}^{n} a_j \pi^j \right) b_m \pi^m$$

$$+ \left(\sum_{j=0}^{n} a_j \pi^j \right) b_{m-1} \pi^{m-1} + \cdots$$

$$+ \left(\sum_{j=0}^{n} a_j \pi^j \right) b_1 \pi + \left(\sum_{j=0}^{n} a_j \pi^j \right) b_0$$

In this product what is the coefficient of π^{n+m}? of π^0? of π^{n+m-1}?

In answer to our question of how we might construct a larger ring from a given ring, let us generalize this ring $\mathbf{Q}[\pi]$. Let R be a ring with identity and let x denote an element which is not in R. If x and R are both included in some larger ring, then any expression of the form

$$a_n x^n + a_{n-1} x^{n-1} + \cdots + a_1 x + a_0$$

with coefficients a_j in R, is an element of this larger ring. However, we do not assume that x and R are included in a larger ring. Instead, we simply form the expressions

$$a_n x^n + a_{n-1} x^{n-1} + \cdots + a_1 x + a_0$$

where n is a nonnegative integer and $a_j \in R$ for $j = 0, 1, 2, ..., n$. We stipulate that the element x has the following property: Two expressions of the form

$$a_0 + a_1 x + \cdots + a_n x^n \quad \text{and} \quad b_0 + b_1 x + \cdots + b_m x^m$$

where $a_j, b_k \in R$ for $j = 0, 1, ..., n$ and $k = 0, 1, ..., m$, are equal if and only if they are equal term by term. Thus

$$a_0 + a_1 x + \cdots + a_n x^n = b_0 + b_1 x + \cdots + b_m x^m$$

if and only if $n = m$ and $a_j = b_j$ for $j = 0, 1, ..., n$. An element x with this property is called an *indeterminate* over R.

Using $\mathbf{Q}[\pi]$ as a guide, we now define a set which contains both x and the elements of R.

31
Definition   Let $(R, +, \cdot)$ be a ring with identity and let x be an indeterminate over R. We denote by $R[x]$ the set of all formal expressions

A $a_n x^n + a_{n-1} x^{n-1} + \cdots + a_1 x + a_0$

where n is a nonnegative integer and $a_j \in R$ for $j = 0, 1, ..., n$. We define $1 \cdot x = x$ and for any $a \in R$ we define ax^0 to be the element a. We call the element a_j in the expression $a_j x^j$ the *coefficient* of x^j. Any expression of the form A above is called a *polynomial in x* with coefficients in R.

Thus $R[x]$ is the set of all polynomials in x with coefficients in R.

32
Problem   a   Give several examples of elements of $\mathbf{Z}[x]$.

b   Give several examples of elements of $\mathbf{Z}_4[x]$.

Let $(R, +, \cdot)$ be a ring with identity. We call the polynomial

$$0x^n + 0x^{n-1} + \cdots + 0x + 0$$

the *zero polynomial* and normally denote it simply by 0.

For every polynomial in $R[x] - \{0\}$ there is a largest nonnegative integer m such that the coefficient of x^m is different from zero. This integer m is called the *degree* of the polynomial and the coefficient a_m of x^m is called the *leading coefficient* of the polynomial. The zero polynomial has degree zero by definition.

If the polynomial $f(x) \in R[x]$ has degree m, we may still write

$$f(x) = a_n x^n + a_{n-1} x^{n-1} + \cdots + a_m x^m + a_{m-1} x^{m-1} + \cdots$$
$$+ a_1 x + a_0$$

where $n > m$, but with the understanding that $a_k = 0$ for $k = m+1, \ldots, n$. For example

$$2x^2 + 1 = 0x^4 + 0x^3 + 2x^2 + 0x + 1$$

Thus, when convenient, we can assume that two polynomials have the same number of terms although their degrees may be different.

On the other hand, when we are working with specific polynomials we usually find it convenient to omit all the terms with a zero coefficient.

33
Definition   The sum $f(x) + g(x)$ of two polynomials

$$f(x) = \sum_{j=0}^{n} a_j x^j \qquad \text{and} \qquad g(x) = \sum_{j=0}^{n} b_j x^j$$

in $R[x]$ is defined to be the polynomial

$$f(x) + g(x) = \sum_{j=0}^{n} (a_j + b_j) x^j$$
$$= (a_n + b_n) x^n + (a_{n-1} + b_{n-1}) x^{n-1} + \cdots$$
$$+ (a_0 + b_0)$$

Thus the coefficient of x^k in the sum $f(x) + g(x)$ is the sum of the coefficients of x^k in $f(x)$ and $g(x)$. Remember that if the degree of $f(x)$ is $m < n$, then $a_k = 0$ for $k = m+1, \ldots, n$ and similarly for $g(x)$.

34
Problem   a   In $\mathbf{Z}[x]$ find the sum of the polynomials $f(x) = 2x^3 + 1$ and $g(x) = x^2 + 1$.

b   In $\mathbf{Z}_4[x]$ find the sum of the polynomials

$$f(x) = 2_4 x^3 + 3_4 x + 2_4 \quad \text{and} \quad g(x) = 2_4 x^3 + 2_4 x^2 - 3_4$$

35
Definition   The product of two polynomials $f(x) = ax^n$ and $g(x) = bx^m$ in $R[x]$ is the polynomial

B $f(x)g(x) = abx^{n+m}$

The product of the two polynomials $f(x) = \sum_{j=0}^{n} a_j x^j$ and $g(x) = bx^m$ is defined to be the polynomial

C $f(x)g(x) = a_n x^n (bx^m) + a_{n-1} x^{n-1} (bx^m) + \cdots$

$$+ a_1 x(bx^m) + a_0 bx^m$$

Finally, we define the product of two general polynomials to be the polynomial

D $f(x)g(x) = \left(\sum_{j=0}^{n} a_j x^j \right) \left(\sum_{k=0}^{m} b_k x^k \right)$

$$= \left(\sum_{j=0}^{n} a_j x^j \right) b_m x^m + \left(\sum_{j=0}^{n} a_j x^j \right) b_{m-1} x^{m-1} + \cdots$$

$$+ \left(\sum_{j=0}^{n} a_j x^j \right) b_1 x + \left(\sum_{j=0}^{n} a_j x^j \right) b_0$$

Note that the definition of a product is a three-stage affair. In actually computing a product of two polynomials one starts with definition D, then applies definition C, and finally definition B.

36
Problem   a   Find the product of the pairs of polynomials in Problem 34. What is the degree of the product in each case?

b   If $(R, +, \cdot)$ is a ring with identity, find the product of the polynomials

$$f(x) = a_2 x^2 + a_1 x + a_0 \qquad \text{and}$$

$$g(x) = b_3 x^3 + b_2 x^2 + b_1 x + b_0$$

in $R[x]$. Write the product in the form $\sum_{k=0}^{n} c_k x^k$. If $a_2 b_3 \neq 0$, what is the degree of $f(x) g(x)$?

37
Problem   a   Let

$$f(x) = \sum_{j=0}^{n} a_j x^j \qquad \text{and} \qquad g(x) = \sum_{k=0}^{m} b_k x^k$$

Find the coefficients of x^{n+m}, of x^{n+m-1}, of x, and of x^0 in the product $f(x) g(x)$.

b   Show that $a_j b_i$ appears in a coefficient of x^k in the product $f(x) g(x)$ if and only if $j + i = k$, or, equivalently, $i = k - j$. Then show that the coefficient of x^k in the product $f(x) g(x)$ is _____ .

38
Problem   a   Let $f(x)$ and $g(x)$ be polynomials of degrees n and m, respectively, in $R[x]$ and let $n \geq m$. Then the degree of the sum $f(x) + g(x)$ is no more than _____, while the degree of the product $f(x) g(x)$ is no more than _____. Complete and prove the statement.

b   Show by example that equality need not hold in either case.

c   Give an example of polynomials whose sum and product have the maximum degree stated above.

Now, at last, we are ready to prove that $R[x]$ is a ring which properly contains the original ring R.

39
Theorem   Let $(R, +, \cdot)$ be a ring with identity. Then $(R[x], +, \cdot)$ is a ring with identity, called the ring of polynomials over R. Moreover, R is a proper subring of $R[x]$.

The theorem is proved in part in the following problem; the proof is completed in the exercises.

40
Problem   First prove that $(R[x], +)$ is a commutative group. (Use the summation notation $\sum_{j=0}^{n} a_j x^j$.) The associative and distributive properties of multiplication are left for Exercises 3 and 4. Find the multiplicative identity of $R[x]$. Then prove that R is a proper subring of $R[x]$.

41
Theorem   Let $(R, +, \cdot)$ be a ring. Then $R[x]$ is a commutative ring if and only if R is a commutative ring.

The proof of this theorem is left for Exercise 5.

EXERCISES 1   Which of the following are subrings of $\mathbf{Z}[x]$? Justify your answers.

a $\{a_n x^n + a_{n-1} x^{n-1} + \cdots + a_1 x : a_k \in \mathbf{Z}, n \in \mathbf{Z}^+\}$. Since n may vary in $\mathbf{Z}^+$, this is the set of all polynomials with zero constant terms.

b $\{a_n x^n + a_{n-1} x^{n-1} + \cdots + a_5 x^5 + a_4 x^4 : a_k \in \mathbf{Z}, 4 \le k \le n, n \ge 4\}$

c $\{a_5 x^5 + \cdots + a_1 x + a_0 : a_k \in \mathbf{Z}, k = 0, 1, ..., 5\}$

d $\{(x - a) f(x) : f(x) \in \mathbf{Z}[x]\}$, where $a \in \mathbf{Z}$ is fixed. This is the set of all polynomials in $\mathbf{Z}[x]$ which are multiples of $x - a$.

2   Prove that in the ring $\mathbf{Q}[\pi]$

$$\sum_{j=0}^{n} a_j \pi^j = \sum_{k=0}^{m} b_k \pi^k$$

where n and m are nonnegative integers and $a_j, b_k \in \mathbf{Q}$ for $0 \le j \le n$, $0 \le k \le m$, if and only if $m = n$ and $a_j = b_j$ for $j = 0, 1, ..., n$.

3   Let $(R, +, \cdot)$ be a ring with identity. Prove that multiplication is associative in $R[x]$.

4   Let $(R, +, \cdot)$ be a ring with identity. Prove that multiplication is distributive over addition in $R[x]$.

5   Prove Theorem 41.

6   Prove that $\mathbf{Z}_n[x]$ is an infinite ring for every integer $n \geq 2$.

7   Prove that if R is one of the rings $\mathbf{Z}$, $\mathbf{Q}$, or $\mathbf{R}$, then for every $f(x), g(x) \in R[x] - \{0\}$ the degree of the product $f(x) g(x)$ is the sum of the degrees of $f(x)$ and $g(x)$. Symbolically, if we denote the degree of a polynomial $p(x)$ by $\deg(p(x))$, then

$$\deg(f(x) g(x)) = \deg(f(x)) + \deg(g(x))$$

where $f(x)$ and $g(x)$ are nonzero polynomials in the rings $\mathbf{Z}[x]$, $\mathbf{Q}[x]$, or $\mathbf{R}[x]$. What special property of the rings $\mathbf{Z}$, $\mathbf{Q}$, or $\mathbf{R}$ have you used in your proof?

8a   In Problem 26 we described the smallest subring of $\mathbf{R}$ which contained both $\mathbf{Q}$ and an irrational number α. In general, let R be any subring of a ring $\bar{R}$ with identity and α any element in $\bar{R} - R$. Show that there exists a smallest subring $R[\alpha]$ of $\bar{R}$ which contains R and α and describe the elements of $R[\alpha]$.

b   Let $R = \mathbf{Q}[\sqrt{2}]$. Describe the elements of $R[\sqrt{3}]$. This is the ring $\mathbf{Q}[\sqrt{2}]$ with $\sqrt{3}$ adjoined. One usually writes $\mathbf{Q}[\sqrt{2}, \sqrt{3}]$ for this ring.

9a   The equation $\alpha^2 - 2 = 0$ has no solution in $\mathbf{Q}$. Show that there is a solution to the equation in $\mathbf{Q}[\sqrt{2}]$.

b   Show that both the equations $\alpha^2 - 2 = 0$ and $\alpha^4 - 2 = 0$ have solutions in $\mathbf{Q}[\sqrt[4]{2}]$.

c   Let R be a subring of $\mathbf{R}$ with identity. Suppose that the equation $\alpha^n - a = 0$, $a \in R^+ = \{x : x \in R, x > 0\}$, does not have a solution in R. Let $\alpha = \sqrt[n]{a}$ be a symbol which represents a solution to the equation. Construct a ring in which the equation has a solution and describe the elements of this ring.

*10   Let α be a real number which is not in $\mathbf{Z}$. Let

$$\mathbf{Z}[\alpha] = \left\{ \sum_{j=0}^{n} a_j \alpha^j \colon a_j \in \mathbf{Z},\ n \in \mathbf{Z}^+ \cup \{0\} \right\}$$

a   Prove that $\mathbf{Z}[\alpha]$ is a subring of $\mathbf{R}$.
b   Prove that if S is a subring of $\mathbf{R}$ which contains $\mathbf{Z}$ and α, then $\mathbf{Z}[\alpha] \subseteq S$. (Thus $\mathbf{Z}[\alpha]$ is the smallest ring which contains $\mathbf{Z}$ and α.)
c   Prove that $\mathbf{Z}[\alpha]$ is a proper subring of $\mathbf{Q}[\alpha]$.
d   Prove that if $c \in \mathbf{Z}^+$ and $\alpha = \sqrt{c} \notin \mathbf{Z}$, then

$$\mathbf{Z}[\alpha] = \{a + b\sqrt{c} \colon a, b \in \mathbf{Z}\}$$

11   Let $c \in \mathbf{Q}$ be a number such that $\sqrt{c} \notin \mathbf{Q}$.
a   Prove that $\mathbf{Q}[\sqrt{c}] = \{a + b\sqrt{c} \colon a, b \in \mathbf{Q}\}$.
b   Prove that if $a + b\sqrt{c} \in \mathbf{Q}[\sqrt{c}] - \{0\}$, then $(a + b\sqrt{c})^{-1}$ is an element of $\mathbf{Q}[\sqrt{c}]$.

12a   Let $(R, +, \cdot)$ be a ring with identity and let x be an indeterminate over R. We have constructed the ring $R[x]$. Now let y be an indeterminate over $R[x]$ which commutes with x. Describe the elements of $R[x][y]$. This ring is often denoted by $R[x, y]$.
b   Describe a method for constructing the ring $R[x_1, x_2, \ldots, x_n]$ of polynomials in n indeterminates $x_1, x_2, \ldots, x_n$ which commute with each other. Give several examples of elements of $R[x_1, x_2, \ldots, x_n] - R$.

3.6 Integral Domains

So far we have seen great variety in the properties of multiplication in various rings. We have investigated general rings in which multiplication may be only associative and distributive over addition. We have also encountered rings which have a multiplicative identity and rings in which multiplication is commutative. We now focus our attention on the cancellation property for multiplication in a ring. This property holds in some rings and fails dramatically in others. Throughout this section we deal with *nontrivial* rings (i.e., rings with more than one element).

42

Problem

Consider the following two properties in a ring R:

a   For all $a, b, c \in R$ if $ac = bc$ and $c \neq 0$, then $a = b$.

b   For all $s, t \in R$ if $st = 0$, then $s = 0$ or $t = 0$.

Determine whether or not each of these properties is true in $\mathbf{Z}_6$.

43

Problem

Prove the following theorem:

Theorem

Let $(R, +, \cdot)$ be a ring. Then the following statements are equivalent (i.e., both statements are true or both are false).

a   For all $a, b, c \in R$ if $ac = bc$ and $c \neq 0$, then $a = b$.

b   For all $s, t \in R$ if $st = 0$, then $s = 0$ or $t = 0$. ▲

In a given ring R the theorem guarantees that statements a and b are equivalent; it does not guarantee that statements a and b are true.

Theorem 43 can be written in the following form:

43'

Theorem

If $(R, +, \cdot)$ is a ring, then the following statements are equivalent:

a For all $a, b, c \in R$ if $ac = bc$ and $c \neq 0$, then $a = b$.

b' For all $s, t \in R$ if $s \neq 0$ and $t \neq 0$, then _____ .

If statement b' above fails in a given ring, a special name is given to those elements which make it fail.

44
Definition
Let $(R, +, \cdot)$ be a ring. If $s, t \in R$ and $s \neq 0$ and $t \neq 0$ but $st = 0$, then s and t are called *divisors of zero* or *zero divisors*.

45
Problem
Find all the divisors of zero in $\mathbf{Z}_6$; in $\mathbf{Z}_5$.

If the equivalent statements a and b in Theorem 43 (or a and b' in Theorem 43') hold in a commutative ring with identity, then the ring is given a special name.

46
Definition
An *integral domain* is a nontrivial commutative ring $(R, +, \cdot)$ with identity such that cancellation holds for multiplication: for every $a, b, c \in R$ if $ac = bc$ and $c \neq 0$, then $a = b$.

47
Problem
With the usual operations, which of the following systems are integral domains? Justify your answers. See Appendix 3 for properties of the real numbers.

a $(\mathbf{Z}, +, \cdot)$
b $(\mathbf{Q}, +, \cdot)$
c $(\mathbf{R}, +, \cdot)$
d $(\mathbf{Z}_6, +, \cdot)$

48
Problem
Let $\mathbf{Q}[\sqrt{2}] = \{a + b\sqrt{2}: a, b \in \mathbf{Q}\}$. We have seen that $\mathbf{Q}[\sqrt{2}]$ is a subring of $\mathbf{R}$ with the usual operations in $\mathbf{R}$. Prove or disprove that $(\mathbf{Q}[\sqrt{2}], +, \cdot)$ is an integral domain. Remember that the elements of $\mathbf{Q}[\sqrt{2}]$ are all real numbers.

We have seen that if statement b′ of Theorem 43′ fails, then a ring must have zero divisors. Since this statement is closely tied to cancellation for multiplication, we are led to ask the following question:

49
Problem

Can an integral domain $(D, +, \cdot)$ have any divisors of zero? Justify your answer. Restate the definition of an integral domain in terms of divisors of zero instead of cancellation.

Let us determine the values of $n \in \mathbf{Z}^+$ for which $\mathbf{Z}_n$ is an integral domain. First let us explore the possibility of divisors of zero in $\mathbf{Z}_n$.

50
Problem

Prove that if $n = km$, where n, k, and m are integers greater than 1, then k_n and m_n are divisors of zero in the ring $\mathbf{Z}_n$. You must prove that neither k_n nor m_n is the zero element of $\mathbf{Z}_n$.

51
Problem

Complete correctly and prove the following statement: The ring $\mathbf{Z}_n$ is an integral domain if and only if n is _____ _____ . ▲

EXERCISES 1a In $(M_2(\mathbf{R}), +, \cdot)$ does the cancellation property (statement a in Problem 43) hold for multiplication? Why?

b Is $M_2(\mathbf{R})$ an integral domain? Why?

2 Find a subring of $M_2(\mathbf{R})$ which is an integral domain.

3a Prove that if $(R, +, \cdot)$ is a ring and $s \in R$ is a divisor of zero, then s does not have a multiplicative inverse.

b Is the converse statement true? That is, if $s \in R$ does not have a multiplicative inverse, then is s necessarily a divisor of zero?

4 Let D be an integral domain. If S is a subring of D, is S necessarily an integral domain? Justify your answer.

5   Let $F(\mathbf{R}, \mathbf{R})$ be the ring of all functions from $\mathbf{R}$ into itself with the operations of pointwise addition and multiplication. (See Exercise 3.1–6.) Show that $F(\mathbf{R}, \mathbf{R})$ is not an integral domain.

6   Is $\mathbf{Z}[x]$, the ring of polynomials over $\mathbf{Z}$ in an indeterminate x, an integral domain? Justify your answer.

7   Prove that if $(R, +, \cdot)$ is an integral domain and if $f(x), g(x) \in R[x] - \{0\}$, then the degree of the product $f(x)g(x)$ is the sum of the degrees of $f(x)$ and $g(x)$. Symbolically,

$$\deg(f(x)g(x)) = \deg(f(x)) + \deg(g(x))$$

8   Let $(R, +, \cdot)$ be a ring with identity. Prove that $R[x]$ is an integral domain if and only if R is an integral domain.

*9   Let R and $\bar{R}$ be rings and $\phi: R \to \bar{R}$ an isomorphism. Show that if R is an integral domain, then $\bar{R}$ is an integral domain. The converse is true also since if ϕ is an isomorphism, then the inverse function ϕ^{-1} is an isomorphism. (See Exercise 2.5–11.)

*10   Prove that if $c \in \mathbf{Z}^+$ and $\sqrt{c} \notin \mathbf{Z}$, then the ring

$$\mathbf{Z}[\sqrt{c}] = \{a + b\sqrt{c}: a, b \in \mathbf{Z}\}$$

is an integral domain.

*11   You have previously encountered complex numbers $a + bi$, where $a, b \in \mathbf{R}$. The letter i denotes the so-called imaginary number such that $i^2 = -1$. Recall that

$(a + bi) + (c + di) = $ _____   and

$(a + bi) \cdot (c + di) = $ _____

The point of the following problem is to construct the set of complex numbers from the familiar set $\mathbf{R}^2$.

Let $\mathbf{C} = \mathbf{R}^2 = \{(a, b): a, b \in \mathbf{R}\}$. By definition of a cartesian product, $(a, b) = (c, d)$ if and only if $a = c$ and $b = d$. We have seen that the sum of two elements (a, b) and (c, d) of $\mathbf{C}$ is defined to be

$$(a, b) + (c, d) = (a + c, b + d)$$

With this addition $\mathbf{C}$ is a commutative group. (See Exercises 1.1–4 and 1.2–10.)

The product of two elements (a, b) and (c, d) of $\mathbf{C}$ is defined to be

$$(a, b) \cdot (c, d) = (ac - bd, ad + bc)$$

a   Prove that $(\mathbf{C}, +, \cdot)$ is a commutative ring with identity.

b   Show that every nonzero element of $\mathbf{C}$ has a multiplicative inverse.

c   Is $(\mathbf{C}, +, \cdot)$ an integral domain? Justify your answer.

d   Find an element $(\alpha, \beta) \in \mathbf{C}$ such that $(\alpha, \beta)^2 = (-1, 0)$.

e   Prove that $(\mathbf{R}, +, \cdot)$ is isomorphic to the subring of $\mathbf{C}$ consisting of all elements $(a, 0)$ with $a \in \mathbf{R}$.

3.7 Fields

We have seen many commutative rings with identity in which every nonzero element has a multiplicative inverse. Such rings are called fields. In this section the theory of fields helps us to prove some interesting and useful results in number theory. At the end of the section we discuss a bit of the history of fields.

52
Definition
A *field* $(F, +, \cdot)$ is a nontrivial commutative ring F with identity such that every nonzero element of F has a multiplicative inverse in F.

53
Problem
Which of the following sets are fields with the usual operations of addition and multiplication? Justify your answers.

a **R**
b **Q**
c **Z**
d **Z**$_5$
e **Z**$_6$

A ring is a group under addition. But when is the set of nonzero ring elements a group under multiplication? The following theorem gives an answer to this question in the case when the ring is commutative.

54
Problem
Prove the following theorem:

Theorem
Let R be a commutative ring. Then R is a field if and only if $R - \{0\}$ is a group under multiplication.

We know that every integral domain is a ring. The next problem continues this chain by showing that every field is an integral domain.

55

Problem   a   Prove that if $(F, +, \cdot)$ is a field, then it is an integral domain.

        b   Is every integral domain also a field? Justify your answer by a proof or by an example of an integral domain which is not a field.

There is a converse to the implication of Problem 55a if the integral domain is finite. This is the content of the following theorem.

56

Problem   Prove the following theorem:

Theorem   Any finite integral domain is a field: If $(F, +, \cdot)$ is an integral domain and F is a finite set, then $(F, +, \cdot)$ is a field.

           You must prove that every element $a \in F - \{0\}$ has a multiplicative inverse. To do so consider the set $\{a, a^2, a^3, \ldots\}$. Can all these powers be distinct?

57

Problem   Complete correctly and prove the following theorem:

Theorem   The ring $(\mathbf{Z}_n, +, \cdot)$ is a field if and only if n is _____ .

We have seen that in a group $(G, \circ)$ the equation $a \circ x = b$ has a unique solution $x =$ _____ in G (Section 1.3). The equation $ax = b$ need not have any solution in a ring R, however. For example, the equation $2x = 4$ has the unique solution $x = 2$ in $\mathbf{Z}$, but the equation $2x = 1$ does not have a solution in $\mathbf{Z}$. On the other hand, if $a, b \in \mathbf{Q}$ and $a \neq 0$, then the equation $ax = b$ has the unique solution $x =$ _____ in $\mathbf{Q}$. In the following problem we see that if F is a field, then every linear equation $ax = b$, $a, b \in F$ and $a \neq 0$, has a solution in F.

58

Problem   a   Prove that if $(F, +, \cdot)$ is a field and $a, b \in F$ with $a \neq 0$, then the equation $ax = b$ has a unique solution for x in F.

b   Prove that a commutative ring R with identity is a field if and only if for every $a, b \in R$ with $a \neq 0$ the equation $ax = b$ has a solution $x \in R$.

59
Definition   A subset S of a field $(F, +, \cdot)$ is a *subfield* of F if and only if $(S, +, \cdot)$ is a field.

60
Problem   We have already seen that a subset S of a ring R is a subring of R if and only if for every $a, b \in S$ both $a - b$ and ab are in S. Find a corresponding necessary and sufficient condition for S to be a subfield of the field F and prove that your answer is correct.

We have seen that every nontrivial ring R contains at least the improper ideals $\{0\}$ and R. It also can be shown that some rings which are not even integral domains have no proper ideals (see Exercise 3.3–9). This lack of ideals is true in general of fields, as shown in the next problem.

61
Problem   a   Prove that a field F has no proper ideals.

b   Show by example that there exist integral domains which contain proper ideals.

Many beginning students write $(a+b)^n = a^n + b^n$, where $a, b \in \mathbf{Z}$ and $n \in \mathbf{Z}^+$, only to be informed that this result is not true. Now we prove that if a_p and b_p are elements of $\mathbf{Z}_p$, where p is a prime, then, in fact, $(a_p + b_p)^p = (a_p)^p + (b_p)^p$. We also prove that if p is a prime and $a \in \mathbf{Z}$ is not a multiple of p, then p divides both $a^p - a$ and $a^{p-1} - 1$. (For example, this would say that 13 divides $x^{12} - 1$ for $x \in \mathbf{Z} - \{13k: k \in \mathbf{Z}\}$.)

62
Problem   To illustrate these results from number theory, choose a specific prime integer $p > 3$. Choose two specific elements $a_p, b_p \in \mathbf{Z}_p - \{0_p\}$.

a   Calculate $(a_p)^{p-1}$ and $(b_p)^{p-1}$.

b   Calculate $(a_p + b_p)^p$ and $(a_p)^p + (b_p)^p$.

A proof of the preceding results in general uses the following problem.

63
Problem   a   If n is an integer such that $\mathbf{Z}_n$ is a field, what is the order of the multiplicative group $\mathbf{Z}_n - \{0_n\}$?

b   Let n be an integer such that $\mathbf{Z}_n$ is a field and let $a_n \in \mathbf{Z}_n - \{0_n\}$. Show that the order of the element a_n in the multiplicative group $\mathbf{Z}_n - \{0_n\}$ is a divisor of the integer $n-1$.   ▲

64
Problem   Prove the following theorem:

Theorem   Let p be a prime.

a   If $a_p \in \mathbf{Z}_p - \{0_p\}$, then $(a_p)^{p-1} = 1_p$ and $(a_p)^p = a_p$.

b   If $a \in \mathbf{Z}$ and a is not a multiple of p, then $a^{p-1} \equiv 1 \pmod{p}$.   ▲

c   If $a \in \mathbf{Z}$, then $a^p \equiv a \pmod{p}$.

The results in Problem 64b and 64c are known as Fermat's Minor Theorem. The Frenchman Pierre de Fermat (1601–1665) was a lawyer for whom mathematics was a hobby. Nevertheless, he made many valuable contributions to number theory and several other areas of mathematics.

65
Problem   Prove the following theorem:

Theorem   Let p be a prime.

a   If $a, b \in \mathbf{Z}$, then

$$(a+b)^p \equiv a^p + b^p \pmod{p}$$

Pierre de Fermat

b   If $a_p, b_p \in \mathbf{Z}_p$, then

$$(a_p + b_p)^p = (a_p)^p + (b_p)^p$$

66

Problem   Show that 13 divides $x^{12} - 1$, where x is an integer which is not a multiple of 13.

The concept of a field was introduced by Abel in a paper published in 1829. Slightly later Galois used the concept of a field although neither he nor Abel used the name that we know today or dealt with anything but fields such as **Q** or **R** whose elements are numbers. Both men meant by a field a set of numbers which is closed under addition, subtraction, multiplication, and division by nonzero elements.

Galois was especially interested in fields such as

$$\mathbf{Q}(\alpha) = \left\{ \left(\sum_{j=0}^{n} a_j \alpha^j \right) \middle/ \left(\sum_{k=0}^{m} b_k \alpha^k \right) : a_j, b_k \in \mathbf{Q}, \right.$$
$$\left. n, m \in \mathbf{Z}^+ \cup \{0\}, \text{ and } \sum_{k=0}^{m} b_k \alpha^k \neq 0 \right\}$$

where α is a real number. Such a field is now called an extension field.

The name field (*Körper* in the original German) was devised by Dedekind, who also stated a set of axioms for number fields in 1871. It was Heinrich Weber (1842–1913) who in the late nineteenth century began the study of abstract fields. Among other things, he presented an abstract formulation of Galois's work on the solutions of polynomial equations. Weber actually considered groups and fields to be the two major concepts of abstract algebra and considered fields to be extensions of groups. His axioms defining an abstract field are the same as those stated in Definition 52 if we write out the definition of a commutative ring. However, Weber did require that inverses be unique (a condition which can actually be proved, as we showed in Section 1.3).

Heinrich Weber

At the end of the nineteenth century, the fields that were known were those of the rational, real, and complex numbers, algebraic number fields such as $\{a+b\sqrt{-5}: a,b \in \mathbf{Q}\}$, and the fields of rational functions in one or several variables (i.e., functions which are quotients of polynomials with coefficients in a given ring of numbers).

EXERCISES 1   Determine which of the following sets are fields. Justify your answers.

a $\mathbf{Q}[\sqrt{2}] = \{a+b\sqrt{2}: a, b \in \mathbf{Q}\}$ with the usual addition and multiplication of numbers. (See Problem 48 and Exercise 1.2–6.)

b The set of complex numbers, $\mathbf{C} = \{(a, b): a, b \in \mathbf{R}\}$, with the addition defined by setting $(a, b) + (c, d) = (a+c, b+d)$ and the product by $(a, b) \cdot (c, d) = (ac-bd, ad+bc)$. (See Exercise 3.6–11.)

c $\mathbf{Z}[x]$, the ring of polynomials over $\mathbf{Z}$ in x

2 Find the multiplicative inverses for several elements in $\mathbf{Z}_{11}$.

3 In any field F an operation of division can be defined by setting $a/b = ab^{-1}$, where $a, b \in F$ and $b \neq 0$.

a In $\mathbf{Z}_7$ calculate $4_7/3_7$.

b In $\mathbf{Z}_{11}$ calculate $5_{11}/6_{11}$.

c Let F be a field. Prove the following statements:

$$\frac{a}{b} \cdot \frac{b}{a} = 1 \qquad\qquad c \cdot \frac{a}{b} = \frac{ca}{b}$$

$$\frac{a}{b} + \frac{c}{d} = \underline{\hspace{2cm}} \qquad\qquad \frac{a}{b} \cdot \frac{c}{d} = \underline{\hspace{2cm}}$$

$$\frac{a+b}{c} = \frac{a}{c} + \frac{b}{c} \qquad\qquad \frac{a/b}{c/d} = \frac{ad}{bc}$$

4 Make addition and multiplication tables for a field with four elements. Can this field be isomorphic to $(\mathbf{Z}_4, +, \cdot)$? (Be certain to check the distributive property.)

5 Prove that if F is a field and R is a ring which is isomorphic to F, then R is a field.

6 An interesting question in number theory is the following: Let m and n be positive with $n > m$. If $2^n - 2^m$ divides $3^n - 3^m$, then is it true that $2^n - 2^m$ divides $x^n - x^m$ for every integer $x \geq 2$? In this exercise we consider two pairs of values for m and n.

a Show that $2^3 - 2$ divides $x^3 - x$ for every integer $x \geq 2$.

b Show that $2^8 - 2^2$ divides $3^8 - 3^2$. Then prove that $2^8 - 2^2$ divides $x^8 - x^2$ for every integer $x \geq 2$. ●

7 Let F be a finite field with more than two elements. Show that the sum of all the elements in F is zero.

8   Let c be an element of $\mathbf{Z}^+$ which is not a perfect square so that $\sqrt{c} \notin \mathbf{Z}$.

a   We know from Section 3.5 that

$$\mathbf{Q}[\sqrt{c}] = \{a + b\sqrt{c}: a, b \in \mathbf{Q}\}$$

is a commutative ring with identity. Is $\mathbf{Q}[\sqrt{c}]$ a field? Justify your answer.

b   From Exercise 3.6–10 we know that $\mathbf{Z}[\sqrt{c}]$ is an integral domain. Is $\mathbf{Z}[\sqrt{c}]$ a field? Justify your answer.

9   Let

$$Q = \{(a_1, a_2, a_3, a_4): a_i \in \mathbf{R}, \ i = 1, 2, 3, 4\}$$

Two elements of Q are equal if and only if their components are equal:

$$(a_1, a_2, a_3, a_4) = (b_1, b_2, b_3, b_4)$$

if and only if $a_i = b_i$ for $i = 1, 2, 3, 4$. We define the sum of two elements of Q by setting

$$(a_1, a_2, a_3, a_4) + (b_1, b_2, b_3, b_4) = (c_1, c_2, c_3, c_4)$$

where $c_i = a_i + b_i$ for $i = 1, 2, 3, 4$. A scalar multiple $\alpha(a_1, a_2, a_3, a_4)$ for $\alpha \in \mathbf{R}$ is defined by

$$\alpha(a_1, a_2, a_3, a_4) = (\alpha a_1, \alpha a_2, \alpha a_3, \alpha a_4)$$

Let $\mathbf{1} = (1, 0, 0, 0)$, $\mathbf{i} = (0, 1, 0, 0)$, $\mathbf{j} = (0, 0, 1, 0)$, and $\mathbf{k} = (0, 0, 0, 1)$.

a   Find $3(2, -1, 3, 1) + 2(-3, -5, 2, 0)$.

b   Show that every element of Q can be written in the form

$$a_1\mathbf{1} + a_2\mathbf{i} + a_3\mathbf{j} + a_4\mathbf{k}$$

c   Show that $(Q, +)$ is a commutative group.

10   Let Q be the set defined in Exercise 9. Define a product for $\mathbf{1}$, $\mathbf{i}$, $\mathbf{j}$, and $\mathbf{k}$ by Table 3.1. If $x \in \{\mathbf{1}, \mathbf{i}, \mathbf{j}, \mathbf{k}\}$, define the

Table 3.1

·	**1**	**i**	**j**	**k**
1	**1**	**i**	**j**	**k**
i	**i**	**−1**	**k**	**−j**
j	**j**	**−k**	**−1**	**i**
k	**k**	**j**	**−i**	**−1**

product of $A = a_1\mathbf{1} + a_2\mathbf{i} + a_3\mathbf{j} + a_4\mathbf{k}$ and $B = b\mathbf{x}$ by

$$A \cdot B = (a_1\mathbf{1} + a_2\mathbf{i} + a_3\mathbf{j} + a_4\mathbf{k})(b\mathbf{x})$$

$$= a_1 b(\mathbf{1} \cdot \mathbf{x}) + a_2 b(\mathbf{i} \cdot \mathbf{x}) + a_3 b(\mathbf{j} \cdot \mathbf{x}) + a_4 b(\mathbf{k} \cdot \mathbf{x})$$

If $A = a_1\mathbf{1} + a_2\mathbf{i} + a_3\mathbf{j} + a_4\mathbf{k}$ and $B = b_1\mathbf{1} + b_2\mathbf{i} + b_3\mathbf{j} + b_4\mathbf{k}$ are elements of Q, define their product by

$$A \cdot B = A \cdot (b_1\mathbf{1} + b_2\mathbf{i} + b_3\mathbf{j} + b_4\mathbf{k})$$

$$= A(b_1\mathbf{1}) + A(b_2\mathbf{i}) + A(b_3\mathbf{j}) + A(b_4\mathbf{k})$$

a For example,

$$(2\mathbf{i} - 3\mathbf{j})(4\mathbf{i} + \mathbf{k}) = (2\mathbf{i} - 3\mathbf{j})(4\mathbf{i}) + (2\mathbf{i} - 3\mathbf{j})(\mathbf{k})$$

$$= \underline{\hspace{6cm}}$$

b Find the products $(4\mathbf{i} - 3\mathbf{j} + 2\mathbf{k})(\mathbf{1} + \mathbf{i} + \mathbf{j} + \mathbf{k})$ and $(a\mathbf{1} + b\mathbf{i} + c\mathbf{j} + d\mathbf{k})(a\mathbf{1} - b\mathbf{i} - c\mathbf{j} - d\mathbf{k})$.

c Prove that $a_1\mathbf{1} + a_2\mathbf{i} + a_3\mathbf{j} + a_4\mathbf{k} = (0, 0, 0, 0)$ if and only if $a_1^2 + a_2^2 + a_3^2 + a_4^2 = 0$.

d Assume that the multiplication defined above is a properly defined binary operation which is associative and distributive over addition. Prove that $(Q, +, \cdot)$ is a ring with identity and that multiplication is not commutative on Q.

e Prove that every nonzero element of Q has a multiplicative inverse. Do not attempt to solve the equation $AX = \mathbf{1}$, where $A \in Q$ is fixed; instead use part b. Remember that you must prove that the inverse is an element of Q.

The set Q is an example of a division algebra—a ring with identity and a scalar multiplication in which every nonzero element has an inverse. This ring was first defined by William Hamilton (1805–1865), who called these "numbers" the quaternions. The four components can be interpreted as giving location in terms of angles and distance and as such the quaternions have a useful interpretation for physics and engineering.

William Rowan Hamilton

*11   Just as there is a division algorithm for the integral domain **Z**, so is there a division algorithm for the integral domain $F[x]$ of all the polynomials over a field F. This can be stated as follows:

Theorem   Let F be a field and $f(x), g(x) \in F[x] - \{0\}$. Then there exist polynomials $q(x)$ and $r(x)$ in $F[x]$ such that

$$f(x) = g(x) q(x) + r(x)$$

and $r(x) = 0$ or $\deg(r(x)) < \deg(g(x))$. The polynomial $q(x)$ is said to be the quotient and $r(x)$ is said to be the remainder on division of $f(x)$ by $g(x)$.

a For each of the polynomials $f(x), g(x) \in \mathbf{Z}[x]$ below, find the quotient and remainder on division of $f(x)$ by $g(x)$.

$f(x)$	$g(x)$
$x^3 - x^2 + 3$	$x^2 + 4$
$4x^2 - 5$	$3x^3$
$x^5 + 1$	$x - 1$

b Let F be a field and let $f(x), g(x) \in F[x] - \{0\}$. To prove the division algorithm let

$$S = \{f(x) - g(x)h(x): h(x) \in F[x]\}$$

Prove that there exists an element $q(x) \in F[x]$ such that

$$r(x) = f(x) - g(x)q(x)$$

is zero or has the smallest degree of all polynomials in S. Then prove by contradiction that

$$\deg(r(x)) < \deg(g(x))$$

if $r(x) \neq 0$. ●

12 Let n be a fixed positive integer. Prove that an element $a_n \in \mathbf{Z}_n$ has a multiplicative inverse if and only if a and n are relatively prime (i.e. the greatest common divisor of a and n, denoted by $\gcd(a, n)$, is 1). ●

13 Consider the multiplicative group $\mathbf{Z}_{17} - \{0_{17}\}$.
a List the distinct elements of

$$\langle 4_{17} \rangle = \{(4_{17})^k: k \in \mathbf{Z}^+\}$$

the multiplicative subgroup generated by the element 4_{17}. Then find a value of n such that $(\langle 4_{17} \rangle, \cdot)$ is isomorphic to the additive group $\mathbf{Z}_n$.
b Repeat part a with the subgroup $\langle 2_{17} \rangle$.
c Determine the elements of $\langle 3_{17} \rangle$. Is the multiplicative group $\mathbf{Z}_{17} - \{0_{17}\}$ a cyclic group?

14a In the multiplicative group $\mathbf{Z}_{13} - \{0_{13}\}$ list the distinct elements of the subgroup

$$\langle 4_{13} \rangle = \{(4_{13})^k : k \in \mathbf{Z}^+\}$$

Then find a value of n such that $(\langle 4_{13} \rangle, \cdot)$ is isomorphic to the additive group $\mathbf{Z}_n$.

b Prove that the multiplicative group $\mathbf{Z}_{13} - \{0_{13}\}$ is a cyclic group.

Exercises 13 and 14 are examples of a theorem which states that if F is a finite field, then the multiplicative group $F - \{0\}$ is cyclic. For the outline of the proof of this theorem see Exercise 5.1–13.

3.8 Fields of Quotients

The set $\mathbf{Z}$ is an integral domain but only 1 and -1 have multiplicative inverses in $\mathbf{Z}$. However, all the quotients a/b with $b \neq 0$, $a, b \in \mathbf{Z}$, are in the field $\mathbf{Q}$, which contains $\mathbf{Z}$. This field has the operation of addition defined by

$$\frac{a}{b} + \frac{c}{d} = \frac{ad + bc}{bd}$$

and the operation of multiplication defined by

$$\frac{a}{b} \cdot \frac{c}{d} = \frac{ac}{bd}$$

Care must be taken with these operations because a rational number can be written in many different ways, but we do know that $a/b = c/d$ if and only if $ad = bc$.

Using these ideas as motivation, let us take an arbitrary integral domain D and show that it can be "placed inside" a field in which every nonzero element actually has a multiplicative inverse. This field is called the field of quotients of D.

Let D be an integral domain. As the first step in the construction of the field of quotients, let

$$S_D = \{(a, b): a, b \in D, b \neq 0\}$$

67
Definition

Two pairs (a, b) and (c, d) in S_D are equivalent, denoted by $(a, b) \sim (c, d)$, if and only if $ad = bc$.

68
Problem

Prove that the relation "$\sim$" on D given in Definition 67 is an equivalence relation on S_D. (See Appendix 4.)

In your proof you may not assume that nonzero elements of D have multiplicative inverses or that division is defined in D. Remember that the point of this work is to *construct* multiplicative inverses for the nonzero elements of D.

69
Definition   Let D be an integral domain. For every $(a, b) \in S_D$ let

$$[a, b] = \{(c, d) : (c, d) \in S_D \text{ and } (c, d) \sim (a, b)\}$$

Then $[a, b]$ is the equivalence class of the element (a, b) of S_D.

70
Problem   Let $D = \mathbf{Z}$ in this problem only. Prove that $[2, 3] = [4, 6]$. Find several pairs of integers a and b such that $[a, b] = [2, 3]$.

Let D be an integral domain and $a, b, a_1, b_1 \in D$ with $b, b_1 \neq 0$. Remember that $[a, b] = [a_1, b_1]$ if and only if $(a, b) \sim (a_1, b_1)$.

71
Problem   If $[a, b] = [a_1, b_1]$, find a relationship among the elements a, b, a_1, and b_1 of D.

Let D be an integral domain and let

$$Q(D) = \{[a, b] : (a, b) \in S_D\}$$

An element of $Q(D)$ is an equivalence class of (admissible) ordered pairs of elements from D.

72
Problem   List several elements of $Q(\mathbf{Z})$. Is $[2, 0]$ in $Q(\mathbf{Z})$?

If $Q(D)$ is to be a field, we must define operations of addition and multiplication on $Q(D)$. We use the operations for the rational numbers as a guide.

73
Definition   Addition $(+)$ for $Q(D)$ is defined by setting

$$[a, b] + [c, d] = [ad + bc, bd]$$

for every $[a, b], [c, d] \in Q(D)$. Multiplication ($\cdot$) is defined by setting

$$[a, b] \cdot [c, d] = [ac, bd]$$

for every $[a, b], [c, d] \in Q(D)$.

74
Problem

In $Q(\mathbf{Z})$ compute the sum $[1, 3] + [-2, 5]$ and the product $[1, 3] \cdot [-2, 5]$.

75
Problem

Let D be an integral domain. Prove that if $[a, b] = [a_1, b_1]$ and $[c, d] = [c_1, d_1]$, then

$$[a, b] \cdot [c, d] = [a_1, b_1] \cdot [c_1, d_1]$$

(that is, $[ac, bd] = [a_1 c_1, b_1 d_1]$).

Problem 75 shows that multiplication is a properly defined binary operation in $Q(D)$. Addition also is a properly defined binary operation in $Q(D)$. The proof of this fact is left for Exercise 2.

76
Theorem

If D is an integral domain, then the set $Q(D)$ is a field with the operations of addition and multiplication given in Definition 73. The set $Q(D)$ is called the *field of quotients* of D.

A partial proof of Theorem 76 is given in the following problem.

77
Problem

a Prove that $(Q(D), +)$ is a commutative group.

b Find the multiplicative identity for $Q(D)$ and justify your choice.

c   Show that if $[a, b] \neq [0, 1]$, then $[a, b]$ has a multiplicative inverse.

The proof that $Q(D) - \{[0, 1]\}$ is a commutative group under multiplication is left for Exercise 3, and the proof that multiplication is distributive over addition in $Q(D)$ is left for Exercise 4.

78
Problem   Let D be an integral domain.
         a   Prove that the set

$$\bar{D} = \{[a, 1]: a \in D\}$$

is a subring of $Q(D)$.

         b   Prove that D is isomorphic to $\bar{D}$. To do so define a function $\phi: D \to \bar{D}$ and prove that ϕ is an isomorphism.

For convenience the notation a/b is often used for the equivalence class $[a, b]$, where a and b are elements of the integral domain D and $b \neq 0$. This agrees with the familiar notation for rational numbers.

EXERCISES   1a   In $Q(\mathbf{Z}_5)$ show that $[a_5, b_5] = [a_5 b_5^{-1}, 1_5]$ if $b_5 \neq 0_5$.
         b   List the distinct equivalence classes in the field of quotients for $\mathbf{Z}_5$. Prove that this field of quotients is isomorphic to $\mathbf{Z}_5$ itself.

         2   Let D be an integral domain. Prove that addition is a properly defined binary operation on $Q(D)$.

         3   Let D be an integral domain. Prove that $Q(D) - \{[0, 1]\}$ is a commutative group under multiplication.

         4   Let D be an integral domain. Prove that multiplication is distributive over addition in $Q(D)$.

5 Let D be an integral domain and let F be a field which contains D. Prove that there exists a subfield F' of F such that F' contains D and F' is isomorphic to $Q(D)$. (This shows that $Q(D)$ is the "smallest" field containing D since any field which contains D must contain an isomorphic copy of $Q(D)$.) ●

6 Prove that the set

$$D = \{a/5^m : a \in \mathbf{Z}, m \in \mathbf{Z}^+\}$$

is an integral domain and find a subfield of $\mathbf{Q}$ which is isomorphic to the field of quotients $Q(D)$.

7 Prove that $\mathbf{Q}$, the field of rational numbers, is isomorphic to $Q(\mathbf{Z})$, the field of quotients of $\mathbf{Z}$. First you must define a correspondence $\mathbf{Q} \to Q(\mathbf{Z})$ and prove that it is a properly defined function; then you must prove that it is a ring isomorphism (or use Exercise 5).

8 The ring $2\mathbf{Z}$ of even integers is not an integral domain since it does not contain an identity. Yet this ring has no zero divisors. We also know that $2\mathbf{Z}$ is contained in the field $\mathbf{Q}$. In this exercise we construct a field of quotients for rings such as $2\mathbf{Z}$ and show in part d that $\mathbf{Q}$ is isomorphic to the field of quotients of $2\mathbf{Z}$ and hence is the smallest field containing $2\mathbf{Z}$.

In general, let $R \neq \{0\}$ be a commutative ring with no zero divisors. Let us construct a field of quotients for R.

Let

$$S_R = \{(a,b) : a, b \in R \text{ and } b \neq 0\}$$

For the pairs $(a,b), (c,d) \in S_R$ define $(a,b) \sim (c,d)$ if and only if $ad = bc$.

a Show that the relation $\sim$ on S_R is an equivalence relation on S_R.

b Let a/b be the equivalence class of (a,b):

$$a/b = \{(c,d) : (c,d) \in S_R \text{ and } (c,d) \sim (a,b)\}$$

Let

$$Q(R) = \{a/b: (a,b) \in S_R\}$$

Define addition $(+)$ and multiplication $(\cdot)$ on $Q(R)$ as follows:

$$(a/b) + (c/d) = (ad+bc)/(bd)$$

$$(a/b) \cdot (c/d) = (ac)/(bd)$$

Prove that addition and multiplication are properly defined binary operations on $Q(R)$.

c   Prove that $(Q(R), +, \cdot)$ is a field. You may use any of the previous proofs which do not depend on the existence of an identity in R.

d   Prove that $Q(2\mathbf{Z})$ is isomorphic to the field of rational numbers $\mathbf{Q}$. Remember that the isomorphism must be a ring isomorphism.

9   Let c be an element of $\mathbf{Z}^+$ which is not a perfect square so that $\sqrt{c} \notin \mathbf{Z}$. From Exercise 3.6–10 we know that

$$\mathbf{Z}[\sqrt{c}] = \{a + b\sqrt{c}: a, b \in \mathbf{Z}\}$$

is an integral domain. Thus we can form the field of quotients $Q(\mathbf{Z}[\sqrt{c}])$. Define $\phi: Q(\mathbf{Z}[\sqrt{c}]) \to \mathbf{Q}[\sqrt{c}]$ by setting $\phi([x, y]) = xy^{-1}$ for every $[x, y] \in Q(\mathbf{Z}[\sqrt{c}])$.

a   Prove that ϕ is a properly defined function with values in $\mathbf{Q}[\sqrt{c}]$.

b   Prove that ϕ is an isomorphism from $Q(\mathbf{Z}[\sqrt{c}])$ onto $\mathbf{Q}[\sqrt{c}]$. Thus, if $c \in \mathbf{Z}^+$, the field of quotients of the integral domain $\mathbf{Z}[\sqrt{c}]$ is isomorphic to a subfield of $\mathbf{R}$, namely $\mathbf{Q}[\sqrt{c}]$.

REVIEW

Important Phrases

ring
ring with identity
commutative ring
subring
proper subring
left ideal
right ideal
(two-sided) ideal
integral domain
field

subfield
divisor of zero
subtraction
division
(ring) homomorphism
(ring) isomorphism
polynomial in x over R
ring of polynomials over R
degree of a polynomial
field of quotients

Symbols

$(R, +, \cdot)$
$a_n \cdot b_n$
$a - b$
a/b
$aR,\ Ra$
$\ker(\phi)$

$\phi(R)$
$\sum_{j=0}^{n} a_j x^j$
$\mathbf{Q}[\alpha]$
$R[x]$
$Q(D)$
$[a, b] \in Q(D)$

Examples

Rings: $2\mathbf{Z}$, $\mathbf{Z}$, $\mathbf{Q}$, $\mathbf{R}$, $M_2(\mathbf{R})$, $\mathbf{Z}_n$, $n\mathbf{Z}$, $\mathbf{Q}[\sqrt{2}]$, $\mathbf{Q}[\pi]$

Integral domains: $\mathbf{Z}$, $\mathbf{Q}$, $\mathbf{R}$, $\mathbf{Z}_n$ for n _____ , $\mathbf{Q}[\sqrt{2}]$

Fields: $\mathbf{Q}$, $\mathbf{R}$, $\mathbf{Z}_n$ for n _____

In the exercises: $(F(X, R), +, \cdot)$, $(\hom(G), +, \circ)$, $(\mathbf{C}, +, \cdot)$, $(R[x_1, x_2, \ldots, x_n], +, \cdot)$, $(Q, +, \cdot)$

Questions

1 What are the axioms for a ring? for an integral domain? for a field?

2 State four elementary properties of a ring that follow from the group properties. State several properties of a ring that result from the existence of multiplication and the distributive law.

3 If a multiplicative identity exists in a ring, is it unique? Can an element of a ring have more than one multiplicative inverse?

4   Describe all the subrings and all the ideals of **Z**.

5   What is a minimal necessary and sufficient condition for a subset of a ring to be a subring? What is a corresponding criterion for a subset of a field to be a subfield?

6   If R is a ring and $a \in R$, is the set aR a left ideal or a right ideal in R? Is the set Ra a left ideal or a right ideal in R?

7   Let ϕ be a homomorphism from a ring R into a ring $\bar{R}$. Is the kernel of ϕ a subring of R? Is it an ideal in R? Is the image set $\phi(R)$ a subring of $\bar{R}$? Is $\phi(R)$ an ideal in $\bar{R}$?

8   Is the degree of a product $f(x) g(x)$ of polynomials over a ring R necessarily the sum of the degrees of $f(x)$ and $g(x)$? What is the largest the degree of the sum, $f(x) + g(x)$, can be?

9   What is the basic difference between the rings $\mathbf{Q}[\sqrt{2}]$ and $\mathbf{Q}[\pi]$?

10   To what condition on divisors of zero is cancellation for multiplication equivalent in a ring? Can an integral domain have divisors of zero?

11   For what values of n is $\mathbf{Z}_n$ an integral domain? a field?

12   What is a condition which is sufficient to insure that an integral domain is a field?

13   List all the ideals of a field.

14   Let $(R, +, \cdot)$ be a ring. What must be true of $(R - \{0\}, \cdot)$ if R is a field? If R is a commutative ring with identity and every equation of the form $ax = b$, where $a, b \in R$ and $a \neq 0$, has a solution $x \in R$, then what more can be said of R?

15   Give an example of a ring which is not an integral domain and of an integral domain which is not a field.

16   Describe the construction of the field of quotients of an integral domain.

The following questions are answered in the exercises:

17 If R and $\bar{R}$ are rings and $\phi: R \to \bar{R}$ is a homomorphism, then it is often true that the properties of R are inherited by $\bar{R}$. For which of the following properties is this true in general? For which is it true if ϕ maps R onto $\bar{R}$? For which is it true if ϕ is an isomorphism?
a R is a commutative ring.
b R is a ring with identity.
c R is an integral domain.
d R is a field.
e R contains a proper two-sided ideal S.

18 Let ϕ be a homomorphism from a ring R onto a ring $\bar{R}$. If $S \subseteq R$ is an ideal, then is $\phi(S)$ an ideal in $\bar{R}$? If $\bar{S}$ is an ideal in $\bar{R}$, then is $\phi^{-1}(\bar{S})$ an ideal in R?

19 Give an example of a ring which is not a field and which contains no proper ideals.

20 For what kind of a ring R is it known that

$$\deg(f(x)\,g(x)) = \deg(f(x)) + \deg(g(x))$$

for all nonzero polynomials $f(x), g(x) \in R[x]$? For what kind of ring R is $R[x]$ necessarily an integral domain? Is $R[x]$ ever a field?

21 If an integral domain D is contained in a field F, then describe a subfield of F which is isomorphic to the field of quotients $Q(D)$.

Chapter 4　Group Theory, II

In this chapter we study three special topics in group theory. We investigate special subgroups of the group of all permutations of the set $\{1, 2, ..., n\}$. Before showing the existence of these subgroups we study special permutations called cycles and transpositions. We show that every permutation can be expressed as a product of cycles or as a product of transpositions.

In Section 4.3 we consider a subset of the collection of all permutations on a group G. We show that this subset, which consists of all isomorphisms of G onto itself, is a group under composition.

In Section 4.4 we demonstrate a method of building a group by defining an operation on the cartesian product of two given groups. Finally, we examine groups which can be represented as a comparable "internal product" of two proper subgroups.

4.1 Cycles and Transpositions in Permutation Groups

In Section 1.5 we introduced the symmetric group S_n consisting of all permutations of the set $\{1, 2, ..., n\}$ (that is, all one-to-one functions which map this set onto itself). We expressed an element f of the group S_n in the two-line notation

$$f = \begin{pmatrix} 1 & 2 & \cdots & n \\ a_1 & a_2 & \cdots & a_n \end{pmatrix}$$

where $f(j) = a_j$ for $j = 1, 2, ..., n$. In this section we show that every permutation in S_n can be written as the composite of certain special permutations called cycles or of even simpler permutations called transpositions.

Each element of S_3 is an example of a cycle. For instance, if f is the permutation

$$f = \begin{pmatrix} 1 & 2 & 3 \\ 3 & 1 & 2 \end{pmatrix}$$

we have $f(1) = 3$, $f(3) = 2$, and $f(2) = 1$. This permutation f can be pictured with a circular rotation of the symbols $1, 2, 3$, as shown in Figure 4.1. This

Figure 4.1

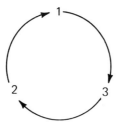

permutation f, which takes 1 onto 3, 3 onto 2, and 2 onto 1, is written in the shorthand notation $f = (1 \quad 3 \quad 2)$. In this one-line notation the image of each element appears immediately to the right of the element, except that the image of the last element is the first element in the line. In this notation $(3 \quad 2 \quad 1)$ also stands for the permutation

$$\begin{pmatrix} 1 & 2 & 3 \\ 3 & 1 & 2 \end{pmatrix}$$

Thus a permutation does not have a unique representation in terms of the one-line notation.

In general an element which is mapped onto itself by a permutation is omitted from the one-line notation. Thus in S_3 the one-line notation (1 2) stands for the permutation

$$\begin{pmatrix} 1 & 2 & 3 \\ 2 & 1 & 3 \end{pmatrix}$$

If every element is mapped onto itself by a permutation, then we write the permutation as (1) or (2) or (3).

1

Problem   Write each permutation in S_3 in the one-line notation.

There are cycles in each of the groups S_n ($n \geq 2$). For example, let $f \in S_4$ with $f(1) = 2$, $f(2) = 3$, $f(3) = 4$, and $f(4) = 1$. In the one-line notation $f =$ (1 2 3 4), and f is a cycle. The permutation f can be pictured with a circular rotation of the symbols 1, 2, 3, 4, as shown in Figure 4.2.

Figure 4.2

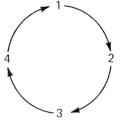

Note that there are several ways to write the same cycle in one-line notation. For example, the cycle (1 2 3 4) can also be written (2 3 4 1), (3 4 1 2), or (4 1 2 3). All of these stand for the same permutation, namely

$$\begin{pmatrix} 1 & 2 & 3 & 4 \\ 2 & 3 & 4 & 1 \end{pmatrix}$$

2

Problem   Give an example of a cycle in S_6 and picture it with a circular rotation of its symbols.

Now let us define formally the term "cycle."

3

Definition   A permutation $f \in S_n$ is a *cycle of length* k if and only if there is a subset $\{a_1, a_2, ..., a_k\}$ of $\{1, 2, ..., n\}$ such that $f(a_1) = a_2$, $f(a_2) = a_3$, ..., $f(a_{k-1}) = a_k$, $f(a_k) = a_1$, and such that $f(i) = i$ for every

$$i \in \{1, 2, ..., n\} - \{a_1, a_2, ..., a_k\}$$

The cycle f is written $(a_1 \quad a_2 \quad ... \quad a_k)$ in the one-line notation; the symbols mapped onto themselves are omitted from the notation.

Note that by definition if f is a cycle of length one, then f maps some element a_1 onto itself and $f(i) = i$ for $i \in \{1, 2, ..., n\} - \{a_1\}$. Thus a cycle of length one maps every element onto itself. Such a cycle is denoted by (1) or (2) or (k) for any $k = 1, 2, ..., n$. The identity permutation is the only cycle of length one.

We sometimes say that a cycle $(a_1 \quad a_2 \quad ... \quad a_k)$ of length $k \geq 2$ moves the k elements in $\{a_1, a_2, ..., a_k\}$ and leaves fixed the elements in $\{1, 2, ..., n\} - \{a_1, a_2, ..., a_k\}$. If $k = 1$, then every element of $\{1, 2, ..., n\}$ is left fixed.

4

Problem   Write each of the following cycles in the one-line notation and find the length of each cycle.

a
$$\begin{pmatrix} 1 & 2 & 3 & 4 & 5 \\ 3 & 1 & 4 & 2 & 5 \end{pmatrix}$$

b
$$\begin{pmatrix} 1 & 2 & 3 & 4 & 5 \\ 4 & 2 & 1 & 3 & 5 \end{pmatrix}$$

$$c \quad \begin{pmatrix} 1 & 2 & 3 & 4 \\ 1 & 2 & 4 & 3 \end{pmatrix}$$

$$d \quad \begin{pmatrix} 1 & 2 & 3 & 4 & 5 \\ 4 & 3 & 1 & 5 & 2 \end{pmatrix}$$

5
Problem   In S_5 let $f = (1 \quad 2 \quad 3 \quad 4 \quad 5)$ and $g = (1 \quad 2 \quad 5 \quad 3 \quad 4)$.

a   Compute the composite function

$$f \circ g = (1 \quad 2 \quad 3 \quad 4 \quad 5) \circ (1 \quad 2 \quad 5 \quad 3 \quad 4)$$

Caution   Remember that in computing the composite of two permutations you must begin with the permutation at the
right. Thus $(f \circ g)(1) = f(g(1)) = f(2) = 3$, and

$$f \circ g = (1 \quad 3 \quad \underline{\hspace{3cm}})$$

Now compute $(f \circ g)(3)$ and complete the cycle.

b   Compute $g \circ f$. Is $f \circ g = g \circ f$?

Not all permutations are cycles. For example, the permutation

$$g = \begin{pmatrix} 1 & 2 & 3 & 4 \\ 2 & 1 & 4 & 3 \end{pmatrix}$$

is not a cycle. (Why?) However, we can write g as the composite

$$g = \begin{pmatrix} 1 & 2 & 3 & 4 \\ 2 & 1 & 3 & 4 \end{pmatrix} \circ \begin{pmatrix} 1 & 2 & 3 & 4 \\ 1 & 2 & 4 & 3 \end{pmatrix}$$

or as the composite $g = (1 \quad 2) \circ (3 \quad 4)$ in the one-line notation.

6
Problem   a   In S_6 express the composite

$$(1 \quad 3 \quad 5 \quad 6) \circ (2 \quad 6 \quad 1)$$

in the two-line notation:

$$(1 \quad 3 \quad 5 \quad 6) \circ (2 \quad 6 \quad 1) = \begin{pmatrix} 1 & 2 & 3 & 4 & 5 & 6 \\ & & & & & \end{pmatrix}$$

Remember that the cycle (2 6 1) leaves 3, 4, and 5 fixed.

b   Show that the composite function

(1   3   5   6) ∘ (2   6   1)

also can be written as the composite of the cycles (1 2) and (3 5 6).

c   Compute (2   6   1) ∘ (1   3   5   6) in the two-line notation. Does this composite function equal the one in part a?

7
Problem   Is the composite of two cycles necessarily a cycle? Justify your answer.

8
Definition   Two cycles $(a_1 \quad a_2 \quad ... \quad a_k)$ and $(b_1 \quad b_2 \quad ... \quad b_m)$ are *disjoint* if and only if the sets $\{a_1, a_2, ..., a_k\}$ and $\{b_1, b_2, ..., b_m\}$ are disjoint:

$$\{a_1, a_2, ..., a_k\} \cap \{b_1, b_2, ..., b_m\} = \varnothing$$

Thus two cycles are disjoint if and only if the elements moved by one are left fixed by the other.

We have seen several examples of composites of cycles, both disjoint and non-disjoint. Let us explore these composites further and determine when cycles can commute.

9
Problem   a   Express the composite functions (1   3) ∘ (2   4) and (2   4) ∘ (1   3) in the two-line notation. Are they equal?

b   Let $f = (1 \quad 2 \quad 5)$ and $g = (3 \quad 4)$. Is $f \circ g = g \circ f$?

c   In Problem 5 we considered the cycles $f = (1 \quad 2 \quad 3 \quad 4 \quad 5)$ and $g = (1 \quad 2 \quad 5 \quad 3 \quad 4)$. Is $f \circ g = g \circ f$? In Problem 6 we considered the cycles $f = (1 \quad 3 \quad 5 \quad 6)$ and $g = (2 \quad 6 \quad 1)$. Is $f \circ g = g \circ f$ for this pair of cycles?

d   We have seen examples of composites of disjoint and non-disjoint cycles. Which of the following statements do you think is correct? If f and g are nondisjoint cycles in S_n, then $f \circ g = g \circ f$. If f and g are disjoint cycles in S_n, then $f \circ g = g \circ f$. Prove your answer by letting $(a_1 \quad a_2 \quad ... \quad a_k)$ and $(b_1 \quad b_2 \quad ... \quad b_m)$ be _____ cycles in S_n and showing that they commute:

$$(a_1 \quad a_2 \quad ... \quad a_k) \circ (b_1 \quad b_2 \quad ... \quad b_m) =$$
$$(b_1 \quad b_2 \quad ... \quad b_m) \circ (a_1 \quad a_2 \quad ... \quad a_k)$$

We have seen that every element of S_3 is a cycle. This is not true, however, in S_n if $n > 3$. We prove below that every permutation can be expressed as the composite of disjoint cycles. Before proving this theorem let us look at a few examples of permutations which are not cycles and see how they can be expressed as a composite of pairwise-disjoint cycles.

10
Problem

Express each of the following permutations as a composite of two or more pairwise-disjoint cycles:

a $\begin{pmatrix} 1 & 2 & 3 & 4 & 5 \\ 3 & 1 & 2 & 5 & 4 \end{pmatrix}$

b $\begin{pmatrix} 1 & 2 & 3 & 4 & 5 & 6 \\ 3 & 4 & 1 & 2 & 6 & 5 \end{pmatrix}$

c $\begin{pmatrix} 1 & 2 & 3 & 4 & 5 & 6 \\ 5 & 6 & 2 & 3 & 1 & 4 \end{pmatrix}$

d $\begin{pmatrix} 1 & 2 & 3 & 4 & 5 & 6 & 7 \\ 4 & 6 & 1 & 3 & 7 & 2 & 5 \end{pmatrix}$

11
Problem   Let

$$\begin{pmatrix} 1 & 2 & \dots & n \\ a_1 & a_2 & \dots & a_n \end{pmatrix}$$

be a permutation in S_n. Using Problem 10 as a guide, demonstrate a procedure for "factoring" this permutation into cycles (i.e., for finding pairwise-disjoint cycles whose composite is the permutation).

With Problem 11 we have proved the first statement of the following theorem. The proof of the second statement concerning the uniqueness of the decomposition is left for Exercise 8.

12
Theorem   Any permutation can be expressed as a single cycle or as a composite of cycles which are pairwise disjoint. This decomposition is unique except for the order of factors and the inclusion of cycles of length one.

A cycle $(s \ t)$ of length two serves to transpose two elements of the set $\{1, 2, \dots, n\}$ while leaving the remaining $n-2$ elements fixed. For this reason a cycle of length two is given a special name.

13
Definition   A cycle of length two is called a *transposition*.

Note that any transposition can be written in the form $(s \ t)$ with $s < t$ because $(t \ s) = (s \ t)$.

14
Problem   a   Show that the cycle $(1 \ 2 \ 3)$ can be written as the composite $(1 \ 3) \circ (1 \ 2)$ of transpositions.

b   Express the cycle $(1 \ 2 \ 3 \ 4)$ as a composite of transpositions.

c Express the cycle (1 2 3 4 5) as a composite of transpositions.

d Express an arbitrary cycle $(a_1 \quad a_2 \quad \ldots \quad a_k)$ as a composite of transpositions.

15
Problem

Prove the following theorem:

Theorem

Any permutation can be expressed as a composite of transpositions.

Note from the examples in Problem 14 that these transpositions are not necessarily disjoint.

16
Problem

Express each of the following permutations as a composite of transpositions.

a (1 4 2)

b (1 3 5 6)

c $\begin{pmatrix} 1 & 2 & 3 \\ 1 & 2 & 3 \end{pmatrix}$

d $\begin{pmatrix} 1 & 2 & 3 & 4 & 5 \\ 3 & 1 & 2 & 5 & 4 \end{pmatrix}$

Theorem 15 shows that the transpositions in the symmetric group S_n are the basic building blocks of the group. In order to find all the elements of the group, we find the

$$\frac{n(n-1)}{2}$$

transpositions in the group and form the composites of these transpositions. This is much easier in theory than in practice if n is large.

EXERCISES 1   Express each of the following permutations as a composite of disjoint cycles.

a $\begin{pmatrix} 1 & 2 & 3 & 4 & 5 & 6 & 7 & 8 \\ 3 & 4 & 5 & 6 & 1 & 8 & 7 & 2 \end{pmatrix}$

b $\begin{pmatrix} 1 & 2 & 3 & 4 & 5 & 6 & 7 \\ 4 & 5 & 7 & 1 & 2 & 3 & 6 \end{pmatrix}$

c $\begin{pmatrix} 1 & 2 & 3 & 4 & 5 & 6 & 7 & 8 & 9 \\ 7 & 8 & 9 & 1 & 2 & 3 & 4 & 5 & 6 \end{pmatrix}$

2   Express each of the following permutations as a composite of disjoint cycles.
a   (1 3 2 4) ∘ (3 4 5)
b   (4 6 3) ∘ (3 6 2) ∘ (1 5 3)
c   (7 8 6 2) ∘ (3 4 2) ∘ (1 6 5 8)

3   Express each permutation in Exercise 1 as a composite of transpositions.

4   Express each permutation in Exercise 2 as a composite of transpositions.

5   Make a list of all the elements in S_4. Begin by listing all the cycles of lengths two, three, and four.

6a   Find the inverse of the transposition $(s \; t)$.
b   Show that the "factorization" of a permutation into transpositions is not unique.

7   Find the inverse of the cycle $(a_1 \; a_2 \; \ldots \; a_k)$.

8   Prove that the decomposition of a permutation which is not a cycle into a composite of pairwise-disjoint cycles is unique except for the order of factors and the inclusion of cycles of length one.

9   Recall that the order of an element $f \in S_n$ is the smallest positive integer m such that f^m is equal to the identity permutation in S_n. (See Section 2.2.) Find the order of each of the following permutations:
a   (1 2 3)
b   (1 2 3 4)

10 Complete the following statement and then prove the following theorem:

Theorem A cycle $(a_1 \quad a_2 \quad \ldots \quad a_k)$ of length k in S_n has order _____ . ●

11 Let $f = \alpha \circ \beta$, where α and β are disjoint cycles, in which case $\alpha \circ \beta = \beta \circ \alpha$. Then $f^2 = (\alpha \circ \beta)^2 = \alpha^2 \circ \beta^2$. (Why?) Show that $f^3 = \alpha^3 \circ \beta^3$ and that $f^m = \alpha^m \circ \beta^m$ for every positive integer m.

12 Use the results of Exercises 10 and 11 to find the order of each of the following permutations:
a $(2 \quad 1 \quad 3) \circ (5 \quad 6 \quad 7 \quad 8)$
b $(2 \quad 1 \quad 4) \circ (3 \quad 5)$
c $(2 \quad 4 \quad 1) \circ (3 \quad 5 \quad 7 \quad 6)$
d $(1 \quad 2 \quad 3 \quad 4) \circ (5 \quad 6 \quad 9 \quad 10 \quad 7 \quad 8)$
e $(1 \quad 2 \quad 6) \circ (3 \quad 4) \circ (5 \quad 7 \quad 9 \quad 8 \quad 10)$

13 Use the results of Exercises 10, 11, and 12 to complete the following statement and then prove the theorem:

Theorem The order of a permutation is the _____ of the orders of the disjoint cycles whose composite is the permutation.

14 Complete the following statement with a condition on k and then prove the proposition: If $f = (a_1 \quad a_2 \quad \ldots \quad a_k)$ is a cycle of length $k > 2$ and k is _____ , then $f \circ f$ is a cycle. ●

4.2 Even and Odd Permutations

In this section we continue the study of the permutation groups S_n for $n = 2, 3, 4, \ldots$. Until now we have avoided the issue of subgroups in S_n except for the small values $n = 3$ and $n = 4$ (and Cayley's Theorem). However, with the aid of cycles and of a special polynomial we can show that S_n consists of two disjoint collections of permutations, the "even" and the "odd" permutations. We also prove that the set of all even permutations is a subgroup of S_n.

To resolve some technical difficulties we first consider a special polynomial in n variables. This polynomial will help us to distinguish between a permutation which transposes an even number of pairs of elements of the set $\{1, 2, \ldots, n\}$ and one which transposes an odd number of pairs.

**17
Definition**

Let $n \geq 2$ be a fixed integer. Define a polynomial $P^{(n)}$ with integer coefficients in the n distinct variables $x_1, x_2, \ldots, x_n$ by setting

$$P^{(n)} = \prod_{1 \leq i < j \leq n} (x_i - x_j)$$

where $\prod$ denotes the product.

**18
Problem**

Write out the factors in $P^{(3)}$ and in $P^{(4)}$:

$$P^{(3)} = (x_1 - x_2)(\underline{\hspace{2cm}})(\underline{\hspace{2cm}})$$
$$P^{(4)} = \underline{\hspace{4cm}}$$

**19
Definition**

Let $n \geq 2$ be a fixed positive integer and let $\theta \in S_n$. Thus θ is a permutation of the set $\{1, 2, \ldots, n\}$. We define a polynomial corresponding to θ by setting

$$P_\theta^{(n)} = \prod_{1 \leq i < j \leq n} (x_{\theta(i)} - x_{\theta(j)})$$

Let us compare $P_\theta^{(n)}$ with $P^{(n)}$. To find the factors in $P_\theta^{(n)}$ simply replace each factor $(x_i - x_j)$ in $P^{(n)}$ by the factor $(x_{\theta(i)} - x_{\theta(j)})$. Thus $P_\theta^{(n)}$ is a polynomial in the n variables $x_1, x_2, \ldots, x_n$ with the subscripts permuted by the permutation θ.

Let $n = 3$ and let $\theta = (1 \quad 2) \in S_3$. Then

$$P_\theta^{(3)} = (x_2 - x_1)(x_2 - x_3)(x_1 - x_3) = -P^{(3)}$$

20

Problem

Let $n = 3$. For every permutation $\theta \in S_3$ compute $P_\theta^{(3)}$ and find a relationship between $P_\theta^{(3)}$ and $P^{(3)}$. Save these results for use in later problems.

21

Problem

Let $n \geq 2$ be a fixed integer. Show that for every $\theta \in S_n$ we have $P_\theta^{(n)} = P^{(n)}$ or $P_\theta^{(n)} = -P^{(n)}$.

22

Definition

Let $n \geq 2$ be a fixed integer. A permutation $\theta \in S_n$ is an *even* permutation if and only if $P_\theta^{(n)} = P^{(n)}$; it is an *odd* permutation if and only if $P_\theta^{(n)} = -P^{(n)}$. We denote by A_n the set of all even permutations in S_n:

$$A_n = \{\theta: \theta \in S_n \text{ and } P_\theta^{(n)} = P^{(n)}\}$$

Problem 21 shows that every element of S_n is either an even permutation or an odd permutation. Since A_n is the set of even permutations, $S_n - A_n$ is the set of odd permutations.

23

Problem

Let $n = 3$.

a   Determine the set A_3 of all even permutations in S_3 and the set $S_3 - A_3$ of all odd permutations in S_3.

b   Is the set of even permutations a subgroup of S_3? Is the set of odd permutations a subgroup of S_3?

c   What is the relationship between the order of A_3 and the order of S_3? What is the index of A_3 in S_3?

24
Problem   Is the identity permutation even or odd in S_n? Explain.

25
Problem   Prove the following lemma:

Lemma   Let $n \geq 2$ be a fixed integer. Every transposition $(s \quad t)$
                 with $s < t$ in S_n is an _____ permutation. ▲

If $\alpha, \beta \in S_n$, then $\alpha \circ \beta \in S_n$. To compute $P^{(n)}_{\alpha \circ \beta}$ note that

$$P^{(n)}_{\alpha \circ \beta} = \prod_{1 \leq i < j \leq n} (x_{\alpha \circ \beta(i)} - x_{\alpha \circ \beta(j)})$$

$$= \prod_{1 \leq i < j \leq n} (x_{\alpha(\beta(i))} - x_{\alpha(\beta(j))})$$

Thus in order to compute $P^{(n)}_{\alpha \circ \beta}$, we first apply the permutation β to $P^{(n)}$, obtaining $P^{(n)}_{\beta} = P^{(n)}$ or $P^{(n)}_{\beta} = -P^{(n)}$. To this result we apply the permutation α. If you wish, try this with two permutations in S_3 or S_4.

26
Problem   Let $n \geq 2$ be a fixed integer and $\alpha, \beta \in S_n$. In each of the
                 cases in Table 4.1 determine whether $\alpha \circ \beta$ is an even or an
                 odd permutation.

Table 4.1

α	β	$\alpha \circ \beta$
even	even	
even	odd	
odd	even	
odd	odd	

Theorem 15 states that every permutation can be expressed as a composite of transpositions. For example

$$(1 \quad 2 \quad 3) = (1 \quad 3) \circ (1 \quad 2) \qquad \text{and}$$
$$(1 \quad 2 \quad 3 \quad 4) = (1 \quad 4) \circ (1 \quad 3) \circ (1 \quad 2)$$

This gives us a convenient means of identifying even and odd permutations.

27
Problem

Prove the following propositions: Let $n \geq 2$ and let $\theta \in S_n$. If θ can be expressed in at least one way as a composite of an even number of transpositions, then θ is an _____ permutation. If θ can be expressed in at least one way as a composite of an odd number of transpositions, then θ is an _____ permutation.

As an almost immediate consequence of the propositions in Problem 27, we have the following theorem:

28
Theorem

Let $n \geq 2$. A permutation $\theta \in S_n$ is an even permutation if and only if θ can be expressed in at least one way as a product of an _____ number of transpositions.

29
Problem

Prove the following theorem:

Theorem

Let $n \geq 2$. The set A_n of all even permutations is a subgroup of S_n. ▲

The subgroup A_n of S_n is called the *alternating group* on n symbols.

Recall that the symmetric group S_n has order _____. The following problem and Problem 31 help determine the order of the subgroup A_n of S_n.

30
Problem

Prove the following lemma:

Lemma   Any two odd permutations in S_n belong to the same left coset of A_n. In other words, if α and β are odd permutations in S_n, then α is a member of the left coset $\beta \circ A_n$.   ▲

**31
Problem**   Prove the following lemma:

Lemma   Let $n \geq 2$ be a fixed integer. The subgroup A_n of S_n has exactly _____ distinct cosets in S_n (that is, A_n is a subgroup of index _____ in S_n).

**32
Problem**   Prove the following theorem:

Theorem   Let $n \geq 2$ be a fixed integer. Then the subgroup A_n of S_n has order _____ , and A_n is a normal subgroup of S_n.

EXERCISES 1   Determine whether each of the following permutations is even or odd:

a $\begin{pmatrix} 1 & 2 & 3 & 4 & 5 \\ 3 & 1 & 4 & 2 & 5 \end{pmatrix}$ d $\begin{pmatrix} 1 & 2 & 3 & 4 & 5 \\ 4 & 3 & 1 & 5 & 2 \end{pmatrix}$

b $\begin{pmatrix} 1 & 2 & 3 & 4 & 5 \\ 4 & 2 & 1 & 3 & 5 \end{pmatrix}$ e $\begin{pmatrix} 1 & 2 & 3 & 4 & 5 & 6 & 7 & 8 \\ 3 & 4 & 5 & 6 & 1 & 8 & 7 & 2 \end{pmatrix}$

c $\begin{pmatrix} 1 & 2 & 3 & 4 & 5 \\ 1 & 2 & 4 & 3 & 5 \end{pmatrix}$ f $\begin{pmatrix} 1 & 2 & 3 & 4 & 5 & 6 & 7 \\ 4 & 5 & 7 & 1 & 2 & 3 & 6 \end{pmatrix}$

2a   List all the elements of the alternating group A_4 in S_4.   ●
 b   Show that A_4 has subgroups with orders two, three, and four, respectively.
 c   Show that A_4 is the subgroup described in Exercise 2.3–14. In that exercise we saw that A_4 has no subgroup of order six.

3   Make a list of the odd permutations in S_4. These permutations constitute one of the two cosets of A_4 in S_4.

4   Show that the cycle $(a_1 \quad a_2 \quad \ldots \quad a_k)$ of length k in S_n is an even permutation if k is _____ and an odd permutation if k is _____ .

5   Define a function ϕ from S_n into $\mathbf{Z}_2$ by setting

$$\phi(\sigma) = \begin{cases} 0_2 & \text{if } \sigma \text{ is an even permutation} \\ 1_2 & \text{if } \sigma \text{ is an odd permutation} \end{cases}$$

Prove that ϕ is a homomorphism and that $\ker(\phi) = A_n$.

4.3   Automorphisms and Conjugates

Let us return to our study of homomorphisms and isomorphisms of groups by considering those isomorphisms which map a group G onto itself. We have already seen that the set $S(G)$ of all one-to-one functions which map G onto itself is a group, the group of permutations on G. Then we can ask whether the collection of all isomorphisms $\phi: G \to G$ is a subgroup of $S(G)$. Before answering this question we develop some terminology and notation.

33
Definition   An *automorphism* of a group G is an isomorphism of G onto itself.

Every group G has at least one automorphism, namely the identity function I defined by $I(x) = x$ for every $x \in G$.

34
Problem   a   Let $\mathscr{I}$ be the multiplicative group of all nonsingular 2×2 matrices. Show that the function $\phi: \mathscr{I} \to \mathscr{I}$ defined by setting

$$\phi(X) = \begin{pmatrix} 1 & 1 \\ 0 & 1 \end{pmatrix} \cdot X \cdot \begin{pmatrix} 1 & -1 \\ 0 & 1 \end{pmatrix}$$

for all $X \in \mathscr{I}$ is an automorphism of $\mathscr{I}$. Note that

$$\phi(X) = AXA^{-1} \qquad \text{where} \quad A = \begin{pmatrix} 1 & 1 \\ 0 & 1 \end{pmatrix}$$

     b   Show that the function $\phi: \mathbf{Z}_6 \to \mathbf{Z}_6$ defined by setting $\phi(a_6) = 5_6 a_6$ for every $a_6 \in \mathbf{Z}_6$ is an automorphism of the additive group $\mathbf{Z}_6$.

35
Problem   Let G be a group and let $a \in G$ be fixed. Define a function $\phi_a: G \to G$ by setting

$$\phi_a(x) = a \circ x \circ a'$$

for every $x \in G$. Prove that ϕ_a is an automorphism of G. (The function ϕ in Problem 34a is an example of such an automorphism.)

Any automorphism of G of the form ϕ_a defined in Problem 35 is called an *inner automorphism* of G. An *outer automorphism* of the group G is an automorphism of G which is not an inner automorphism.

36
Problem

Define $\phi: \mathbf{Z} \rightarrow \mathbf{Z}$ by setting $\phi(x) = -x$ for every $x \in \mathbf{Z}$. Prove that the function ϕ is an outer automorphism of $(\mathbf{Z}, +)$.

Now let us explore the behavior of an inner automorphism of a group G. First let us look at an example.

37
Problem

Consider the group $(S_3, \circ)$ and the permutation

$$a = \begin{pmatrix} 1 & 2 & 3 \\ 2 & 1 & 3 \end{pmatrix}$$

a   Describe ϕ_a by finding $\phi_a(x)$ for every $x \in S_3$.

b   Let K be a normal subgroup of order three in S_3. Show that $\phi_a(x) \in K$ for every $x \in K$. Thus the normal subgroup K is mapped onto itself by ϕ_a.

c   Choose a subgroup H of order two in S_3 such that $a \notin H$. Is H mapped onto itself by ϕ_a? Find the image set $\phi_a(H)$ and the set

$$a \circ H \circ a' = \{a \circ h \circ a' : h \in H\}$$

and compare them. Compare H and $\phi_a(H)$. Is H a normal subgroup of S_3?

We have seen that if $(G, \circ)$ is a group and $\phi: G \to G$ is a homomorphism, then the image set $\phi(G) = \{\phi(x): x \in G\}$ is a subgroup of G (Theorem 51 in Chapter 2). If H is a subgroup of G, then we can define a function $\phi_1: H \to G$ by setting $\phi_1(x) = \phi(x)$ for every $x \in H$. This function ϕ_1 is a homomorphism. (Why?) Thus the image set $\phi_1(H) = \phi(H)$ is a subgroup of G.

38

Problem   Let $(G, \circ)$ be a group, H a subgroup of G, and $a \in G$. Find an automorphism of G such that the set $a \circ H \circ a'$ is the image of H under the automorphism. This proves that $a \circ H \circ a'$ is a subgroup.

If H is a subgroup of a group G, then the subgroup $a \circ H \circ a'$ is called a *conjugate of H* by the element a. For $x \in G$ a *conjugate of x* by a is the element $a \circ x \circ a'$. See Exercises 9 and 10 for work with conjugates.

39

Problem   Let H be a normal subgroup of the group G and let $a \in G$ be fixed. How are H and $a \circ H \circ a'$ related? (See Theorem 80 in Chapter 2 for equivalent forms of the definition of normal subgroup.)

40

Problem   Prove the following theorem:

Theorem   Let $(G, \circ)$ be a group. A subgroup H of G is normal in G if and only if H is mapped onto itself by every inner automorphism of G (that is, $\phi_a(H) = H$ for every $a \in G$).

Now let us return to our original question in this section: Is the collection of all automorphisms on G a subgroup of $S(G)$, the group of all permutations on G? The question is answered in the following theorem.

41

Problem   Prove the following theorem:

Theorem   Let $(G, \circ)$ be a group. The set $\mathscr{A}(G)$ of all automorphisms of G is a group with the operation of composition of functions. ▲

How do the inner automorphisms of a group G fit into the structure of the group $\mathscr{A}(G)$? The next two problems answer this question.

42

Problem   a   Prove that the set $\mathscr{H}$ of all inner automorphisms of a group $(G, \circ)$ is a subgroup of the group $\mathscr{A}(G)$ of all automorphisms of G.

      b   Let $\psi \in \mathscr{A}(G)$ and $\phi_a \in \mathscr{H}$. Compute $(\psi \circ \phi_a \circ \psi^{-1})(x)$ for every $x \in G$.

43

Problem   Use Problem 42 to prove the following theorem:

Theorem   Let $(G, \circ)$ be a group. Then the set $\mathscr{H}$ of all inner automorphisms of G is a normal subgroup of $\mathscr{A}(G)$, the group of all automorphisms of G.

We have seen an example of an outer automorphism for $(\mathbf{Z}, +)$ but no examples of inner automorphisms. The next problem describes all the inner automorphisms for $(\mathbf{Z}, +)$ as well as all other commutative groups.

44

Problem   Let $(G, +)$ be a commutative group. Completely describe the group of all inner automorphisms of G. This result is true for any commutative group, regardless of the symbol used for the operation.

EXERCISES 1   Find an outer automorphism of the additive group $\mathbf{Z}_n$.

      2   Let us extend the result of Problem 36. Let $(G, \circ)$ be a group and define $\phi(x) = x'$ for every $x \in G$.

   a   Prove that if G is a commutative group, then ϕ is an auto-morphism of G.

   b   Is the converse true? Explain.

3   Find all the inner automorphisms of $(D_4, \circ)$, the group of symmetries of the square.

4a   Find all the inner automorphisms of $(S_3, \circ)$.

   b   Is there an outer automorphism of $(S_3, \circ)$? Explain.

5   Find all the automorphisms of $(\mathbf{Z}, +)$.   ●

6   Find all the automorphisms of $(\mathbf{Q}, +)$.   ●

7   Find all the automorphisms of $(\mathbf{Z}_p, +)$, where p is a prime.

8   Let $(G, \circ)$ be a group. Recall that the center of G is the set

$$Z(G) = \{x: x \in G \text{ and } x \circ y = y \circ x \text{ for every } y \in G\}$$

(See Exercises 2.7–9 and 2.7–10.) Prove that if $a \in Z(G)$, then $\phi_a(x) = x$ for every $x \in G$. Prove or disprove the converse.

9   Let $(G, \circ)$ be a group. We say that x is a conjugate of y if and only if there exists $a \in G$ such that $x = a \circ y \circ a'$. Prove that the relation "x is a conjugate of y" is an equivalence relation on G.

10a   Let $(G, \circ)$ be a group. By Exercise 9 the relation "x is a conjugate of y" is an equivalence relation. For this relation prove that the center $Z(G)$ of G is the union of all the equivalence classes containing exactly one element.

   b   Prove that if G is a finite group, then the number of conjugacy equivalence classes containing one element divides the order of G.

11   Let $(G, \circ)$ be a group and let $Z(G)$ denote the center of G. Prove that the quotient group $G/Z(G)$ is isomorphic to the group $\mathcal{H}$ of all inner automorphisms of G.   ●

12 **Definition** Let $(G, \circ)$ be a group and let T be a non-empty subset of G. The *normalizer* of T is the set

$$N(T) = \{a : a \in G \text{ and } T \circ a = a \circ T\}$$

a Prove that $N(T) = \{a : a \in G \text{ and } a \circ T \circ a' = T\}$.
b Prove that $N(T)$ is a subgroup of G.

13 Let x be an element of the group G.
a Prove that $N(\{x\}) = \{a : a \in G \text{ and } x \circ a = a \circ x\}$.
b Prove that x is left fixed by the inner automorphism ϕ_a if and only if a is left fixed by the inner automorphism ϕ_x.
c Prove that $b \in N(\{x\})$ if and only if $x \in N(\{b\})$.

14 For every element $x \in S_3$ find the normalizer $N(\{x\})$. (See Exercise 13a.)

15 Let H be a subgroup of the group G.
a Prove that H is a normal subgroup of $N(H)$.
b Prove that $N(H)$ is the largest subgroup of G in which H is a normal subgroup. To do so prove that if K is a subgroup of G and if H is a normal subgroup of K, then $K \subseteq N(H)$.
c Prove that H is normal in G if and only if $N(H) = \underline{\hspace{2cm}}$.

4.4 External Direct Products

The familiar coordinate plane $\mathbf{R}^2$ is constructed by forming all ordered pairs (a, b) with $a \in \mathbf{R}$ and $b \in \mathbf{R}$. We saw in Exercise 1.2–10 that the set $\mathbf{R}^2$ is a group with an operation $(+)$ defined by addition of coordinates: $(a, b) + (c, d) = (a+c, b+d)$.

In this section we generalize the example of $\mathbf{R}^2$ and show how to construct a new group from any two given groups H and K. This new group is proved to be "large" in the sense that it contains a subgroup isomorphic to H and another subgroup isomorphic to K.

45
Definition

Let $(H, \circ)$ and $(K, *)$ be groups. The *external direct product* of H and K is the cartesian product

$$H \times K = \{(h, k): h \in H, \ k \in K\}$$

with an operation defined as follows:

$$(h, k) \ \square \ (h_1, k_1) = (h \circ h_1, k * k_1)$$

for every $h, h_1 \in H$ and $k, k_1 \in K$. The external direct product of H and K is denoted by $H \times K$.

46
Problem

Prove the following theorem:

Theorem

If $(H, \circ)$ and $(K, *)$ are groups, then $(H \times K, \square)$ is a group.

If $(H, \cdot)$ and $(K, \cdot)$ are both multiplicative groups, the operation on $H \times K$ is written

$$(h, k) \cdot (h_1, k_1) = (hh_1, kk_1)$$

and is called multiplication. If $(H, +)$ and $(K, +)$ are both additive groups, the operation on $H \times K$ is written

$$(h, k) + (h_1, k_1) = (h+h_1, k+k_1)$$

and is called addition. In this case some authors refer to $H \times K$ as the *external direct sum* of H and K.

47

Problem a Consider the groups $(\mathbf{Z}_2, +)$ and $(\mathbf{Z}_3, +)$. List the elements of $\mathbf{Z}_2 \times \mathbf{Z}_3$. What is the order of the group $\mathbf{Z}_2 \times \mathbf{Z}_3$?

    b Let $(H, \circ)$ and $(K, *)$ be finite groups. Express the order of the group $(H \times K, \square)$ in terms of the order of H and the order of K.

Recall that if $(G, +)$ is a group, then the multiple na $(n \in \mathbf{Z})$ of $a \in G$ is defined inductively as follows: $0 \cdot a = 0$, $n \cdot a = (n-1) \cdot a + a$ for $n \in \mathbf{Z}^+$, and $(-n) \cdot a = n(-a)$ for $n \in \mathbf{Z}^+$. Similarly, if $(G, \circ)$ is a nonadditive group, the powers a^n $(n \in \mathbf{Z})$ of an element $a \in G$ are defined as follows: $a^0 = e$, $a^n = a^{n-1} \circ a$ for $n \in \mathbf{Z}^+$, and $a^{-n} = (a')^n$ for $n \in \mathbf{Z}^+$.

The following problem tells us how to compute powers or multiples in $H \times K$ for certain groups H and K. It is useful when we want to find the order of elements of $H \times K$.

48

Problem   Let H and K be groups and let (h, k) be an element of $H \times K$. Let n be a positive integer.

    a If H and K are multiplicative groups, compute $(h, k)^2$ and $(h, k)^3$. Then $(h, k)^n = ($ _____ , _____ $)$.

    b If H and K are additive groups, compute $2(h, k)$ and $3(h, k)$. Then $n(h, k) = ($ _____ , _____ $)$.

In the following problems we look at further examples of the direct product and explore the relationship of the order of $(h, k) \in H \times K$ and the orders of $h \in H$ and $k \in K$.

49

Problem   Consider the additive groups $\mathbf{Z}_2$ and $\mathbf{Z}_3$.

    a Find the order of every element in $\mathbf{Z}_2 \times \mathbf{Z}_3$.

b Is $\mathbf{Z}_2 \times \mathbf{Z}_3$ a cyclic group? (See Section 2.6 for the definition of cyclic group.)

c Prove or disprove that $\mathbf{Z}_2 \times \mathbf{Z}_3$ is isomorphic to the additive group $\mathbf{Z}_6$.

50
Problem

Consider the additive groups $\mathbf{Z}_4$ and $\mathbf{Z}_6$.

a Find the smallest positive integer j such that $j \cdot a_4 = 0_4$ for every $a_4 \in \mathbf{Z}_4$.

b Find the smallest positive integer m such that $m \cdot b_6 = 0_6$ for every $b_6 \in \mathbf{Z}_6$.

c Find the smallest positive integer n such that $n \cdot (a_4, b_6) = (0_4, 0_6)$ for every $(a_4, b_6) \in \mathbf{Z}_4 \times \mathbf{Z}_6$.

d Decide whether or not $\mathbf{Z}_4 \times \mathbf{Z}_6$ is a cyclic group.

e Prove or disprove that $\mathbf{Z}_4 \times \mathbf{Z}_6$ is isomorphic to the additive group $\mathbf{Z}_{24}$.

51
Problem

Let H and K be finite groups and let $h \in H$ and $k \in K$. Express the order of the element $(h, k) \in H \times K$ in terms of the order of h and the order of k.

In Section 2.6 we saw that each of the additive groups $\mathbf{Z}_n$, $n \in \mathbf{Z}^+$, is a cyclic group and that every cyclic group of order n is isomorphic to $\mathbf{Z}_n$. Now we wish to answer the following question: For which positive integers m and n is the external direct product $\mathbf{Z}_m \times \mathbf{Z}_n$ a cyclic group? This is the content of the following theorem.

52
Problem

Complete the following statements and prove the theorem:

Theorem a   The external direct product of the additive groups Z_m and Z_n is a cyclic group if and only if_____ .

b   The additive group $Z_m \times Z_n$ is isomorphic to the additive group Z_{mn} if and only if _____ .

53
Theorem   Let $(H, \circ)$ and $(K, *)$ be groups. Then the external direct product $H \times K$ is commutative if and only if H and K are both commutative.

Leave the proof of the theorem for Exercise 1.

We made the statement at the beginning of the section that $H \times K$ was "large" in the sense that it contains a subgroup isomorphic to H and another subgroup isomorphic to K. In the following problems we define and study these subgroups and their quotient groups.

54
Definition   If H and K are groups, let

$$\widetilde{H} = H \times \{e_K\} = \{(h, e_K): h \in H\} \quad \text{and}$$
$$\widetilde{K} = \{e_H\} \times K = \{(e_H, k): k \in K\}$$

Note that $\widetilde{H}$ and $\widetilde{K}$ are defined to be subsets of $H \times K$.

55
Problem   In $Z_2 \times Z_3$ find the elements of the sets $\widetilde{Z}_2$ and $\widetilde{Z}_3$. Compute all possible sums, $(a_2, 0_3) + (0_2, b_3)$, of two elements with the first element in $\widetilde{Z}_2$ and the second in $\widetilde{Z}_3$.

56
Problem   Prove the following theorem:

Theorem   Let H and K be groups. Then

a $\widetilde{H}$ and $\widetilde{K}$ are normal subgroups of $H \times K$;

b　$\widetilde{H} \cap \widetilde{K} = \{$_____$\}$;

c　every element $g \in H \times K$ has exactly one representation of the form $g = \widetilde{h} \circ \widetilde{k}$, where $\widetilde{h} \in \widetilde{H}$ and $\widetilde{k} \in \widetilde{K}$;

d　H is isomorphic to $\widetilde{H}$ and K is isomorphic to $\widetilde{K}$.

57
Problem　　Show that the quotient group $(\mathbf{Z}_2 \times \mathbf{Z}_3)/\widetilde{\mathbf{Z}}_2$ is isomorphic to the group _____. Remember that an element of the quotient group is a coset of the form $(a_2, b_3) + \widetilde{\mathbf{Z}}_2$. Find all the distinct cosets of $\widetilde{\mathbf{Z}}_2$.

One of the most useful results of Chapter 2 is the First Isomorphism Theorem. This theorem states that if ϕ is a homomorphism from a group G *onto* a group $\bar{G}$ and if $\ker(\phi) = K$, then the quotient group G/K is isomorphic to $\bar{G}$. Thus, for example, if we wish to prove that the quotient group $(H \times K)/\widetilde{H}$ is isomorphic to a group $\bar{G}$, we need only define a function ϕ from $H \times K$ *onto* $\bar{G}$ and prove that ϕ is a homomorphism with $\widetilde{H} = \ker(\phi)$.

58
Problem　a　Prove the following lemma:

Lemma　　Let H and K be groups. Then there is a homomorphism ϕ from $H \times K$ onto H such that $\ker(\phi) = \widetilde{K}$.　▲

b　State a similar result for the group K.

59
Problem　　Complete the following statement and prove the theorem:

Theorem　　Let H and K be groups. Then the quotient group $(H \times K)/\widetilde{H}$ is isomorphic to ____ and the quotient group $(H \times K)/\widetilde{K}$ is isomorphic to ____ .

EXERCISES 1   Prove Theorem 53.

2   If H and K are finite cyclic groups, find a condition on the orders of H and K which guarantees that $H \times K$ is a cyclic group. Prove your result.

3   Prove or disprove that $\mathbf{Z} \times \mathbf{Z}$ is a cyclic group under addition.

4   Let H and K be groups and let H_1 and K_1 be subgroups of H and K, respectively. Prove that $H_1 \times K_1$ is a subgroup of $H \times K$.

5   Find all the subgroups of $\mathbf{Z} \times \mathbf{Z}$ under addition.

6   Let $(H_1, \circ), (H_2, \circ), \ldots, (H_n, \circ)$ be groups. Define an external direct product $H_1 \times H_2 \times \cdots \times H_n$ and an operation for the external direct product. Prove that $H_1 \times H_2 \times \cdots \times H_n$ with this operation is a group.

7a   Prove or disprove that the additive group $\mathbf{Z}_2 \times \mathbf{Z}_3 \times \mathbf{Z}_5$ is isomorphic to the additive group $\mathbf{Z}_{30}$.
 b   Prove or disprove that $\mathbf{Z}_2 \times \mathbf{Z}_4 \times \mathbf{Z}_5$ is isomorphic to the additive group $\mathbf{Z}_{40}$.

4.5   Internal Direct Products

In Section 4.4 we regarded $(H, \circ)$ and $(K, *)$ as any two groups and formed the external direct product $H \times K$. In this section we say what it means for a group G to be the internal direct product of two normal subgroups H and K. We show that several familiar groups can be expressed as the internal direct product of two normal subgroups. We also find a relationship between the internal and the external direct products of two normal subgroups of a group.

If H and K are subgroups of a group G, then $H \circ K$ is defined to be the set

$$H \circ K = \{h \circ k \colon h \in H,\ k \in K\}$$

60

Problem

Prove that the set $H \circ K$ is a normal subgroup of a group G if H and K are normal subgroups of G.   ▲

See Exercise 2.7–15 for examples of what happens if H and K are not normal subgroups.

61

Definition

Let H and K be normal subgroups of the group G. Then G is the *internal direct product* of H and K if and only if $G = H \circ K$ and $H \cap K = \{e\}$.

62

Problem   a

In the additive group $M_2(\mathbf{R})$ let

$$H = \left\{ \begin{pmatrix} a & 0 \\ 0 & d \end{pmatrix} \colon a, d \in \mathbf{R} \right\} \qquad \text{and}$$

$$K = \left\{ \begin{pmatrix} 0 & b \\ c & 0 \end{pmatrix} \colon b, c \in \mathbf{R} \right\}$$

Prove that $M_2(\mathbf{R})$ is the internal direct product of H and K.

b   Show that the additive group

$$\mathbf{Q}[\sqrt{2}] = \{a + b\sqrt{2}: a, b \in \mathbf{Q}\}$$

is the internal direct product of two proper subgroups.

63
Problem   Prove the following theorem:

Theorem   Let G be a group which is the internal direct product of
                       the normal subgroups H and K. Then $h \circ k = k \circ h$ for every
                       $h \in H$ and $k \in K$. ▲

Note that Theorem 63 does not say that G is a commutative group. It simply
says that elements h and k commute if they are chosen from the normal subgroups H and K, respectively, where $H \cap K = \{e\}$ and $H \circ K = G$.

64
Problem   Prove the following theorem:

Theorem   Let H and K be normal subgroups of the group G. Then G
                       is the internal direct product of H and K if and only if every
                       element $g \in G$ has exactly one representation of the form
                       $g = h \circ k$, where $h \in H$ and $k \in K$.

We have seen that the external direct product $H \times K$ of the groups H and K
contains two normal subgroups $\widetilde{H}$ and $\widetilde{K}$ such that every element $g \in H \times K$ is
uniquely represented as the composite $g = \widetilde{h} \circ \widetilde{k}$, where $\widetilde{h} \in \widetilde{H}$ and $\widetilde{k} \in \widetilde{K}$
(Theorem 56). Thus the external direct product can be written also as an
internal direct product $\widetilde{H} \circ \widetilde{K}$.

65
Problem   a   Show that the additive group $\mathbf{Z}_6$ is the internal direct
                       product of two subgroups with orders two and three,
                       respectively.

b   Show that the additive group $\mathbf{Z}_6$ is isomorphic to the external direct product of the subgroups in part a.

66
Problem

Prove the following theorem:

Theorem

The group $(G, \circ)$ is the internal direct product of two normal subgroups H and K if and only if G is isomorphic to the external direct product $H \times K$. ▲

67
Problem

Prove the following theorem:

Theorem

If the group $(G, \circ)$ is the internal direct product of two normal subgroups H and K, then G/H is isomorphic to K and G/K is isomorphic to H.

Theorem 52b states that the additive group $\mathbf{Z}_m \times \mathbf{Z}_n$ is isomorphic to the additive group $\mathbf{Z}_{mn}$ if and only if _____ . Let us use this result and Theorem 66 to determine when $\mathbf{Z}_{mn}$ is an internal direct product.

68
Problem

Complete the following statement and prove the theorem:

Theorem

The additive group $\mathbf{Z}_{mn}$ is the internal direct product of two subgroups with orders m and n, respectively, if and only if

_____ .

EXERCISES   1   Find several ways to represent the additive group $M_2(\mathbf{R})$ as an internal direct product of two proper subgroups.

2   Show that the multiplicative group

$$\left\{ \begin{pmatrix} a & 0 \\ 0 & d \end{pmatrix} : a, d \in \mathbf{R}, \ ad \neq 0 \right\}$$

can be represented as the internal direct product of two proper subgroups.

3   Determine whether or not each of the following groups can be represented as an internal direct product of two proper subgroups. Justify your conclusions.

a $(\mathbf{Z}, +)$

b $(S_3, \circ)$

c $(D_4, \circ)$

4   Find all values of n for which the group $(\mathbf{Z}_n, +)$ can be represented as an internal direct product of two proper subgroups. Justify your conclusion.

5   Let G be a group which is isomorphic to the external direct product $H_1 \times K_1$ of two groups H_1 and K_1. Prove that G is the internal direct product of two normal subgroups of G.

6   Illustrate Theorem 67 with two proper subgroups of the additive group $\mathbf{Z}_{21}$.

7   Consider the set $\mathbf{Z}[\sqrt{2}] = \{a + b\sqrt{2} : a, b \in \mathbf{Z}\}$.

a   Show that $\mathbf{Z}[\sqrt{2}]$ is a subgroup of $\mathbf{R}$ under addition.

b   Show that $\mathbf{Z}[\sqrt{2}]$ is the internal direct product of two proper subgroups H and K. Then illustrate Theorem 67 by explicitly displaying an isomorphism between $\mathbf{Z}[\sqrt{2}]/H$ and K and an isomorphism between $\mathbf{Z}[\sqrt{2}]/K$ and H.

8   Prove that the additive group $\mathbf{Q}$ cannot be represented as an internal direct product of two proper subgroups.

9   Prove that the additive group $\mathbf{R}$ cannot be represented as an internal direct product of two proper subgroups.

10   Let $(G, \circ)$ be a group. Let $H_1, H_2, \ldots, H_n$ be normal subgroups of G. Let

$$H_1 \circ H_2 \circ \cdots \circ H_n$$
$$= \{h_1 \circ h_2 \circ \cdots \circ h_n : h_j \in H_j \text{ for } j = 1, 2, \ldots, n\}$$

a   Prove by induction that $H_1 \circ H_2 \circ \cdots \circ H_n$ is a normal subgroup of G.

b We say that G is the internal direct product of the normal subgroups $H_1, H_2, ..., H_n$ if and only if every element $g \in G$ can be uniquely represented as a composite of the form $g = h_1 \circ h_2 \circ \cdots \circ h_n$, where $h_j \in H_j$ for $j = 1, 2, ..., n$. Prove that if G is the internal direct product of the normal subgroups $H_1, H_2, ..., H_n$, then

$$G = H_1 \circ H_2 \circ \cdots \circ H_n \qquad \text{and}$$

$$H_i \cap H_j = \{e\} \qquad \text{for every } i, j \in \{1, 2, ..., n\}, \ i \neq j$$

11 Let $(G, +)$ be a finite commutative group of order n. If p is a prime that divides n, let H_p be the set of all elements of G whose order is a power of p. Then H_p is a subgroup of G (Exercise 2.2–12). Show that if $n = p_1^{k_1} p_2^{k_2} \cdots p_r^{k_r}$, where $p_1, p_2, ..., p_r$ are distinct primes and $k_1, k_2, ..., k_r \in \mathbf{Z}^+$, then G is the internal direct product of the subgroups $H_{p_1}, H_{p_2}, ..., H_{p_r}$:

$$G = H_{p_1} + H_{p_2} + \cdots + H_{p_r} \quad \bullet$$

Exercise 2.8–11 shows that each of the sets H_{p_j} contains an element different from the identity.

REVIEW

Important Phrases

cycle
transposition
length of a cycle
pairwise-disjoint cycles
even permutation
odd permutation
alternating group

automorphism
inner automorphism
outer automorphism
conjugate of a subgroup
conjugate of an element
external direct product
internal direct product

Symbols

$(a_1 \quad a_2 \quad \cdots \quad a_k)$
$P^{(n)}$
$P_\theta^{(n)}$
A_n
$a \circ H \circ a'$
ϕ_a

$\mathscr{A}(G)$
$\mathscr{H}$
$H \times K$
$\tilde{H} = H \times \{e_K\}$
$\tilde{K} = \{e_H\} \times K$
$G = H \circ K$

Questions 1   Demonstrate a procedure for factoring any permutation into a composite of cycles. Is this decomposition unique?

2   Demonstrate a procedure for factoring any permutation into a composite of transpositions. Is this decomposition unique?

3   Is a transposition an odd or an even permutation? When is the composite of k transpositions even? When is it odd?

4   Under what conditions on $\alpha, \beta \in S_n$ is the composite $\alpha \circ \beta$ an even permutation? an odd permutation?

5   What is the index of the alternating group A_n in S_n? What is the order of A_n? Is A_n a normal subgroup of S_n?

6   State a criterion in terms of inner automorphisms for determining whether or not a subgroup is normal.

7   Is the collection $\mathscr{A}(G)$ of all automorphisms a group under composition? Is the set $\mathscr{H}$ of all inner automorphisms of G a subgroup of $\mathscr{A}(G)$? Is it a normal subgroup? For what groups G is $\mathscr{H}$ a nontrivial subgroup of $\mathscr{A}(G)$?

8   Under what condition on m and n is the external direct product $\mathbf{Z}_m \times \mathbf{Z}_n$ a cyclic group which is isomorphic to $\mathbf{Z}_{mn}$? Under what condition on m and n is $\mathbf{Z}_{mn}$ the internal direct product of two subgroups, one with order m and the other with order n?

9   If H and K are normal subgroups of a group G, is $H \circ K$ a subgroup of G? Is $H \circ K$ a normal subgroup? If $H \cap K \neq \{e\}$ or $H \circ K \neq G$, then can every element of G be uniquely represented in the form $g = h \circ k$, where $h \in H$ and $k \in K$?

10   If G is the internal direct product of two (proper) normal subgroups, then is G isomorphic to an external direct product of nontrivial groups? Is the converse true?

11   If $G = H \times K$, then to what group is $G/\tilde{H}$ isomorphic? If G is the internal direct product of normal subgroups H and K, then to what group is G/H isomorphic?

Chapter 5   Quotient Rings And Ideals

In Chapter 2 we saw that normal subgroups played an important role in the construction of quotient rings. In this chapter we see that ideals play a similar role in the formation of "quotient rings." Once we have such quotient rings we investigate the conditions under which they are integral domains and/or fields. These conditions give us two classes of ideals, the "prime" ideals and the "maximal" ideals. As an application we study a ring of continuous functions and its maximal ideals.

We begin with some topics from the theory of polynomial rings. These rings furnish some interesting examples in the later sections.

5.1　Ideals in Polynomial Rings

In high school one studies polynomial expressions and equations. In the calculus one learns that polynomials with integral or rational coefficients can be considered as functions. In fact, we show in this section that if $(R, +, \cdot)$ is a commutative ring with identity and $f(x) \in R[x]$, then we can define a "polynomial function" on R by using $f(x)$. This function can then be used to determine whether or not the polynomial $x - a$, $a \in R$, is a factor of the polynomial $f(x)$.

1
Definition　　Let $(R, +, \cdot)$ be a commutative ring with identity. For every polynomial

$$f(x) = \sum_{k=0}^{n} a_k x^k \in R[x]$$

we denote by $f(r)$ the element

$$f(r) = \sum_{k=0}^{n} a_k r^k$$

in R. The correspondence $r \to f(r)$, where $r \in R$, defines a function $f : R \to R$ which we call a *polynomial function f* with the rule of correspondence $r \to f(r)$.

For example, the polynomial expression

$$f(x) = x^3 - x^2 - 4x + 4$$

in $\mathbf{Z}[x]$ determines the polynomial function $f : \mathbf{Z} \to \mathbf{Z}$ defined by setting

$$f(r) = r^3 - r^2 - 4r + 4$$

for every $r \in \mathbf{Z}$.

2
Problem　　a　In $\mathbf{Z}[x]$ let

$$f(x) = x^3 - x^2 - 4x + 4$$

Find $f(1)$, $f(2)$, and $f(-1)$. Show that $x-1$ and $x-2$ are factors of $f(x)$; you may do this by showing that

$$f(x) = (x-1)(x-2)\, g(x)$$

for some $g(x) \in \mathbf{Z}[x]$.

b　In $\mathbf{Z}_5[x]$ let $f(x) = 1_5 x^5 - 1_5 x$. Find $f(a_5)$ for every $a_5 \in \mathbf{Z}_5$.

3
Problem

Show that if $(R, +, \cdot)$ is a commutative ring with identity and $f(x), g(x) \in R[x]$ with $f(x) = g(x)$, then $f(r) = g(r)$ for every $r \in R$.

If $(R, +, \cdot)$ is one of the integral domains $\mathbf{Z}$, $\mathbf{Q}$, or $\mathbf{R}$, then the converse of the proposition in Problem 3 is true. This is proved in Exercise 7.

4
Definition

Let R be a commutative ring with identity and let $f(x) \in R[x]$.

a　A polynomial $g(x) \in R[x]$ is a *factor* of $f(x)$ if and only if there exists a polynomial $q(x)$ in $R[x]$ such that

$$f(x) = g(x)\, q(x)$$

b　An element $a \in R$ is a *zero* of the polynomial function f if and only if $f(a) = 0$.

Experience tells us that a quadratic polynomial

$$a_2 x^2 + a_1 x + a_0 \in \mathbf{Z}[x]$$

has a factor $x-a$ if and only if a is a zero of the polynomial, that is,

$$a_2 a^2 + a_1 a + a_0 = 0$$

We want to show that a similar result is true for any polynomial in $R[x]$, where R is a commutative ring with identity. As a first step in that direction let us devise a method for dividing a polynomial $f(x) \in R[x]$ by the polynomial $x-a$.

If $f(x) \in R[x]$ with $\deg(f(x)) = n \geq 1$, then

$$f(x) = a_n x^n + a_{n-1} x^{n-1} + \cdots + a_1 x + a_0$$

with $a_n \neq 0$. But

$$a_n x^n = a_n x^{n-1}(x-a) + a_n a x^{n-1}$$

so that

$$f(x) = a_n x^{n-1}(x-a) + a_n a x^{n-1} + \sum_{j=0}^{n-1} a_j x^j$$

**5
Problem**

Use the process outlined above to determine whether or not $x-1$ is a factor in $\mathbf{Z}[x]$ of the polynomial

$$x^3 + 2x + 3 = x^2(x-1) + \underline{\hspace{3cm}}$$

**6
Theorem**

Let R be a commutative ring with identity and let $f(x) \in R[x]$. Then the element $a \in R$ is a zero of the polynomial function f if and only if $x-a$ is a factor of the polynomial $f(x)$. Equivalently, $f(a) = 0$ for $a \in R$ if and only if

$$f(x) = (x-a) q(x)$$

for some polynomial $q(x) \in R[x]$.

Prove Theorem 6 by solving the following problem:

**7
Problem**   a

Show that if $f(x) \in R[x]$, where R is a commutative ring with identity, and if

$$f(x) = (x-a) q(x)$$

then $f(a) = 0$.

b   Prove the converse by means of the second principle of induction. To do so let P_n be the proposition: For every polynomial $f(x)$ of degree n in $R[x]$, if $f(a) = 0$, then $x-a$ is a factor of $f(x)$. Show that the statement P_1 is true.

Assume that the statements P_k, $1 \leq k \leq n$, are all true. Then for every polynomial $f(x)$ of degree $k \leq n$, if $f(a) = 0$, then $x-a$ is a factor of $f(x)$. To prove that P_{n+1} is true let $\bar{f}(x)$ be any polynomial of degree $n+1$ such that $\bar{f}(a) = 0$ and prove that

$$\bar{f}(x) = (x-a)\, q(x)$$

for some $q(x) \in R[x]$. To do so apply the technique discussed before Problem 5 to the polynomial $\bar{f}(x)$ of degree $n+1$.

8
Problem

Find all the zeros in **Z** of the polynomial function

$$f(r) = r^3 - r^2 - 4r + 4$$

How many zeros does the polynomial function $g(r) = r^2 - 2$ have in **Z**? in **Q**? in **R**?

9
Problem

Prove the following theorem:

Theorem

Let R be an integral domain and let $f(x) \in R[x]$ be a polynomial of degree $n \geq 1$. Then the polynomial function f has at most n zeros and the polynomial $f(x)$ has at most n factors of the form $x-a$, $a \in R$.   ▲

A correct proof of Theorem 9 requires use of the condition that R is an integral domain. The following example shows that the conclusion of Theorem 9 may fail dramatically if R is not an integral domain.

10
Problem

Consider the first-degree polynomial $f(x) = 6_{12}x$ in $\mathbf{Z}_{12}[x]$. Show that the polynomial function f has six zeros in $\mathbf{Z}_{12}$ and that the polynomial $f(x)$ has six different factors of degree one in $\mathbf{Z}_{12}[x]$. Is $f(x)$ the product of these six factors?

Now that we have studied factors and zeros of polynomials in $R[x]$, let us focus our attention on the ideals of $R[x]$.

11
Problem

Let R be a commutative ring with identity and let $a \in R$ be a fixed element. Show that the set

$$S_a = \{f(x): f(x) \in R[x], f(a) = 0\}$$

is an ideal in $R[x]$ and that

$$S_a = (x-a)R[x]$$
$$= \{(x-a)g(x): g(x) \in R[x]\}$$

We have seen that every ideal in $\mathbf{Z}$ can be written in the form $n\mathbf{Z}$, where $n \in \mathbf{Z}$ is fixed. Problem 11 shows that at least some ideals in $R[x]$ are similar to the ideals in $\mathbf{Z}$ in the sense that they can be written as a "multiple," $(x-a)R[x]$, of the ring $R[x]$. We also have seen in Section 3.3 that if R is a commutative ring with identity, then every set of the form rR ($r \in R$) is an ideal in the ring R. Thus, if $p(x) \in R[x]$, then $p(x)R[x]$ is an ideal in $R[x]$.

12
Definition

Let R be a commutative ring with identity. An ideal S in R is a *principal ideal* if and only if

$$S = aR = \{ar: r \in R\}$$

for some $a \in R$. A principal ideal is often denoted by (a), where

$$(a) = aR = \{ar: r \in R\}$$

Note that a principal ideal does not have to be a proper ideal. In fact, the ideal {0} is the principal ideal

$$(0) = \{0 \cdot r \colon r \in R\}$$

while the ring R is itself a principal ideal, the ideal

$$(1) = \{1 \cdot r \colon r \in R\}$$

The following problem gives an example of a principal ideal and of an ideal which is not a principal ideal.

13
Problem   a   Show that the set

$$\{(x+2)f(x) + (x+4)g(x) \colon f(x), g(x) \in \mathbf{Q}[x]\}$$

is a principal ideal in $\mathbf{Q}[x]$, namely the ideal (1).   ▲

b   Show that the set

$$\{(x+2)f(x) + (x+4)g(x) \colon f(x), g(x) \in \mathbf{Z}[x]\}$$

is not a principal ideal in $\mathbf{Z}[x]$. First show that $x+2$, $x+4$, and 2 are all in the ideal.

We have seen that in the ring **Z** every ideal is a principal ideal. A ring with this property is given a special name.

14
Definition   A commutative ring R with identity is a *principal ideal ring* if and only if every ideal in R is a principal ideal.

Problem 13 shows that $\mathbf{Z}[x]$ is not a principal ideal ring. In Problem 15 we show that if F is a field, then $F[x]$ is a principal ideal ring. In order to prove this result about the ring of polynomials over the field F, we need the following division algorithm for polynomials. (See Exercise 3.7–11.)

Theorem   Let $(F, +, \cdot)$ be a field and let $f(x), g(x) \in F[x]$ with $g(x) \neq 0$. Then there exist polynomials $q(x), p(x) \in F[x]$ such that

$$f(x) = g(x) q(x) + p(x)$$

and either $p(x) = 0$ or

$$\deg(p(x)) < \deg(g(x))$$

15
Problem   Prove the following theorem:

Theorem   Let $(F, +, \cdot)$ be a field. Then $F[x]$ is a principal ideal ring. Thus, if $S \subseteq F[x]$ is an ideal, then there exists a polynomial $d(x) \in S$ such that

$$S = (d(x))$$
$$= \{d(x) g(x): g(x) \in F[x]\} \quad \blacktriangle$$

EXERCISES 1   Show that in $\mathbf{Z}_5[x]$ the polynomials $x - 2_5$ and $x - 4_5$ are factors of the polynomial $x^5 - x$.

2   Give an example of two different polynomials $f(x)$ and $g(x)$ in $\mathbf{Z}_5[x]$ such that $f(a_5) = g(a_5)$ for every $a_5 \in \mathbf{Z}_5$. The existence of these polynomials is assured since there are an infinite number of polynomials in $\mathbf{Z}_5[x]$ but _____ distinct polynomial functions.

3   Give an example of a polynomial in $\mathbf{Z}[x]$ of degree two with two factors of the form $ax + b$ in $\mathbf{Z}[x]$ which has no zeros in $\mathbf{Z}$.

4   Prove that for the polynomial $f(x) = x^3$ in $\mathbf{Z}_8[x]$ the polynomial function $f(r) = r^3$ has the zeros 0_8, 2_8, 4_8, and 6_8. Then show that there are four different factorizations of the polynomial $f(x) = x^3$ in $\mathbf{Z}_8[x]$.

5 As an illustration of Theorems 6 and 9, find the zeros of the polynomial functions $f, g: \mathbf{Z}_3[x] \to \mathbf{Z}_3$ defined by

$f(r) = r^2 + r + 1_3$ and

$g(r) = r^4 + 2_3$

Find the factors $x - a$ of the polynomials

$f(x) = x^2 + x + 1_3$ and

$g(x) = x^4 + 2_3$

6 Let R be an integral domain, $f(x), g(x) \in R[x]$, and $f(x) = g(x)$. Show that if $f(x) = x^k p(x)$ and $g(x) = x^k q(x)$ for some $p(x), q(x) \in R[x]$, then $p(x) = q(x)$.

7a Let R be one of the rings $\mathbf{Z}$, $\mathbf{Q}$, or $\mathbf{R}$ and let $f(x), g(x) \in R[x]$. Show that the polynomial functions f and g are equal if and only if the polynomials $f(x)$ and $g(x)$ are equal. In other words, $f(r) = g(r)$ for every $r \in R$ ($R = \mathbf{Z}, \mathbf{Q}, \mathbf{R}$) if and only if $f(x) = g(x)$. ●

  b Why does the proof in part a fail for polynomials in $\mathbf{Z}_5[x]$?

8 **Definition** Let $(F, +, \cdot)$ be a field and let $f(x)$ and $g(x)$ be polynomials in $F[x] - \{0\}$. A polynomial $d(x) \in F[x]$ is a *greatest common divisor* of $f(x)$ and $g(x)$ if and only if (i) $d(x)$ divides both $f(x)$ and $g(x)$ and (ii) if $p(x)$ divides both $f(x)$ and $g(x)$, then $p(x)$ divides $d(x)$.

  a Find the greatest common divisor of each of the following pairs of polynomials in $\mathbf{Q}[x]$.

$f(x)$	$g(x)$
$x^3 - x^2 + 2x - 2$	$x^2 + 2$
$x^3 - x^2 + 2x - 2$	$x^3 - x^2 - 4x + 4$
$x^4 - 4$	$x^3 - 1$

  b Can two polynomials have more than one greatest common divisor? Explain.

*9   Prove the following theorem concerning the existence of a greatest common divisor for polynomials over a field:

> **Theorem**   Let $(F, +, \cdot)$ be a field and let $f(x)$ and $g(x)$ be polynomials in $F[x] - \{0\}$. Then $f(x)$ and $g(x)$ have a greatest common divisor $d(x)$. Moreover, there exist $p(x), q(x) \in F[x]$ such that
>
> $$d(x) = f(x)\, p(x) + g(x)\, q(x)$$ •

10   **Definition**   Let R be a commutative ring with identity. A polynomial $p(x) \in R[x]$ is *irreducible* if and only if the following condition holds: $p(x)$ has positive degree and if $p(x) = a(x)\, b(x)$, then $\deg(a(x)) = 0$ or $\deg b((x)) = 0$ (that is, $a(x)$ or $b(x)$ is a constant polynomial).

   a   Give several examples of irreducible polynomials in $\mathbf{Z}[x]$.
   b   Give an example of a polynomial which is irreducible in $\mathbf{Q}[x]$ but not irreducible in $\mathbf{R}[x]$.

*11   Prove that if $(F, +, \cdot)$ is a field, $p(x)$ is an irreducible polynomial in $F[x]$, and $p(x)$ divides $f(x)\, g(x)$, where $f(x), g(x) \in F[x]$, then $p(x)$ divides $f(x)$ or $p(x)$ divides $g(x)$. •

*12   Let $(R, +, \cdot)$ be a commutative ring with identity and $r \in R$. Define a function $\phi_r \colon R[x] \to R$ by setting

$$\phi_r(f(x)) = f(r) = \sum_{k=0}^{n} a_k r^k$$

   for every polynomial $f(x) = \sum_{k=0}^{n} a_k x^k \in R[x]$.
   a   In $\mathbf{Z}[x]$ find $\phi_0(f(x))$ and $\phi_2(f(x))$ when $f(x) = 3x^3 - 4x - 5$ and when $f(x) = x^4 - 16$.
   b   Let $(R, +, \cdot)$ be a commutative ring with identity and $r \in R$. Prove that the function ϕ_r defined above is a homomorphism from $R[x]$ *onto* R.
   c   Find the kernel of ϕ_r.

13 As an application of Theorem 9, let us prove the following theorem:

Theorem Let $(F, +, \cdot)$ be a finite field. Then the multiplicative group $F - \{0\}$ is a cyclic group.

a Prove that if $(G, \circ)$ is a finite commutative group with identity e such that every equation $x^n = e$, $n \in \mathbf{Z}^+$, has at most n solutions, then G is a cyclic group. ●

b Prove that if F is a finite field, then $(F - \{0\}, \cdot)$ is a cyclic group.

c Show that $(\mathbf{Z}_n - \{0_n\}, \cdot)$ is a cyclic group if _____ .

5.2 Quotient Rings

We have seen that every ring is first of all a commutative group under addition. Thus for every subring of the given ring there is a quotient group under addition. In this section we consider conditions under which a product can be defined for this quotient group in order to make it a ring.

If $(R, +, \cdot)$ is a ring and S is a subring of R, then S is a normal subgroup of the additive group R. Thus the collection R/S of all the cosets of S is a group with the operation of addition defined by

$$(a+S) + (b+S) = (a+b) + S$$

for every $a, b \in R$.

Recall the following facts about R/S:

a   If $a \in R$, then _____ is the coset in R/S to which the element a belongs.

b   For $a, b \in R$, $a+S = b+S$ if and only if _____ $\in S$.

c   The zero element in R/S is the coset _____ .

d   An element s is in S if and only if $s+S =$ _____ .

Following the example of the definition of addition of cosets, we define a "product" of two elements $a+S$ and $b+S$ of the quotient group R/S by setting

$$(a+S) \cdot (b+S) = (ab) + S$$

Thus the "product" of two cosets $a+S$ and $b+S$ is the coset to which the element ab belongs. In Problem 18 we determine those subrings S of R for which this product is properly defined (i.e., if $a+S = a_1+S$ and $b+S = b_1+S$, then $(ab)+S = (a_1 b_1)+S$).

16

Problem   Recall that the quotient group $\mathbf{Z}/4\mathbf{Z}$ under addition is equal to the group $\mathbf{Z}_4$ and that a product has been defined for $\mathbf{Z}_4$ by setting $a_4 \cdot b_4 =$ _____ for every $a_4, b_4 \in \mathbf{Z}_4$. Show that the product defined above for cosets is the same as this product for $\mathbf{Z}_4$; that is, show that

$$(a+4\mathbf{Z}) \cdot (b+4\mathbf{Z}) = (ab) + 4\mathbf{Z} = (ab)_4$$

17

Problem

Let

$$S = \left\{ \begin{pmatrix} a & 0 \\ c & 0 \end{pmatrix} : a, c \in \mathbf{R} \right\}$$

Then S is a left ideal, but not a two-sided ideal, in $M_2(\mathbf{R})$. Prove that while

$$\begin{pmatrix} 1 & 1 \\ 1 & 1 \end{pmatrix} + S = \begin{pmatrix} 2 & 1 \\ 3 & 1 \end{pmatrix} + S$$

the "products"

$$\left[\begin{pmatrix} 1 & 1 \\ 1 & 1 \end{pmatrix} + S \right] \cdot \left[\begin{pmatrix} 1 & 1 \\ 0 & 2 \end{pmatrix} + S \right] \quad \text{and}$$

$$\left[\begin{pmatrix} 2 & 1 \\ 3 & 1 \end{pmatrix} + S \right] \cdot \left[\begin{pmatrix} 1 & 1 \\ 0 & 2 \end{pmatrix} + S \right]$$

defined above are not the same.

18

Problem

Let $(R, +, \cdot)$ be a ring and let S be a subring of R. We have defined a multiplication on R/S by setting

$$(a+S) \cdot (b+S) = (ab) + S$$

for every $a, b \in R$. Prove that this multiplication is a properly defined binary operation on R/S if and only if S is an ideal in R. ▲

Now that we have found all the subrings (namely the ideals) for which multiplication is a properly defined binary operation on the quotient group, let us prove that with this multiplication R/S is a ring if S is an ideal.

19

Problem

Prove the following theorem:

Theorem

Let R be a ring and S an ideal in R. Then $(R/S, +, \cdot)$ is a ring.

Let $(R, +, \cdot)$ be a ring and S an ideal in R. Define $\pi: R \to R/S$ by setting $\pi(a) = a + S$ for every $a \in R$. We have already seen that π is a group homomorphism from the additive group R onto the additive group R/S (Theorem 94 in Chapter 2). This function π is called the canonical homomorphism.

20

Problem   Show that the function $\pi: R \to R/S$ defined by $\pi(a) = a + S$ for every $a \in R$ is a ring homomorphism.

We have seen that if R and $\bar{R}$ are rings and $\phi: R \to \bar{R}$ is a (ring) homomorphism, then

$$\ker(\phi) = \{x: \phi(x) = \bar{0}\}$$

is an ideal in R. Thus we can form the quotient ring $R/\ker(\phi)$. We want to compare this quotient ring $R/\ker(\phi)$ and the ring $\bar{R}$.

21

Problem   For the rings $\mathbf{Z}$ and $\mathbf{Z}_4$ let $\phi: \mathbf{Z} \to \mathbf{Z}_4$ be defined by setting $\phi(a) = a_4$ for every $a \in \mathbf{Z}$. Then ϕ is a homomorphism (why?) with $\ker(\phi) = S = $ _____ . Define a function $\bar{\phi}: \mathbf{Z}/S \to \mathbf{Z}_4$ by setting $\bar{\phi}(a + S) = \phi(a)$ for every $a \in \mathbf{Z}$. Show that $\bar{\phi}$ is an isomorphism between the two rings. Begin by comparing this definition of $\bar{\phi}$ with the one given in the proof of the First Isomorphism Theorem for Groups (Theorem 101 in Chapter 2).

22

Problem   Let $(R, +, \cdot)$ and $(\bar{R}, +, \cdot)$ be rings and let $\phi: R \to \bar{R}$ be a homomorphism from R onto $\bar{R}$. Let $S = \ker(\phi)$. We have seen that R/S is a ring with the usual addition and multiplication of cosets. Define $\bar{\phi}: R/S \to \bar{R}$ by setting

$$\bar{\phi}(a + S) = \phi(a)$$

for every $a + S \in R/S$.

a   Show quickly that $\bar{\phi}$ is a properly defined group homomorphism which is both one-to-one and onto. Feel free to use Theorem 101 in Chapter 2.

b   Prove that $\bar{\phi}$ is a ring homomorphism.

Problem 22 can be stated in the form of a theorem as follows:

23
Theorem   *First Isomorphism Theorem for Rings.* If $(R, +, \cdot)$ and $(\bar{R}, +, \cdot)$ are rings and ϕ is a homomorphism from R onto $\bar{R}$, then $R/\mathrm{ker}(\phi)$ is isomorphic to $\bar{R}$.

A homomorphic image of a ring R is a ring $\bar{R}$ such that there exists a homomorphism from R *onto* $\bar{R}$. Theorem 23 asserts that every homomorphic image of a ring R is isomorphic to a quotient ring R/S for some ideal $S \subseteq R$. Thus all those homomorphic images which are not isomorphic are included among the quotient rings R/S of R by an ideal S.

In Sections 5.3 and 5.4 we determine under what conditions on the ideal S a quotient ring can be an integral domain or a field.

EXERCISES 1   Find all the quotient rings of the ring $\mathbf{Z}_6$ by an ideal $S \subseteq \mathbf{Z}_6$

2   Show that the only quotient rings for a field F are the rings $F/\{0\}$ and F/F. Describe all the nonisomorphic rings which can be homomorphic images of a field F. Justify your answer.

★3   Prove that if R is a ring with identity and S is a proper ideal of R, then R/S is a ring with identity.

★4   Prove that if R is a commutative ring and S is an ideal of R, then R/S is a commutative ring.

5   Find all the quotient rings of the ring $M_2(\mathbf{R})$ by an ideal $S \subseteq M_2(\mathbf{R})$. ●

6   Let R be a nontrivial ring and $\phi: M_2(\mathbf{R}) \rightarrow R$ a homomorphism from $M_2(\mathbf{R})$ *onto* R. Prove that R is isomorphic to $M_2(\mathbf{R})$.

7   Characterize the set of homomorphisms from $(\mathbf{Z}, +, \cdot)$ into $(\mathbf{Z}, +, \cdot)$.

8   Determine all the possible quotient rings of the ring $\mathbf{Z}$ by an ideal $S \subseteq \mathbf{Z}$.

*9   Let $(R, +, \cdot)$ be a ring with identity and $a \in R$. Let

$$S_a = \{(x-a)\,f(x): f(x) \in R[x]\}$$

a   Prove that $R[x]/S_a$ is an integral domain if R is an integral domain.   ●

b   Prove that $R[x]/S_a$ is a field if R is a field.

5.3 Prime Ideals and Their Quotient Rings

In the last section we saw that if R is a ring and S is a subring of R, then the quotient group R/S is a ring if and only if S is an ideal in R. Thus we were able to completely characterize those subrings for which the quotient group has a properly defined binary operation of multiplication of cosets. In this section we continue our characterization study by determining those ideals for which the quotient ring is an integral domain.

Recall that a commutative ring R with identity is an integral domain if and only if for every $a, b \in R$ such that $ab = 0$ either $a = 0$ or $b = 0$.

24

Problem

Let R be a ring and S an ideal in R such that R/S is an integral domain.

a   If $a, b \in R$ and

$$(a+S) \cdot (b+S) = 0 + S$$

then either $a + S = $ _____ or $b + S = $ _____ .

b   Using the properties of cosets, show that if R/S is an integral domain, $a, b \in R$, and $ab \in S$, then either $a \in S$ or $b \in S$. An ideal with this property is given a special name.

25

Definition

An ideal $S \neq R$ in a ring R is a *prime ideal* in R if and only if for every $a, b \in R$, $ab \in S$ implies either $a \in S$ or $b \in S$. Equivalently, an ideal $S \neq R$ in a ring R is a prime ideal in R if and only if for every $a, b \in R$, $a \notin S$ and $b \notin S$ implies $ab \notin S$.

26

Problem

Determine whether or not the following ideals in $\mathbf{Z}$ are prime ideals. Justify your answers. ▲

a $S = 6\mathbf{Z} = \{6k: k \in \mathbf{Z}\}$
b $S = 7\mathbf{Z} = \{7k: k \in \mathbf{Z}\}$

27

Problem   Find all the prime ideals in **Z**. Justify your answer.

We saw in Problem 24 that if R is a ring and S is an ideal in R such that R/S is an integral domain, then S is a prime ideal. Now let us consider a modified converse. Suppose R is a commutative ring with identity and S is a prime ideal. Is R/S necessarily an integral domain? Let us consider the following examples.

28

Problem   a   Is 7**Z** a prime ideal in **Z**? Is **Z**/7**Z** an integral domain? (Remember that **Z**/7**Z** is equal to Z_7. See Section 2.8.)

            b   Choose another prime ideal S in **Z**. Is **Z**/S an integral domain?

29

Problem   Prove the following theorem:

Theorem   Let R be a commutative ring with identity and S an ideal in R. Then R/S is an integral domain if and only if S is a prime ideal in R.

As an application of Theorem 29 let us consider an example in **Z**$[x]$, the ring of polynomials over **Z**. The ring **Z**$[x]$ is a commutative ring with identity. The set

$$(x) = \{xf(x): f(x) \in \mathbf{Z}[x]\}$$

is an ideal in **Z**$[x]$. (Why?)

30

Problem   a   Define a function $\phi: \mathbf{Z}[x] \to \mathbf{Z}$ by setting

$$\phi(f(x)) = f(0) = a_0$$

for every

$$f(x) = \sum_{k=0}^{n} a_k x^k \in \mathbf{Z}[x]$$

Prove that ϕ is a homomorphism from $\mathbf{Z}[x]$ *onto* $\mathbf{Z}$. Find $\ker(\phi)$.

b   Prove that $\mathbf{Z}[x]/(x)$ is an integral domain.   ▲

c   Prove that (x) is a prime ideal in $\mathbf{Z}[x]$.

EXERCISES   1   Prove that every proper ideal in $\mathbf{Z}$ is contained in at least one prime ideal. Give several examples of this statement.

*2a   Prove that if $(F, +, \cdot)$ is a field and $p(x) \in F[x]$ is irreducible, then the ideal

$$(p(x)) = \{p(x)\, f(x) : f(x) \in F[x]\}$$

is a prime ideal in $F[x]$. See Exercise 5.1–10 for the definition of an irreducible polynomial.

b   Let F be a field. Prove that if $g(x) \in F[x]$ is not irreducible, then the ideal

$$(g(x)) = \{g(x)\, f(x) : f(x) \in F[x]\}$$

is contained in a prime ideal but is not itself a prime ideal.   ●

3   Prove that if $(R, +, \cdot)$ is an integral domain and $a \in R$, then the ideal

$$(x - a) = \{(x - a)\, f(x) : f(x) \in R[x]\}$$

is a prime ideal in $R[x]$.

*4   Determine whether or not the following ideals are prime ideals in the given ring R:
a $R = \mathbf{Q}[x]$, $S = \{(x^2 - 2)\, f(x) : f(x) \in \mathbf{Q}[x]\}$
b $R = \mathbf{R}[x]$, $S = \{(x^2 - 2)\, f(x) : f(x) \in \mathbf{R}[x]\}$
c $R = \mathbf{Q}[x]$, $S = \{xf(x) + 3g(x) : f(x), g(x) \in \mathbf{Q}[x]\}$

5.4 Maximal Ideals and Their Quotient Rings

We have shown that for a commutative ring R with identity and an ideal $S \subseteq R$ the quotient ring R/S is an integral domain if and only if S is a prime ideal in R. We now wish to determine the condition necessary for R/S to be a field.

If R is a commutative ring with identity, then the quotient ring R/S is a commutative ring with identity $1+S$. In this case we need to establish the necessary and sufficient condition for each element $a+S \neq 0+S$ to have a multiplicative inverse. This existence of multiplicative inverses in R/S depends on S being a special type of ideal called a "maximal" ideal.

**31
Definition**   An ideal S in a ring R is a *maximal ideal* in R if and only if

a $S \neq R$ and

b   there is no ideal J in R such that $S \subset J \subset R$ (proper containment).

Note that condition b of Definition 31 says that it is impossible to fit an ideal J strictly between the ideal S and the ring R. There are several useful forms of this condition. Let R be a ring and S an ideal in R with $S \neq R$. Then the following statements are equivalent to condition b of the definition of a maximal ideal:

b′   If J is an ideal in R and $S \subseteq J$, $S \neq J$, then $J = R$.

b″   If J is an ideal in R and $S \subseteq J \subseteq R$, then either $S = J$ or $J = R$.

(Venn diagrams might help you to see the equivalence of these statements.)

**32
Problem**   Find all the ideals of the ring $\mathbf{Z}_8$. Determine whether or not each of these ideals is a maximal ideal.

**33
Problem**   a   Is $4\mathbf{Z}$ a maximal ideal in $\mathbf{Z}$? Is $\mathbf{Z}/4\mathbf{Z}$ a field? Remember that $\mathbf{Z}/4\mathbf{Z} = \mathbf{Z}_4$.

b   Is $5\mathbf{Z}$ a maximal ideal in $\mathbf{Z}$? Is $\mathbf{Z}/5\mathbf{Z}$ a field?

Recall that if F is a field, then F has no proper ideals (i.e., if J is an ideal in F, then either $J = \{0\}$ or $J = F$). (See Problem 61a in Chapter 3.)

In addition to this property of fields, we need the following lemma:

34
Lemma   If R is a ring and S and J are ideals in R with $S \subseteq J$, then the set

$$J/S = \{a + S\colon a \in J\}$$

is an ideal in R/S.

Leave the proof of this lemma for Exercise 4.

The following theorem gives us a necessary condition for a quotient ring to be a field.

35
Problem   Prove the following theorem:

Theorem   Let R be a ring and S an ideal in R such that R/S is a field. Then S is a maximal ideal in R. ▲

We cannot prove a converse to Theorem 35 because if R is not commutative or if R does not have an identity, then R/S need not be a commutative ring with identity. In that case it certainly would not be a field. However, for a commutative ring with identity we have the following theorem:

36
Theorem   Let R be a commutative ring with identity and $S \subseteq R$ an ideal. Then R/S is a field if and only if S is a maximal ideal.

Note that one implication in Theorem 36 is contained in Theorem 35. Prove the "if" part of the theorem by working the following problem:

37

Problem

Let R be a commutative ring with identity. Assume that $S \subset R$ is a maximal ideal in R. In R/S let $a+S \neq 0+S$. We must find a multiplicative inverse of $a+S$ (that is, an element $r+S$ such that _____ .)

Consider the set

$$\bar{J} = \{(a+S)(r+S): r \in R\}$$
$$= \{ar + S: r \in R\}$$

Then $\bar{J}$ is contained in R/S. We wish to prove that $1+S \in \bar{J}$. (Why?) Note that if $\pi: R \to R/S$ is the canonical homomorphism defined by setting $\pi(a) = a+S$ for every $a \in R$, then $\bar{J}$ is the image of the set

$$J = \{ar + s: r \in R \text{ and } s \in S\}$$
$$= aR + S$$

(Why?)

a   Prove that J is an ideal in R.

b   Prove that S is a proper subset of J.

c   Prove that $J = R$ and $\bar{J} = R/S$.

d   Show that $a+S$ has a multiplicative inverse in R/S.

38

Problem

Prove the following theorem:

Theorem

If R is a commutative ring with identity and S is a maximal ideal in R, then S is a prime ideal in R.

The converse of Theorem 38 is not true. In Exercise 7 there is an example in $\mathbf{Z}[x]$ of a prime ideal which is not a maximal ideal.

EXERCISES 1 Find all the maximal ideals in $\mathbf{Z}$. Remember that they must be prime ideals.

2a Find all the proper ideals in $\mathbf{Z}_n$ if $n = p^k$, where $p \geq 2$ is a prime. (Try $n = 4, 8$ first.)
 b Find all the prime and maximal ideals in $\mathbf{Z}_n$ if $n = p^k$, where $p \geq 2$ is a prime.

3a Show that if $R = 2\mathbf{Z}$, the set of all even integers, and $S = \{2r: r \in 2\mathbf{Z}\}$, then S is a maximal ideal in R but not a prime ideal in R.
 b Is the statement of Theorem 38 true for a commutative ring without identity?

4 Prove Lemma 34.

5 Show that if F is a field and $a \in F$, then the ideal

$$(x-a) = \{(x-a)f(x): f(x) \in F[x]\}$$

is a maximal ideal in $F[x]$. ●

6 Show that if F is a field and $g(x) \in F[x]$ is divisible by $q(x)$, where $\deg(q(x)) \geq 1$, then the ideal

$$(g(x)) = \{g(x)f(x): f(x) \in F[x]\}$$

is not a maximal ideal in $F[x]$.

7 Define a function $\phi: \mathbf{Z}[x] \to \mathbf{Z}_2$ by setting

$$\phi\left(\sum_{k=0}^{n} a_k x^k\right) = \begin{cases} 0_2 & \text{if } a_0 \in 2\mathbf{Z} \\ 1_2 & \text{if } a_0 \notin 2\mathbf{Z} \end{cases}$$

for every polynomial $\sum_{k=0}^{n} a_k x^k \in \mathbf{Z}[x]$.
 a Prove that ϕ is a homomorphism from $\mathbf{Z}[x]$ onto $\mathbf{Z}_2$.
 b Show that

$$\ker(\phi) = \{2a + xf(x): a \in \mathbf{Z}, f(x) \in \mathbf{Z}[x]\}$$

 c Let $S = \ker(\phi)$. Show that S is a maximal ideal in $\mathbf{Z}[x]$. ●

d　Show that the ideal

$$(x) = \{xf(x): f(x) \in \mathbf{Z}[x]\}$$

is a prime ideal but not a maximal ideal in $\mathbf{Z}[x]$.　●

8　Let F be a field. In Exercise 5.3–2 we saw that if $p(x) \in F[x]$ is irreducible, then the ideal

$$(p(x)) = \{p(x)f(x): f(x) \in F[x]\}$$

is a prime ideal in $F[x]$. If $p(x) \in F[x]$ is irreducible, is the ideal $(p(x))$ necessarily a maximal ideal?　●

9　Determine whether or not each of the following ideals is a maximal ideal in the given ring R:

a　$R = \mathbf{Q}[x]$, $S = \{(x^2-2)f(x): f(x) \in \mathbf{Q}[x]\}$
b　$R = \mathbf{R}[x]$, $S = \{(x^2-2)f(x): f(x) \in \mathbf{R}[x]\}$
c　$R = \mathbf{Q}[x]$, $S = \{xf(x) + 3g(x): f(x), g(x) \in \mathbf{Q}[x]\}$

5.5 Maximal Ideals in Rings of Functions

In the calculus one learns that a function f defined on the closed interval $[0, 1]$ is continuous at $t_0 \in [0, 1]$ if and only if $\lim_{t \to t_0} f(t) = f(t_0)$. A function f is continuous on the interval $[0, 1]$ if and only if it is continuous at every point in the interval $[0, 1]$.

We have seen examples of rings of functions in Exercise 3.1–6. In this section we illustrate one connection between analysis and abstract algebra. We prove that the set of continuous functions on the interval $[0, 1]$ is a ring and consider some of its maximal ideals.

39
Problem

Which of the following functions are continuous at the point $t_0 = \frac{1}{2}$? Sketch a graph of each function and save the graphs for later use.

a $f(t) = t^2$ for $0 \leq t \leq 1$

b $f(t) = \begin{cases} 1 - 2t & \text{if } 0 \leq t \leq \frac{1}{2} \\ -1 & \text{if } \frac{1}{2} < t \leq 1 \end{cases}$

c $f(t) = \begin{cases} 2t - 1 & \text{if } 0 \leq t \leq \frac{1}{2} \\ 0 & \text{if } \frac{1}{2} < t \leq 1 \end{cases}$

d $f(t) = \begin{cases} 0 & \text{if } 0 \leq t \leq \frac{1}{2} \\ 2t - 1 & \text{if } \frac{1}{2} < t \leq 1 \end{cases}$

If $f: [0, 1] \to \mathbf{R}$ and $g: [0, 1] \to \mathbf{R}$ are functions, then their sum, $f+g$, and product, fg, are defined on the interval $[0, 1]$ by setting

$$(f+g)(t) = f(t) + g(t) \qquad \text{and} \qquad (fg)(t) = f(t) g(t)$$

for $t \in [0, 1]$.

From the calculus we know that if f and g are continuous on the interval $[0, 1]$, then the functions $f+g$ and fg are also continuous on $[0, 1]$. Thus the set of all continuous functions on $[0, 1]$ is closed under the addition and multiplication defined above. This gives us the beginning of a ring which we study below.

40
Definition

Let $C[0,1]$ be the collection of all continuous functions $f: [0,1] \to \mathbf{R}$. For every $f, g \in C[0,1]$ the sum, $f+g$, and the product, fg, are defined as

$$(f+g)(t) = f(t) + g(t) \qquad \text{and} \qquad (fg)(t) = f(t)\,g(t)$$

for $t \in [0,1]$.

41
Theorem

The set $C[0,1]$ of continuous functions $f: [0,1] \to \mathbf{R}$ with the operations of pointwise addition and multiplication is a commutative ring with identity.

A partial proof of Theorem 41 is contained in the following problem:

42
Problem

a   Find the additive identity (the zero of the ring) and the multiplicative identity. Remember that these must be functions from $[0,1]$ into $\mathbf{R}$.

b   Find the additive inverse of $f \in C[0,1]$.

c   Prove that multiplication is distributive over addition in $C[0,1]$.

The rest of the proof of Theorem 41 is left for Exercise 1.

Recall that for functions f, f_1, and f_2 defined on the interval $[0,1]$ we have $f = f_1$ if and only if $f(t) = f_1(t)$ for every $t \in [0,1]$. Thus $f \neq f_2$ if and only if $f(t) \neq f_2(t)$ for at least one $t \in [0,1]$.

A function $f: [0,1] \to \mathbf{R}$ is said to be nonzero if and only if there is a point $t_0 \in [0,1]$ such that $f(t_0) \neq 0$. Problem 39 gives examples of nonzero functions in $C[0,1]$, including at least one which takes on the value of 0 on a subinterval and still is a nonzero function.

43

Problem

Prove that the ring $(C[0, 1], +, \cdot)$ is not an integral domain. To do so find nonzero functions $f, g \in C[0, 1]$ such that $fg = 0$.

In Problems 45 through 50 the following theorems may be useful. They were proved in earlier sections.

Theorem 23 Let R and $\bar{R}$ be rings. If ϕ is a (ring) homomorphism from R onto $\bar{R}$, then $R/\ker(\phi)$ is isomorphic to $\bar{R}$.

Theorem 36 Let M be an ideal in a commutative ring R with identity. Then M is a maximal ideal in R if and only if R/M is a field.

44

Definition

Fix $c \in [0, 1]$ and define a function

$$\phi_c: C[0, 1] \to \mathbf{R}$$

by setting

$$\phi_c(f) = f(c)$$

for every $f \in C[0, 1]$.

45

Problem

Let $c = \frac{1}{4}$. Let f and g be the functions defined on $[0, 1]$ by $f(t) = t^2 - \frac{1}{16}$ and $g(t) = t$, respectively. Find $\phi_c(f)$, $\phi_c(g)$, $\phi_c(f+g)$, and $\phi_c(fg)$.

46

Problem   a

Show that the function $\phi_c: C[0, 1] \to \mathbf{R}$ given in Definition 44 is a ring homomorphism from $C[0, 1]$ onto $\mathbf{R}$.

b Describe all the elements $h \in \ker(\phi_c)$. Sketch graphs of several functions in $\ker(\phi_c)$.

c Prove that $C[0, 1]/\ker(\phi_c)$ is isomorphic to $\mathbf{R}$.

d Prove that $\ker(\phi_c)$ is a maximal ideal in $C[0, 1]$.

47
Problem

Prove that if $c \in [0, 1]$ is fixed and

$$M_c = \{f: f \in C[0, 1] \text{ and } f(c) = 0\}$$

then M_c is a maximal ideal in $C[0, 1]$.

We have seen in Problems 46 and 47 that there are a great many maximal ideals in the ring $C[0, 1]$. In Problem 48 we show that for every subinterval $[c, d]$ of $[0, 1]$ there is a proper ideal in $C[0, 1]$.

48
Problem

Let c and d be fixed so that $0 < c < d < 1$. Let

$$I = \{f: f \in C[0, 1], f(t) = 0 \text{ for } t \in [c, d]\}$$

a Show that I is an ideal in $C[0, 1]$. Find a nonzero function $f \in C[0, 1]$ that is in I and a function $g \in C[0, 1]$ that is not in I.

b If $t \in [c, d]$, find a relationship between I and M_t.

c Is I a prime ideal in $C[0, 1]$? Justify your answer.

d Is I a maximal ideal in $C[0, 1]$? Justify your answer.

If ϕ is a point-evaluation homomorphism of the type given in Definition 44, then the kernel of ϕ is a maximal ideal in $C[0, 1]$. Now let us prove that the kernel of any homomorphism ϕ from $C[0, 1]$ onto $\mathbf{R}$ is a maximal ideal.

49

Problem

Prove that if ϕ is a homomorphism from $C[0,1]$ *onto* **R**, then $\ker(\phi)$ is a maximal ideal.

It is possible, with the use of some analysis theorems beyond the scope of the calculus, to show that if M is a maximal ideal in $C[0,1]$, then there exists $c \in [0,1]$ such that

$$M = M_c = \{f: f \in C[0,1], f(c) = 0\}$$

Thus the maximal ideals in $C[0,1]$ consist exactly of those ideals of functions which vanish at a given point.

50

Problem

Assume that every maximal ideal M in $C[0,1]$ is of the form $M = M_c$ for some $c \in [0,1]$. Let ϕ be a homomorphism from $C[0,1]$ onto **R** with the additional property that $\phi(af) = a\phi(f)$ for every $a \in$ **R** and $f \in C[0,1]$, where af is the function defined on $[0,1]$ by setting

$$(af)(t) = a(f(t)).$$

Prove that for any constant function g with value a we have $\phi(g) = a$ and that there exists $c \in [0,1]$ such that $\phi(f) = f(c)$ for every $f \in C[0,1]$. Thus every homomorphism with this special property from $C[0,1]$ onto **R** is given by evaluation at a point in the interval $[0,1]$.

EXERCISES   1   Finish the proof of Theorem 41.

2   Let $C'[0,1]$ be the collection of all continuous functions $f: [0,1] \to$ **R** such that the first derivative f' of f exists and is continuous on the interval $[0,1]$. Show that $C'[0,1]$ is a proper subring of $C[0,1]$.

3   Let $C'[0,1]$ be the set defined in Exercise 2. Fix $c \in [0,1]$. Let

$$M'_c = \{f: f \in C'[0,1] \text{ and } f(c) = 0\}$$

a   Prove that M_c' is a maximal ideal in $C'[0,1]$.

b   Find a nonzero function $g \in C[0,1]$ such that $g(c) = 0$ and $g \in C'[0,1]$.

c   Show that the set M_c' is different from the maximal ideal M_c of $C[0,1]$ and that

$$M_c' = M_c \cap C'[0,1]$$

4   Let $C'[0,1]$ be the ring defined in Exercise 2. Fix $c \in [0,1]$. Let

$$J_c = \{f: f \in C'[0,1],\ f'(c) = f(c) = 0\}$$

a   Prove that J_c is an ideal in $C'[0,1]$.

b   Is J_c a prime ideal in $C'[0,1]$? a maximal ideal?

5   Fix $c \in [0,1]$. Let $C'[0,1]$ be the ring defined in Exercise 2. Define $D_c: C'[0,1] \to \mathbf{R}$ by setting $D_c(f) = f'(c)$ for every $f \in C'[0,1]$.

a   Is D_c a group homomorphism from $(C'[0,1], +)$ *onto* $(\mathbf{R}, +)$?

b   Is D_c a ring homomorphism from $C'[0,1]$ onto $\mathbf{R}$?

6   Define $\psi: C[0,1] \to \mathbf{R}$ by setting

$$\psi(f) = \int_0^1 f(t)\, dt$$

for every $f \in C[0,1]$.

a   Is ψ a group homomorphism from $(C[0,1], +)$ onto $(\mathbf{R}, +)$?

b   Is ψ a ring homomorphism from $C[0,1]$ onto $\mathbf{R}$?

7   Define a function $D: C'[0,1] \to C[0,1]$, where $C'[0,1]$ is the ring defined in Exercise 2, by setting $D(f) = f'$ for every $f \in C'[0,1]$.

a   Show that D is a group homomorphism from $(C'[0,1], +)$ *onto* $(C[0,1], +)$.

b   Is D a ring homomorphism from $C'[0,1]$ onto $C[0,1]$?

REVIEW

Important Phrases

polynomial function
factor of a polynomial
zero of a polynomial
   function
principal ideal
principal ideal ring
quotient ring
canonical homomorphism

homomorphic image of a ring
prime ideal
maximal ideal
ring of continuous functions

greatest common divisor of
   polynomials
irreducible polynomial

Symbols

(a)
R/S
$C[0, 1]$

$\phi_c(f) = f(c)$
M_c

Questions

1   State a theorem relating factors of the form $x - a$ and the zeros of a polynomial over a commutative ring with identity.

2   Let R be an integral domain. What is the maximum number of zeros of a polynomial $f(x) \in R[x]$ of degree n? What is the maximum number of factors $x - a$ $(a \in R)$ of $f(x) \in R[x]$ if the degree of $f(x)$ is n? If R is not an integral domain, is it possible to place such a maximum on the number of zeros or factors of a polynomial in $R[x]$?

3   What is the division algorithm for the polynomials over a field?

4   For what types of subrings S of a ring R is multiplication a properly defined binary operation on R/S? If R is a commutative ring with identity, then for what types of subrings of R is R/S an integral domain? a field?

5   Give two examples of a principal ideal ring. Give an example of a ring of polynomials which is not a principal ideal ring.

6   State the First Isomorphism Theorem for Rings and explain how to use it to find the nonisomorphic rings which are homomorphic images of a given ring.

7   Is every maximal ideal a prime ideal in a commutative ring with identity? Is every prime ideal a maximal ideal in a commutative ring with identity?

8   How are addition and multiplication defined on $C[0,1]$? Is $(C[0,1], +, \cdot)$ a ring? a commutative ring with identity? an integral domain? a field?

9   Describe a class of homomorphisms from $C[0,1]$ onto $\mathbf{R}$. Describe a class of maximal ideals related to these homomorphisms. Are there any other types of homomorphisms or maximal ideals in $C[0,1]$?

The following questions are answered in the exercises.

10   Let $f(x), g(x) \in R[x]$, where R is a commutative ring with identity, and assume $f(r) = g(r)$ for every $r \in R$. Is it necessarily true that $f(x) = g(x)$? For which rings is it true that $f(r) = g(r)$ for every $r \in R$ implies $f(x) = g(x)$?

11   What is meant by the greatest common divisor of two polynomials? Do two nonzero polynomials over a field necessarily have a greatest common divisor?

12   What is an irreducible polynomial in $R[x]$? If F is a field and $p(x) \in R[x]$ is irreducible, is the ideal $(p(x))$ a prime ideal? a maximal ideal?

13   What are some of the ideals in $C'[0,1]$? Are they also ideals in $C[0,1]$?

The following familiar notation from set theory is used throughout this book.

Symbol	Meaning
$x \in A$	x is an element of the set A
$x \notin A$	x is not an element of A
$\{a_1, a_2, \ldots, a_n\}$	The set whose elements are $a_1, a_2, \ldots, a_n$
$\{x : P(x)\}$	The set of all elements x for which the statement $P(x)$ is true
$\varnothing$	The empty set; the set with no elements
$A \cup B$ (union)	The set of all elements which belong to A or to B or to both
$A \cap B$ (intersection)	The set of all elements which belong to both A and B
$A - B$ (difference)	The set of all elements which belong to A but not to B
$A \subseteq B$ (containment)	A is a subset of B; every element of A is also an element of B
$A = B$	$A \subseteq B$ and $B \subseteq A$; the sets A and B have the same elements
$A \neq B$	$A - B \neq \varnothing$ or $B - A \neq \varnothing$ or both
$A \subset B$ (proper containment)	A is a subset of B and $A \neq B$
$A \times B$ (cartesian product)	The set of all ordered pairs (a, b) such that $a \in A$ and $b \in B$
$A \cap B = \varnothing$	The sets A and B are disjoint

A. Logic

Much of mathematics is written in propositions, which are statements which are either true or false but not both. Simple statements may be put together in many ways to form compound statements which are true or false according to the truth or falsity of the simple statements of which they consist.

The compound statement "P and Q" is true if both P and Q are true. It is false if P is false or Q is false or both P and Q are false. These relationships can be shown compactly as in Table A1, which is called a "truth table" for the statement "P and Q."

Table A1

P	Q	P and Q
T	T	T
T	F	F
F	T	F
F	F	F

The compound statement "P or Q" is true if P is true or Q is true or both are true. It is false if both P and Q are false. Table A2 gives the truth table for the statement "P or Q."

Table A2

P	Q	P or Q
T	T	T
T	F	T
F	T	T
F	F	F

The simple statement "*not P*" is true if P is false and it is false when P is true (see Table A3).

Table A3

P	not P
T	F
F	T

Two statements which have the same truth tables are said to be *logically equivalent*. Statements which do not have all the same truth values are not logically equivalent.

De Morgan's laws assert that the negation of the statement "*P* and *Q*" is logically equivalent to the statement "*not P* or *not Q*." The negation of the statement "*P* or *Q*" is logically equivalent to the statement "*not P* and *not Q*." (See Exercise 1.)

The implication "if *P*, then *Q*" is symbolized by $P \Rightarrow Q$, which is also read "*P* implies *Q*." This statement is true when *P* is true and *Q* is true; it is false when *P* is true and *Q* is false. Since the statement $P \Rightarrow Q$ cannot really be tested when *P* is false, one says that it is true in this case. (An example of this situation is the following sentence: If grass is red, then it is snowing.) The truth table for the implication $P \Rightarrow Q$ is given in Table A4.

Table A4

P	Q	$P \Rightarrow Q$
T	T	T
T	F	F
F	T	T
F	F	T

In the implication $P \Rightarrow Q$, the statement *P* is called the *hypothesis* and *Q* is called the *conclusion*.

The statement $P \Rightarrow Q$ is logically equivalent to the statement "*not P* or *Q*." This is shown by truth tables. (See Exercise 2.)

The negation of the statement "if P, then Q" is equivalent to the statement "P and *not* Q." Thus "*not* $(P \Rightarrow Q)$" means "P and *not* Q." One negates an implication $P \Rightarrow Q$ by saying that the hypothesis P holds but the conclusion Q fails.

The *contrapositive* of the implication $P \Rightarrow Q$ is the implication "*not* $Q \Rightarrow$ *not* P." The contrapositive is logically equivalent to the original implication. The implication $P \Rightarrow Q$ sometimes can be established by proving the contrapositive "*not* $Q \Rightarrow$ *not* P."

The *converse* of $P \Rightarrow Q$ is the implication $Q \Rightarrow P$. The converse is *not* logically equivalent to the original implication. One cannot prove an implication by proving its converse, nor can one assume that the converse $Q \Rightarrow P$ is true simply because $P \Rightarrow Q$ has been proved to be true.

There are several ways of stating the implication $P \Rightarrow Q$. These include the following statements:

> if P, then Q
> P is sufficient for Q
> P only if Q
> Q is necessary for P

The statement "P if and only if Q" is true if P and Q are both true or both false. It is symbolized by $P \Leftrightarrow Q$. The truth table for $P \Leftrightarrow Q$ is given in Table A5.

Table A5	P	Q	$P \Leftrightarrow Q$
	T	T	T
	T	F	F
	F	T	F
	F	F	T

The statement "P if and only if Q" can be written in any of the following forms:

$P \Leftrightarrow Q$
$P \Rightarrow Q$ and $Q \Rightarrow P$
P is equivalent to Q
P is necessary and sufficient for Q

Since the contrapositive of $Q \Rightarrow P$ is equivalent to $Q \Rightarrow P$, the statement "P if and only if Q" is logically equivalent to the statement

$$(P \Rightarrow Q) \text{ and } (not\ P \Rightarrow not\ Q)$$

Let $P(x)$ and $Q(x)$ be statements involving a variable x. For example, let $P(x)$ be the statement $x + 1 > x$. Then $P(x)$ is true for every real number x. As a second example let $Q(x)$ be the statement $x^2 = 1$. Then $Q(x)$ is true for the real numbers $x = 1$ and $x = -1$ and false for all other real numbers.

The notation

$$\forall x \in X \ P(x)$$

is read "for every $x \in X \ P(x)$." The statement $\forall x \in X \ P(x)$ is true if and only if $P(x)$ is true for every element x of the set X under discussion. The statement $\forall x \in X \ P(x)$ is false if and only if $P(x)$ is false for at least one element $x \in X$. Sometimes one writes simply $\forall x \ P(x)$ if it is clear from the context which set X is being considered with $x \in X$.

The notation

$$\exists x \in X \ P(x)$$

is read "there exists $x \in X$ such that $P(x)$." This statement, $\exists x \in X \ P(x)$, is true if and only if there is at least one element in the set X such that $P(x)$ is true. The statement is false if and only if $P(x)$ is false for every $x \in X$. Sometimes one writes

$$\exists x \ P(x)$$

with the understanding that $x \in X$, where X is the set under discussion.

Combining these two notations, we see that the negation of the statement $\forall x \in X \ P(x)$ is the statement

$$\exists x \in X \ not\ P(x)$$

The negation of the statement $\exists x \in X \; P(x)$ is the statement

$$\forall x \in X \; not \; P(x)$$

Since the negation of the statement $P(x) \Rightarrow Q(x)$ is "$P(x)$ and *not* $Q(x)$," the negation of the statement

$$\forall x \; (P(x) \Rightarrow Q(x))$$

is the statement

$$\exists x \; (P(x) \; and \; not \; Q(x))$$

The negation of the statement

$$\forall y \; \exists x \; P(x, y)$$

is obtained in two steps. First we obtain

$$not \; [\forall y \; \exists x \; P(x, y)] \Leftrightarrow \exists y \; not \; (\exists x \; P(x, y))$$

Since the statement

$$not \; (\exists x \; P(x, y))$$

is equivalent to the statement

$$\forall x \; not \; P(x, y)$$

we obtain finally that the negation of $\forall y \; \exists x \; P(x, y)$ is the statement

$$\exists y \; \forall x \; not \; P(x, y)$$

For example, let $x_1, x_2, \ldots$ be a sequence of real numbers. In the calculus or advanced calculus one learns that the limit of the sequence is the number L if and only if for every $\epsilon > 0$ there exists an integer N such that for every $n \geq N$, $|x_n - L| < \epsilon$. In symbolic form we write $\lim_{n \to \infty} x_n = L$ if and only if

$$\forall \epsilon > 0 \; \exists N \; (\forall n \geq N \; |x_n - L| < \epsilon)$$

The negation of this statement is the symbolic statement

$$\exists \epsilon > 0 \; \forall N \; (\exists n \geq N \; |x_n - L| \geq \epsilon)$$

In words the limit of the sequence $x_1, x_2, \ldots$ is not L if and only if there exists $\epsilon > 0$ such that for every integer N, $|x_n - L| \geq \epsilon$ for some $n \geq N$.

EXERCISES 1 Write out the truth tables for the following pairs of statements and use them to prove De Morgan's laws.
a *not* (P and Q): *not* P or *not* Q
b *not* (P or Q); *not* P and *not* Q

2 Write out the truth tables for each of the following statements and compare each table to the table for $P \Rightarrow Q$ to determine whether or not the statement is equivalent to $P \Rightarrow Q$.
a $Q \Rightarrow P$ (the converse)
b *not* $P \Rightarrow$ *not* Q (the inverse)
c *not* $Q \Rightarrow$ *not* P (the contrapositive)
d *not* P or Q

3 Show that the statements $P \Leftrightarrow Q$ and $[(P \Rightarrow Q)$ and $(not \, P \Rightarrow not \, Q)]$ are logically equivalent.

4 Determine whether each of the statements below is true or false. Write the negation of each statement. The symbols **R** and **Z** represent the sets of real numbers and integers, respectively.
a There exist real numbers x, y such that $x + y = 2$ and $xy = 2$.
b $\forall x \in \mathbf{R}$ (if $x < 3x$, then $x < 0$)
c There exists $x \in \mathbf{R}$ such that $x^2 < 0$.
d $\forall x \in \mathbf{Z} \; x > 0$
e $\forall x \in \mathbf{Z} \; \exists y \in \mathbf{Z} \; x < y$
f $\exists x \in \mathbf{Z} \; \forall y \in \mathbf{Z} \; x < y$

B. Methods of Proof

In mathematics one deals with propositions (i.e., statements assumed or proved to be true or false). These propositions usually are classified as axioms, lemmas, theorems, or propositions.

An axiom is a statement which is assumed to be true; often an axiom is self-evident. All areas of mathematics begin with undefined terms and axioms. All the remaining types of statements must be proved to be true.

A lemma is a statement which is used in proving another statement (a proposition or theorem) but is believed to have little interest by itself. A theorem is a major proposition. The distinction between propositions and theorems is often a matter of individual opinion. In fact, even lemmas can become theorems in the sense that they become widely used.

One of the principal tasks of a mathematician is to prove or disprove conjectures. By this we mean that he wishes to establish the correctness of a statement. He does this by means of an argument, an assertion that a statement called the conclusion follows from certain other statements called premises. These premises can include axioms, definitions, and previously proved theorems. In order to constitute a proof of a statement, the argument must be valid. By this we mean that if $P_1, P_2, ..., P_n$ are the premises and Q is the conclusion in the argument, then the compound statement

$$(P_1 \text{ and } P_2 \text{ and } ... \text{ and } P_n) \Rightarrow Q$$

must always be true (i.e., it must be a *tautology*).

The following arguments are all valid:

Fundamental Rule of Inference	Argument by Contrapositive
$P \Rightarrow Q$ P	$\left.\begin{array}{l} P \Rightarrow Q \\ not\ Q \end{array}\right\}$ Premises
$\therefore Q$	$\therefore not\ P$ Conclusion

Chain Rule of Inference	Rule of Separation
$P \Rightarrow Q$ $Q \Rightarrow R$	$P \text{ or } Q$ $not\ P$
$\therefore P \Rightarrow R$	$\therefore Q$

It can be shown that by using these basic valid arguments we can form other arguments which also are valid. For example, suppose we want to determine whether or not the following argument is valid:

$P_1 \Rightarrow P_2$ If John gets up at seven, then he is an early bird.

$P_2 \Rightarrow P_3$ If John is an early bird, then he gets the worm.

P_1 John gets up at seven.

$\therefore P_3$ Therefore, John gets the worm.

By the chain rule of inference we know that the argument

$$P_1 \Rightarrow P_2$$
$$P_2 \Rightarrow P_3$$

$$\therefore P_1 \Rightarrow P_3$$

is valid. Since the argument

$$P_1 \Rightarrow P_3$$
$$P_1$$

$$\therefore P_3$$

also is valid, we see that on combining the two arguments we obtain the argument given initially but with an additional, intermediary, premise $(P_1 \Rightarrow P_3)$. Hence the original argument also is valid.

Very often the statement we want to prove is an implication $P \Rightarrow Q$. There are two ways in which to carry out a proof of such a statement—directly or indirectly.

In a direct proof we assume that the hypothesis, P, of the implication $P \Rightarrow Q$ is true and we attempt to prove that the statement Q is necessarily true as a consequence. In doing so we rule out the one case for which the implication $P \Rightarrow Q$ is false, namely when P is true and Q is false. For example, once we have assumed that the hypothesis P is true, we might attempt to construct a chain of statements of the form $P \Rightarrow P_1$, $P_1 \Rightarrow P_2$, ..., $P_n \Rightarrow Q$, each of which is some axiom, definition, or previously proved theorem. Then the compound statement

$$[P \text{ and } (P \Rightarrow P_1) \text{ and } (P_1 \Rightarrow P_2) \text{ and } ... \text{ and } (P_n \Rightarrow Q)] \Rightarrow Q$$

is a true statement if and only if Q is true. Thus Q must be true.

As an example let us prove the following proposition:

Proposition 1
Let x and y be integers. If x is even and y is odd, then xy is even.

Proof
Let us assume that x is even and y is odd. Since x is even, there exists an integer a such that $x = 2a$. Since y is odd, there exists an integer b such that $y = 2b+1$. Using symbolic notation we obtain the following argument:

$$(x = 2a) \text{ and } (y = 2b+1) \Rightarrow (xy = 2a(2b+1))$$
$$\Rightarrow (xy = 2(2ab+a))$$
$$\Rightarrow (xy = 2c, \text{ where } c = 2ab+a \in \mathbf{Z})$$
$$\Rightarrow (xy \text{ is even})$$

Therefore xy is even.

When you don't know how to start a direct proof, you might try studying examples (the "do-something" approach), working backward, and/or looking for theorems and axioms in which P appears as a hypothesis or Q appears as a conclusion. In working backward when trying to prove $P \Rightarrow Q$, one starts with Q and tries to deduce P or some statement known to be true, forming a chain which one hopes then to reverse. If the chain can be reversed (as often occurs with a set of equations or inequalities), then the proof has been found of the statement $P \Rightarrow Q$. (See the proof of Proposition 5 for an example of this technique.) However, if the chain cannot be reversed (as is often the case), then a proof has not been found.

We have seen that an implication $P \Rightarrow Q$ and its contrapositive *not* $Q \Rightarrow$ *not P* are logically equivalent; these two statements must both be true or they must both be false. Thus, if we have difficulty in proving the statement $P \Rightarrow Q$ directly, we can attempt instead to establish the truth of the contrapositive *not* $Q \Rightarrow$ *not P*. For example, it would be difficult to prove directly that if x is an integer and x^2 is even, then x is even. As an example of a *proof by contraposition*, let us prove this statement.

Proposition 2
Let x be an integer. If x^2 is even, then x is even.

Proof
The proposition is in the form $P \Rightarrow Q$, where P is the statement "x^2 is even" and Q is the statement "x is even." Thus the contrapositive *not $Q \Rightarrow$ not P* is the proposition: "If x is odd (not even), then x^2 is odd (not even)."

Let us assume that x is odd. Then there exists an integer a such that $x = 2a+1$.

$$(x = 2a+1) \Rightarrow (x^2 = (2a+1)(2a+1))$$
$$\Rightarrow (x^2 = 4a^2+4a+1)$$
$$\Rightarrow (x^2 = 2(2a^2+2a)+1)$$
$$\Rightarrow (x^2 = 2b+1, \text{ where } b = 2a^2+2a \in \mathbf{Z})$$

Therefore, x^2 is odd. Since the contrapositive is true, the original statement $P \Rightarrow Q$ is true also.

A proof by contraposition is called an *indirect proof* since we are not proving the given proposition directly. A second type of indirect proof is a *proof by contradiction*. This type is used most often when we know that there are only two or three possibilities available and we want to eliminate all but one. For example, we know that every real number is either positive, negative, or zero, but never more than one of these (law of trichotomy). Thus, if we wanted to prove that a given quantity A was positive, we might assume $A \le 0$ and attempt to arrive at a statement Q which we know to be false.

The general procedure of a proof by contradiction of a statement P is to assume that *not P* is true and to derive from that assumption a statement Q which is known from previous theorems or axioms to be false. Since the statement *not $P \Rightarrow Q$* is known to be true while Q is false, it follows from truth tables that *not P* is false. Hence P must be true.

The proof that the number $\sqrt{2}$ is irrational is an example of the use of contradiction.

Proposition 3
The number $\sqrt{2}$ is irrational.

Proof

Assume that $\sqrt{2}$ is a rational number. Then there exist integers a and b such that $\sqrt{2} = a/b$ and a and b have no factors in common (the fraction is in lowest terms).

$$\left(\sqrt{2} = \frac{a}{b}\right) \Rightarrow \left(2 = \frac{a^2}{b^2}\right)$$

$$\Rightarrow (a^2 = 2b^2)$$
$$\Rightarrow (a^2 \text{ is an even integer})$$
$$\Rightarrow (a \text{ is an even integer}) \qquad \text{(See Proposition 2)}$$
$$\Rightarrow (a = 2c \text{ for some integer } c)$$
$$\Rightarrow (2b^2 = a^2 = 4c^2)$$
$$\Rightarrow (b^2 = 2c^2)$$
$$\Rightarrow (b \text{ is an even integer})$$
$$\Rightarrow (b = 2d \text{ for some integer } d)$$
$$\Rightarrow (a \text{ and } b \text{ have the factor 2 in common})$$

The last statement of the argument above contradicts our choice of a and b as integers which have no factors in common. Thus the assumption that $\sqrt{2}$ is rational is false and we know that $\sqrt{2}$ is an irrational number.

When we have not succeeded in proving a conjecture by any of these direct or indirect means, it may be that the conjecture is not true. There are two standard techniques for disproving conjectures. The first is to find *one* example which does not satisfy the conjecture. This example is usually called a *counterexample*. For example, we can use a counterexample to disprove the conjecture that if $x \in \mathbf{Z}$ and $x > 2$, then $x^2 - 4x \geq 0$ by noting that $3 > 2$ and $3^2 - 4 \cdot 3 = -3 < 0$. Thus the conjecture as it stands is false.

The second technique of attempting to disprove a conjecture is to assume that the conjecture is true and derive additional relationships from it. If we can find a relationship which contradicts an axiom, definition, or previously proved theorem, then the conjecture is false. This particular technique has been used in testing conjectures which eventually have led to the development of new branches of mathematics. This is most notably true in geometry, where the attempts to test Euclid's parallel axiom by assuming that this axiom was not true have led instead to noneuclidean geometries. In the development of these geometries the negation of the parallel axiom was assumed true and theorems were derived from this statement (together with other axioms) which did not contradict known axioms or theorems.

Occasionally, one wants to prove a proposition in the form $P \Leftrightarrow Q$. Since $P \Leftrightarrow Q$ means

$$(P \Rightarrow Q) \text{ and } (Q \Rightarrow P)$$

we can proceed by proving the two statements $P \Rightarrow Q$ and $Q \Rightarrow P$ individually by means of one of the techniques above. However, we have also seen that $P \Leftrightarrow Q$ is equivalent to the statement

$$(P \Rightarrow Q) \text{ and } (not\ P \Rightarrow not\ Q)$$

This often provides a convenient way of proving an equivalence statement: prove $P \Rightarrow Q$ and then prove $not\ P \Rightarrow not\ Q$. As an example, let us prove the following proposition:

Proposition 4
Let x be an integer. Then x is odd if and only if x^2 is odd.

Proof
Let P be the statement "x is odd" and let Q be the statement "x^2 is odd." Then our proposition is in the form $P \Leftrightarrow Q$. In order to prove $P \Leftrightarrow Q$ we want to prove $P \Rightarrow Q$ and $not\ P \Rightarrow not\ Q$.

First let us assume that x is odd. Then there exists an integer a such that $x = 2a+1$.

$$\begin{aligned}(x = 2a+1) &\Rightarrow (x^2 = (2a+1)^2) \\ &\Rightarrow (x^2 = 2(2a^2+2a)+1) \\ &\Rightarrow (x^2 = 2b+1, \text{ where } b = 2a^2+2a \in \mathbf{Z}) \\ &\Rightarrow (x^2 \text{ is odd})\end{aligned}$$

Therefore x^2 is odd if x is odd.

Now let us prove $not\ P \Rightarrow not\ Q$. Assume that x is not odd. Then there exists an integer a such that $x = 2a$.

$$\begin{aligned}(x = 2a) &\Rightarrow (x^2 = (2a)^2) \\ &\Rightarrow (x^2 = 2(2a^2)) \\ &\Rightarrow (x^2 = 2b, \text{ where } b = 2a^2 \in \mathbf{Z}) \\ &\Rightarrow (x^2 \text{ is even})\end{aligned}$$

Therefore the contrapositive $not\ P \Rightarrow not\ Q$ is true and we must also have the implication $Q \Rightarrow P$ true.

A third method of proving an equivalence $P \Leftrightarrow Q$ is to produce a chain of equivalent statements leading from P to Q as follows:

$$P \Leftrightarrow P_1, \ P_1 \Leftrightarrow P_2, \ P_2 \Leftrightarrow P_3, \ \ldots, \ P_n \Leftrightarrow Q$$

For example, we could use this technique to prove the following statement: An integer x is odd if and only if x^{16} is odd. By Proposition 4 we know that an integer x is odd if and only if x^2 is odd. Thus we obtain the chain

$$
\begin{aligned}
(x \text{ is odd}) &\Leftrightarrow (x^2 \text{ is odd}) \\
&\Leftrightarrow ((x^2)^2 = x^4 \text{ is odd}) \\
&\Leftrightarrow ((x^4)^2 = x^8 \text{ is odd}) \\
&\Leftrightarrow ((x^8)^2 = x^{16} \text{ is odd})
\end{aligned}
$$

Other common forms of conjectures can be written symbolically as $\exists x \in X \ P(x)$, $\forall x \in X \ P(x)$, and $\exists$ a unique x such that $P(x)$.

To prove the statement $\exists x \in X \ P(x)$, we need only exhibit or construct in some way *one* element $x \in X$ such that the statement $P(x)$ is true. The actual construction of this element can be very difficult (for example, the demonstration of a solution to the fourth-degree polynomial equation

$$x^4 + a_1 x^3 + a_2 x^2 + a_3 x + a_4 = 0$$

is very complicated). We regularly see this type of proof when we want to solve an equation or inequality because the demonstration of a solution is a proof of existence. As an example let us prove the following proposition:

Proposition 5
Let a and b be real numbers with $a \neq 0$. There exists a real number x such that $ax + b = 0$.

Proof
This is one time when working backward can be very useful. Let us assume that there is such a number x.

$$
\begin{aligned}
(ax + b = 0) &\Rightarrow (ax = -b) \\
&\Rightarrow \left(x = -\frac{b}{a} \right)
\end{aligned}
$$

Now we must show that we can reverse our steps.

Since $a \neq 0$, the number $-(b/a)$ does exist. Let $x = -(b/a)$.

$$\left(x = -\frac{b}{a}\right) \Rightarrow \left(ax+b = a\left(-\frac{b}{a}\right)+b = -b+b = 0\right)$$

Therefore the number $-(b/a)$ has the desired property and we have exhibited the necessary solution.

To prove the statement $\forall x \in X \ P(x)$, we let x represent a fixed but arbitrary element of the set X and prove that for this x the statement $P(x)$ is true. Since x is an arbitrary element of the set X, we have then shown that $P(x)$ is true for every $x \in X$. As an example let us prove the following proposition:

Proposition 6
For every $x \in \mathbf{R}$, $x^2 \geq 0$.

Proof
We need the fact that the product of positive numbers is positive and the law of trichotomy.

Let $x \in \mathbf{R}$. Then either x is positive or x is negative or $x = 0$.

$$(x \text{ positive}) \Rightarrow (x \cdot x = x^2 \text{ is positive})$$
$$\Rightarrow (x^2 > 0)$$
$$(x \text{ negative}) \Rightarrow (-x \text{ is positive})$$
$$\Rightarrow (x^2 = (-x) \cdot (-x) \text{ is positive})$$
$$\Rightarrow (x^2 > 0)$$
$$(x = 0) \Rightarrow (x \cdot x = 0 \cdot 0 = 0)$$

Therefore $x^2 \geq 0$ for every $x \in \mathbf{R}$.

The proof of Proposition 6 also is an example of a proof by cases.

To prove a statement of the form $\exists$ a unique $x \in X$ such that $P(x)$, we must first prove the statement $\exists x \in X \ P(x)$. Then we must prove that there is only one $x \in X$ with this property $P(x)$. One way to prove this latter statement is to assume that there are two elements x_1 and x_2 in X such that $P(x_1)$ and $P(x_2)$ are true and prove that $x_1 = x_2$. This latter part of the proof is called the *uniqueness part* of the proof while the first step is called the *existence part* of the proof.

As an example of a uniqueness proof let us consider the following proposition:

Proposition 7

Let a and b be real numbers with $a \neq 0$. There exists a unique real number x such that $ax+b = 0$.

Proof

Proposition 5 shows us the existence of the number x. Now let us assume that there exist two real numbers x_1 and x_2 such that $ax_1+b = 0$ and $ax_2+b = 0$.

$$[(ax_1+b = 0) \text{ and } (ax_2+b = 0)]$$
$$\Rightarrow (ax_1+b = ax_2+b)$$
$$\Rightarrow (ax_1 = ax_2) \quad \text{(cancellation for addition)}$$
$$\Rightarrow (x_1 = x_2) \quad \text{(cancellation for multiplication)}$$

A second proof of the uniqueness of the solution uses the first part of the proof of Proposition 5, where we showed that if x is a solution to the equation, then $x = -(b/a)$. This proves that there is exactly one solution, namely $-(b/a)$.

Appendix 3   Algebraic and Order Properties of Numbers

Let **Z** denote the set of all integers, **Q** the set of all rational numbers, and **R** the set of all real numbers. The following properties are true for each of these three sets, **Z**, **Q**, and **R**, with the operations of addition and multiplication. Throughout the following the letter X denotes any one of the three sets.

1   Closure of X under addition: For every $a, b \in X$,

$a + b \in X$

(that is, the sum of two elements of X is an element of X).

2   Associativity of addition: For every $a, b, c \in X$,

$a + (b+c) = (a+b) + c$

3   Existence of an additive identity: There is an element $0 \in X$ such that $a+0 = 0+a = a$ for every $a \in X$.

4   Existence of additive inverses: For every $a \in X$, there is an element $-a \in X$ such that $a + (-a) = 0$.

5   Commutativity of addition: For every $a, b \in X$,

$a + b = b + a$

6   Closure of X under multiplication: For every $a, b \in X$,

$ab \in X$

(that is, the product of two elements of X is an element of X).

7   Associativity of multiplication: For every $a, b, c \in X$,

$a(bc) = (ab)c$

8   Existence of a multiplicative identity: There is an element $1 \in X$ such that $a \cdot 1 = 1 \cdot a = a$ for every $a \in X$.

9   Commutativity of multiplication: For every $a, b \in X$,

$$ab = ba$$

10   Distributivity of multiplication over addition: For every $a, b, c \in X$,

$$a(b+c) = ab + ac$$

11   Cancellation for multiplication: If $a, b, c \in X$, $c \neq 0$, and $ac = bc$, then $a = b$.

12   Existence of multiplicative inverses in $\mathbf{Q}$ and $\mathbf{R}$: If X is one of the sets $\mathbf{Q}$ or $\mathbf{R}$ (but not $\mathbf{Z}$), then for every $a \in X - \{0\}$ there is an element $a^{-1} \in X$ such that $a \cdot a^{-1} = 1$.

Subtraction of elements $a, b \in \mathbf{R}$ is defined in terms of additive inverses by setting

$$a - b = a + (-b)$$

Division of elements $a, b \in \mathbf{R}$ with $b \neq 0$ is defined in terms of multiplicative inverses by setting

$$a/b = ab^{-1}$$

In addition to the 12 properties listed above for addition and multiplication, the three sets of numbers $\mathbf{Z}$, $\mathbf{Q}$, and $\mathbf{R}$ have order properties. Since the following statements are true of each of the three sets, we denote any one of them by X.

13   There is a proper, nonempty subset P of X such that
a $0 \notin P$;
b   for every $x \in X$, exactly one of the following conditions holds: $x = 0$, $x \in P$, or $-x \in P$ (law of trichotomy);
c   if $a, b \in P$, then $a + b \in P$ and $ab \in P$.

The elements of the set P are said to be positive elements of X, and we write $x > 0$ if and only if $x \in P$. Using this notation we can rewrite property 13b as follows:

b′   If $x \in X$, then x satisfies *exactly one* of the following: $x = 0$, $x > 0$, or $-x > 0$ (law of trichotomy).

If $a, b \in X$, we say that a is less than b and we write $a < b$ if and only if $b - a \in P$ (or $b - a > 0$). We say that b is greater than a, written $b > a$, if and only if $a < b$. The order relation $<$ has the following properties:

14a Every pair of elements $a, b \in X$ satisfies exactly one of the following: $a = b$, $a < b$, or $b < a$ (law of trichotomy).

b If $a < b$ and $b < c$, then $a < c$ (transitivity property).

c If $a, b \in X$ and $a < b$, then $-b < -a$.

d If $a, b, c, d \in X$, $a < b$, and $c < d$, then $a + c < b + d$.

e If $a, b, c \in X$, $a < b$, and $c > 0$, then $ac < bc$. If $-c > 0$, then $bc < ac$.

The symbol $a \leq b$ means that $a < b$ or $a = b$.

The set $\mathbf{Z}^+$ of all positive integers also has the following properties:

a $1 \in \mathbf{Z}^+$ and 1 is the smallest element of $\mathbf{Z}^+$ (that is, $1 \leq k$ for every $k \in \mathbf{Z}^+$).

b Every element of $\mathbf{Z}^+$ has a successor. Thus, if $k \in \mathbf{Z}^+$, then $k + 1 \in \mathbf{Z}^+$ and $k + 1 > k$.

These are two of the Peano axioms which define the set $\mathbf{Z}^+$. Another of the axioms is the principle of finite induction (see Appendix 5). We show in Appendix 5 that this axiom is a consequence of another axiom.

Often in mathematics one encounters a statement of comparison or relationship among pairs of elements of a given set. A *relation*, or binary relation, on a set A assigns to every pair of elements $a, b \in A$ exactly one statement concerning a and b. This statement assigned to the pair $a, b \in A$ is often written with a symbol such as $a \sim b$. The statement must make sense for every pair $a, b \in A$. If the statement is true, we write $a \sim b$; if it is false, we write $a \nsim b$. Examples of relations on the set of positive integers are "$a = b$," "$a < b$," and "a is a factor of b."

Formally, a binary relation R on a set A is any subset of $A \times A$. For any ordered pair $(a, b) \in A \times A$, either (a, b) belongs to the relation R or (a, b) does not belong to the relation R (but not both). With the relation R we can use a relational symbol such as "$\sim$." If $(a, b) \in R$, we write $a \sim b$; if $(a, b) \notin R$, we write $a \nsim b$.

For example, let

$$R = \{(x, y): x, y \in \mathbf{Z}^+,\ y - x \text{ is positive}\}$$

be the relation "less than" on the set of positive integers, and let "$<$" be the relational symbol. Then $(1, 2)$ is in R so that $1 < 2$, while $(2, 1)$ is not in R so that $2 \nless 1$.

1
Definition   An *equivalence relation* $a \sim b$ on A is a relation which satisfies the following three conditions:

a   Reflexivity: $a \sim a$ for every $a \in A$.

b   Symmetry: If $a \sim b$, then $b \sim a$ for every $a, b \in A$.

c   Transitivity: If $a \sim b$ and $b \sim c$, then $a \sim c$ for every $a, b, c \in A$.

Note that only the relation $a = b$ of the three mentioned above is an equivalence relation. The relation "less than" ($a < b$) is transitive but neither symmetric nor reflexive; the relation "is a factor of" (a is a factor of b) is reflexive and transitive but not symmetric.

2
Example   Each of the following relations is an equivalence relation:

a   In the set of all lines in a given plane, $L_1 \sim L_2$ (often written $L_1 \parallel L_2$) if and only if the line L_1 is parallel to the line L_2. (Any line is assumed to be parallel to itself.)

b   In the set of all triangles in a given plane, $\triangle_1 \simeq \triangle_2$ if and only if the triangle $\triangle_1$ is congruent to the triangle $\triangle_2$. (Recall some high school geometry.)

c   In the set of all triangles in a given plane, $\triangle_1 \sim \triangle_2$ if and only if $\triangle_1$ is similar to $\triangle_2$.

d   In the collection of all finite subsets of a given set, $B \sim C$ if and only if the subsets B and C have the same number of elements.

e   In any nonempty set, $a \sim b$ if and only if $a = b$. This is the equivalence relation of equality.

f   In the set of all integers, $a \sim b$ if and only if $a-b$ is an even integer (that is, $a-b = 2k$ for some integer k).

As a result of the properties which define it, an equivalence relation on a set A makes it possible to partition ("break up") the set A into disjoint subsets; this often proves useful mathematically. We make this formal in Definitions 3 and 5 and Theorem 6.

3
Definition   Let $\sim$ denote an equivalence relation on A. For every $a \in A$ let

$$[a] = \{x: x \in A \text{ and } x \sim a\}$$

The set $[a]$ is called the *equivalence class* of the element a; it consists of all elements $x \in A$ which are equivalent to a under the relation $\sim$.

4
Example

In the set of all integers let $a \sim b$ if and only if $a - b$ is even. The equivalence classes for this equivalence relation are

$$[0] = \{x: x \in \mathbf{Z} \text{ and } x-0 \text{ is even}\} \qquad \text{and}$$

$$[1] = \{x: x \in Z \text{ and } x-1 \text{ is even}\}$$

The class $[0]$ is the set of all even integers and $[1]$ is the set of all odd integers. Note that

$$[-4] = [-2] = [0] = [2], \text{ etc.}$$

while

$$[-3] = [-1] = [1] = [3], \text{ etc.}$$

5
Definition

A *partition* of a set A is a collection of pairwise-disjoint subsets of A whose union is equal to A. Every element of A belongs to one and only one of the subsets which comprise a partition.

In Example 4 the equivalence classes $[0]$ and $[1]$ comprise a partition of $\mathbf{Z}$ because every integer belongs to the set $[0]$ or to the set $[1]$ and $[0] \cap [1] = \varnothing$.

For a second example of equivalence classes and partitions, consider the collection $\mathscr{A}$ of all finite subsets of $\mathbf{Z}^+ = \{1, 2, 3, ...\}$. In this collection we define $B \sim C$ if and only if the subsets B and C have the same number of elements.

The equivalence class $[\{1\}]$ is the set

$$\{X: X \in \mathscr{A} \text{ and } X \sim \{1\}\}$$

Thus the equivalence class $[\{1\}]$ is the collection of all subsets of $\mathbf{Z}^+$ which have exactly one element:

$$[\{1\}] = \{\{1\}, \{2\}, \{3\}, ...\}$$

Similarly, $[\{1, 2\}]$ consists of all subsets of $\mathbf{Z}^+$ which have exactly two elements. The sets $\{3, 11\}$, $\{7, 110\}$, and $\{26, 147\}$ are all elements of the equivalence class $[\{1, 2\}]$.

The partition of $\mathcal{A}$ corresponding to this equivalence relation consists of the pairwise-disjoint equivalence classes $[\{1\}]$, $[\{1, 2\}]$, ..., $[\{1, 2, ..., n\}]$, ... Note that the class $[\{1, 2, ..., n\}]$ consists of all subsets of $\mathbf{Z}^+$ with exactly n elements.

6
Theorem

Let $\sim$ denote an equivalence relation on a set A. The equivalence classes in A have the following properties which hold for every $a, b \in A$:

a $a \in [a]$; every element of A belongs to an equivalence class.

b   If $[a] \cap [b] \neq \varnothing$, then $[a] = [b]$.

c   If $[a] \neq [b]$, then $[a] \cap [b] = \varnothing$; two different equivalence classes have no common elements.

d $[a] = [b]$ if and only if $a \sim b$.

e $[a] \cap [b] = \varnothing$ if and only if $a \nsim b$.

Proof of Property a
Since $a \sim a$ for every $a \in A$ (reflexivity of $\sim$), we must have $a \in [a]$.

Proof of Property b
Let $x \in [a] \cap [b]$. Then, by definition of equivalence class, $x \sim a$ and $x \sim b$, so that $a \sim b$. (Why?) To prove $[a] = [b]$ let us start with $c \in [a]$. But then $c \sim a$. Since $a \sim b$, we have $c \sim b$. Thus $c \in [b]$ and $[a] \subseteq [b]$. In the same way we show that $[b] \subseteq [a]$ and hence it follows that $[a] = [b]$.

The proofs of the remaining three properties (c, d, and e) are left as exercises. Property d is particularly useful when working with equivalence classes.

The following theorem results from properties 6a and 6c of an equivalence relation.

7
Theorem   If $\sim$ is an equivalence relation on the set A, then the collection of all equivalence classes $[a]$, where $a \in A$, is a partition of A.

As a converse to Theorem 7 we have the following theorem:

8
Theorem   Any given partition of a set A induces an equivalence relation $\sim$ on A. The given partition consists of the equivalence classes $[a]$ of the relation $\sim$.

Outline of the Proof
Define a relation $\sim$ on A by saying that $a \sim b$ if and only if a and b belong to the same element of the partition. Prove that $\sim$ is an equivalence relation. Then prove that for every $a \in A$ $[a]$ is equal to the element of the partition which contains a.

EXERCISES 1   Describe the equivalence classes for each of the equivalence relations given in Example 2.

2   Prove properties c, d, and e of Theorem 6.

3   Complete the proof of Theorem 8.

4   Let $\sim$ denote a relation on a set A. Using results on logic, complete the following statements:
a $\sim$ is not reflexive if and only if_____ .
b $\sim$ is not symmetric if and only if _____.
c $\sim$ is not transitive if and only if _____.

5   At first glance it would appear that the properties of symmetry and transitivity of an equivalence relation together imply the reflexivity of the relation. (An argument might be that if $a \sim b$, then $b \sim a$ and hence, by transitivity, $a \sim a$.) Why is this not true?

Appendix 5   Well-Ordering and Induction

A. Well-Ordering

Intuitively we would say that any subset of the positive integers, $\mathbf{Z}^+ = \{1, 2, 3, \dots\}$, has a first, or smallest, element although the same subset may not have a largest element. We use this idea of a smallest element often, as, for example, when we write such a subset as

$$\{3, 5, 8, 12, \dots\}$$

Even a set such as

$$\{x: x \in \mathbf{Z}, x > 12\}$$

has a smallest element, 13, in the set. Let us formalize our intuitive ideas.

1
Definition a Let X be a subset of **R**. An element $a \in \mathbf{R}$ is a *smallest or least* element of X if and only if $a \in X$ and $a \le x$ for every $x \in X$.

b A set S of real numbers is *well-ordered* if and only if every nonempty subset of S contains a smallest element.

We assume the following axiom:

2
Axiom *Well-Ordering Principle.* The set $\mathbf{Z}^+$ of positive integers is well-ordered.

3
Example a The set S of all odd positive integers is well-ordered. To show this it is not sufficient to note that 1 is the smallest element of S. We must show that *every* nonempty subset of S has a least element. Let X be an arbitrary nonempty subset of S. Then $X \subseteq \mathbf{Z}^+$ and by the well-ordering principle X has a smallest element. Thus S is well-ordered.

b   The set **R** is not well-ordered since the subset

$$\mathbf{R}^- = \{x: x \in \mathbf{R} \text{ and } x < 0\}$$

has no smallest element.

c   Let

$$S = \{x: x \in \mathbf{R} \text{ and } x \geq 1\}$$

The set S itself has a least element, namely 1. The subset $\{x: x > 2\}$ does not contain a least element. Thus S is not well-ordered.

The well-ordering principle is useful in proving statements about integers. As an example let us prove the following proposition, which will be useful in Section B.

4
Proposition   *Principle of Finite Induction.* Let S be a set of positive integers such that

a $1 \in S$ and
b   for every k if $k \in S$, then $k+1 \in S$.

Then S is the set of all positive integers.

Proof
Let us assume that $S \neq \mathbf{Z}^+$. Let

$$X = \{n: n \in \mathbf{Z}^+ \text{ and } n \notin S\} = \mathbf{Z}^+ - S$$

Then X is a nonempty subset of $\mathbf{Z}^+$. By the well-ordering principle X contains a smallest element x_0 and $x_0 > 1$ by hypothesis a. Thus the integer $x_0 - 1$ is a positive integer which is not in X. Hence $x_0 - 1 \in S$. But then hypothesis b states that $x_0 = (x_0 - 1) + 1 \in S$, contradicting the fact that $x_0 \in \mathbf{Z}^+ - S$. Thus we must have $X = \emptyset$ and $S = \mathbf{Z}^+$.

EXERCISES 1 Which of the following sets are well-ordered? Justify your answers.
   a   All even integers
   b   All integers larger than -100
   c $\left\{\dfrac{1}{n}: n \in \mathbf{Z}^+\right\}$

   d $\{0\} \cup \left\{\dfrac{1}{n}: n \in \mathbf{Z}^+\right\}$

   (If your answers for parts c and d are different, read carefully the definition of a well-ordered set.)

2 Which of the following sets are well-ordered? Justify your answers.
   a   Even positive integers
   b $\{x: x \in \mathbf{Z} \text{ and } x \geq a\}$ where a is a fixed integer. (You may want to consider two possibilities—$a > 0$ and $a \leq 0$.)
   c $\mathbf{Q}$, the set of all rational numbers
   d $\mathbf{Q}^+ = \{x: x \in \mathbf{Q} \text{ and } x > 0\}$
   e $\{x: x \in \mathbf{Q} \text{ and } x \geq 0\}$

   (If your answers for parts d and e are different, read carefully the definition of a well-ordered set.)

   f $\left\{1 - \dfrac{1}{n}: n \in \mathbf{Z}^+\right\}$

3 Prove that every subset of a well-ordered set is well-ordered.

4 Prove that any finite set of real numbers is well-ordered.

B. Induction

Frequently in mathematics one makes an observation which leads to a conjecture. The observation might be the fact that the sum of the first three or four odd positive integers is a square:

$$1 + 3 + 5 = 9 \qquad \text{and} \qquad 1 + 3 + 5 + 7 = 16$$

One might then ask for how many similar sums of odd integers this occurs. Is it true for all values of n that

$$1 + 3 + 5 + \cdots + (2n-1) = n^2 \text{ ?}$$

This simple-looking statement actually constitutes an infinite number of statements which must be checked or proved: $1 = 1^2$, $1+3 = 2^2$, $1+3+5 = 3^2$, etc. How can this be done? This is where induction plays a role in mathematics. It allows one to prove an infinite number of statements fairly quickly (and, on occasion, it leads to the discovery of those statements).

In general, we use the symbols P_1, P_2, P_3, etc., to stand for the statements under consideration.

5
Theorem
      Principle of Mathematical Induction. Let $\{P_n : n \in \mathbf{Z}^+\}$ be a set of propositions defined for every integer $n \geq 1$ such that

a P_1 is true and
b   for every integer $k \geq 1$ if P_k is true, then P_{k+1} is true.

      Then P_n is true for every integer $n \geq 1$.

In the principle of mathematical induction statements a and b constitute the *hypothesis*. The *conclusion* asserts that P_n is true for every integer $n \geq 1$.

Proof of the Induction Principle
Suppose P_1, P_2, P_3, ... satisfy the hypothesis of the induction principle. We wish to prove the conclusion: P_n is true for every integer $n \geq 1$. We have already proved in Section A that if S is a set of positive integers such that (a) $1 \in S$ and (b) $k \in S$ implies $k+1 \in S$, then S is the set of all positive integers. The hypothesis of the induction principle (Theorem 5) allows us to define a set S which satisfies these conditions.

Let $S = \{n : P_n \text{ is true}\}$. By the induction hypothesis we see that (a) $1 \in S$ and (b) $k \in S$ implies $k+1 \in S$. Thus Proposition 4 (Section A) tells us that $S = \mathbf{Z}^+$. Hence P_n is true for every positive integer n.

The induction principle is a chain-reaction principle. To use this principle we need to know that the chain reaction can be started (that is, P_1 is true) and that it continues at any stage (i.e., the truth of P_k implies the truth of P_{k+1}). Then with our chain started by P_1, we have P_1 implies P_2, P_2 implies P_3, P_3 implies P_4, etc.

Remember that in order to prove a collection of statements $\{P_n: n \in \mathbf{Z}^+\}$ using the principle of mathematical induction, you must do two things:

    α Show that P_1 is true.

    β Prove that for every $k \geq 1$, P_k implies P_{k+1}. To do so assume that P_k is true for some arbitrary, but fixed, k and then prove P_{k+1}.

As an example let us prove the statement

$$1 + 3 + 5 + \cdots + (2n - 1) = n^2$$

for all $n \in \mathbf{Z}^+$.

For every positive integer n let P_n denote the above statement. Thus, in words, P_n states that the sum of the first n odd positive integers is n^2. Since $1 = 1^2$, P_1 is true. Let us assume that P_k is true, that is,

$$1 + 3 + 5 + \cdots + (2k - 1) = k^2$$

We wish to prove P_{k+1}, that is,

$$1 + 3 + \cdots + (2(k+1) - 1) = (k+1)^2$$

From statement P_k we obtain

$$1 + 3 + \cdots + (2k - 1) + (2k + 1) = k^2 + (2k + 1)$$
$$= (k+1)^2$$

Thus the statement P_{k+1} is implied by the statement P_k. The principle of mathematical induction then states that for every positive integer n, P_n is true.

In the preceding example P_n is the name of the entire statement

$$1 + 3 + 5 + \cdots + (2n - 1) = n^2$$

Note that P_n is not the expression

$$1 + 3 + \cdots + (2n - 1)$$

It is *not* correct to write

$$P_n = 1 + 3 + 5 + \cdots + (2n-1)$$

The statements P_n: $n = n+1$ illustrate why it is necessary to show that both conditions of the induction hypothesis are satisfied. Certainly P_1 fails, but if we assume that P_k: $k = k+1$ is true, then by adding 1 to each side we obtain P_{k+1}: $k+1 = (k+1)+1$.

EXERCISES   1a   Consider the following sums:

$$2 + 4 + 6 + \cdots + 2n$$
$$1 + 2 + 3 + \cdots + n$$
$$1^3 + 2^3 + 3^3 + \cdots + n^3$$

We seek a simple formula in terms of n for each of these sums. To find these formulas, compute the indicated sums and fill in the answers in Table A6.

Table A6

n	1	2	3	4	5	6	7	8
$\displaystyle\sum_{k=1}^{n} 2k$						42		
$\displaystyle\sum_{k=1}^{n} k$						21		
$\displaystyle\sum_{k=1}^{n} k^3$						441		*XXX*

State your formulas in terms of n.

$$\sum_{k=1}^{n} 2k = \underline{\hspace{5cm}}$$

$$\sum_{k=1}^{n} k = \underline{\hspace{5cm}}$$

$$\sum_{k=1}^{n} k^3 = \underline{\hspace{5cm}}$$

b   Prove by induction the formula $\sum_{k=1}^{n} 2k = \underline{\hspace{3cm}}$.

c   Prove the formula $\sum_{k=1}^{n} k = \underline{\hspace{3cm}}$.

d   Prove the formula $\sum_{k=1}^{n} k^3 = \underline{\hspace{3cm}}$.

2   Prove by induction the statement

$$P_n:\ 1^2 + 2^2 + \cdots + n^2 = \frac{n(n+1)(2n+1)}{6}$$

3   Let $a \in \mathbf{R}$. Set $a^1 = a$ and recursively define $a^{n+1} = a^n \cdot a$ for every integer $n \geq 1$. Now let m be any fixed positive integer. Use induction on n to prove

a $a^m \cdot a^n = a^{m+n}$ for every integer $n \geq 1$;

b $(a^m)^n = a^{mn}$ for every integer $n \geq 1$.

4   Let $a, b \in \mathbf{R}$. Prove that $(ab)^n = \underline{\hspace{2cm}}$ for every integer $n \geq 1$.

5   This exercise shows the necessity of checking both parts of the induction hypothesis. Try to prove by induction the following incorrect statements. For each statement show that one hypothesis of the induction principle holds but another fails.

a $2 + 4 + \cdots + 2n = n(n+1) + 2$

b $1 + 3 + \cdots + (2n-1) = n^3$

6   Students sometimes claim that the induction principle is invalid. They say that the principle entails assuming the conclusion in order to prove it. To show that this objection is unfounded, compare part b of the induction hypothesis with the conclusion of the principle and use points α and β (page 299).

7   Complete the following statement and prove that it is true for every $n \in \mathbf{Z}^+$: A set with n elements has _____ subsets. Remember that the empty set is counted as a subset. •

8   Prove the following statement: For every $a, r \in \mathbf{Z}^+$ such that $a > 1$ there exists an integer $s \in \mathbf{Z}^+$ such that $a^s > r$.

9   Prove that for every $a, r \in \mathbf{Z}^+$ there exists $s \in \mathbf{Z}^+$ such that $s \cdot a > r$.

C. Other Forms of the Principle of Induction

In proofs by induction it is often useful or necessary to begin the process with an integer different from 1. For example, suppose we want to establish the inequality $n^2 > 2n + 1$. Since $1^2 = 1 < 2 \cdot 1 + 1$, the inequality certainly is not true for $n = 1$. Moreover, it is not true for $n = 2$ although it is true for $n = 3$. Thus we can not immediately apply the principle of induction stated in Theorem 5 (Section B). However, we can handle this problem if we denote our statements by

$$P_n: \quad (n+2)^2 > 2(n+2) + 1 \qquad (n \in \mathbf{Z}^+)$$

or if we prove a new form of the principle of induction which allows us to start with any integer. Let us take the second course of action since it allows us to handle many problems as stated, rather than in a rewritten form.

As another statement of the principle of induction we have the following theorem:

6
Theorem   Let n_0 be an integer and let P_n be a proposition defined for every integer $n \geq n_0$ such that

a P_{n_0} is true and

b   for every integer $k \geq n_0$ the truth of P_k implies the truth of P_{k+1}.

Then P_n is true for every integer $n \geq n_0$.

Proof

Let S be the set of all positive integers n such that the proposition P_{n_0+n-1} is true. As a consequence of hypothesis a we have $1 \in S$. It follows from hypothesis b that if $k \in S$, then $k+1 \in S$, for the truth of P_{n_0+k-1} implies the truth of

$$P_{(n_0+k-1)+1} = P_{n_0+(k+1)-1}$$

But then Proposition 4 (Section A) states that S is the set of all positive integers. Hence P_{n_0+n-1} is true for all positive integers n, so P_n is true for all integers $n \geq n_0$.

As an example of the use of this form of the principle of induction let us prove the inequality $n^2 > 2n+1$ for every $n \geq 3$. As we have noted, the inequality does not hold for $n = 1, 2$. However, $3^2 = 9 > 2 \cdot 3 + 1 = 7$, so the statement P_n: $n^2 > 2n+1$ is true for $n_0 = 3$. Let us assume that P_k is true for some $k \geq 3$. Then $k^2 > 2k+1$ and hence

$$\begin{aligned}
(k+1)^2 &= k^2 + 2k + 1 \\
&> (2k+1) + (2k+1) \\
&= 2(k+1) + 2k \\
&\geq 2(k+1) + 6 \\
&> 2(k+1) + 1
\end{aligned}$$

Thus, if P_k is true, then P_{k+1} is true and Theorem 6 states that P_n: $n^2 > 2n+1$ is true for every $n \geq 3$.

In addition to the variation stated in Theorem 6, there is a second form of the principle of induction. This second form is particularly useful in proving the Fundamental Theorem of Arithmetic, which is stated and proved in Appendix 6E.

7
Theorem

Second Principle of Mathematical Induction. Let P_n be a proposition defined for every integer $n \geq 1$ such that

a P_1 is true and

b   for every integer $k \geq 1$ if $P_1, P_2, ..., P_k$ are all true, then P_{k+1} is true.

Then P_n is true for every integer $n \geq 1$.

Proof

Let S be the set of all positive integers n such that P_n is true. Suppose $S \neq \mathbf{Z}^+$. Then the set $\mathbf{Z}^+ - S$ has a smallest element j (that is, a smallest element such that P_j is false) and $j > 1$ since $1 \in S$ by hypothesis a. Thus $P_1, P_2, \ldots, P_{j-1}$ are all true because j is the smallest element not in S. As a consequence of hypothesis b, P_j must then be true. This gives us the desired contradiction. Thus $S = \mathbf{Z}^+$ and P_n is true for all positive integers.

EXERCISES   1   Note that hypothesis b of the second induction principle (Theorem 7) is a short way of writing an infinite list of implications. Write these implications for $k = 1, 2, 3, 4$. To make the principle seem reasonable, assume that the propositions $P_1, P_2, P_3, \ldots$ satisfy the hypotheses of the second principle of induction. Show directly (without using the conclusion) that P_5 is true by repeated use of the hypotheses.

2   Let P_n be the proposition $2^n > n^2$. Prove that P_n is true for every integer $n \geq$ _____ .

3   Prove that the statement $P_n: 2^n < n!$ $(n \in \mathbf{Z}^+)$ is true for every integer $n \geq$ _____ . (The number $n!$ is the product of all the positive integers from 1 to n. Thus $n! = 1 \cdot 2 \cdot 3 \cdot \cdots \cdot (n-1) \cdot n$.)

4   Give an alternate proof of Theorem 6 using the first principle of mathematical induction (Theorem 5).   ●

Appendix 6   Some Arithmetical Properties of Integers

This appendix is concerned with arithmetical properties of integers related to division. Section A deals with the notation of divisibility of integers, while Section B continues with the division algorithm. In Section C it is shown that any two integers have a greatest common divisor, while in Section D an algorithm is given for finding this greatest common divisor. The final section of this appendix states the Fundamental Theorem of Arithmetic and outlines a proof for it.

The proofs, but not the statements, of some major theorems in this appendix require familiarity with induction and well-ordering, which are dealt with in Appendix 5. On a first reading you may wish to omit the proofs.

A. Divisibility

We begin with a definition and some useful notation.

1
Definition   An integer b is a *factor*, or divisor, of an integer a if and only if $a = bq$ for some integer q. If b is a factor or divisor of a, we also say that a is a *multiple* of b or that a is *divisible* by b.

The notation $b \mid a$ means that b is a divisor of a. We write $b \nmid a$ if and only if b is not a divisor of a.

Caution   The symbol $b \mid a$ should not be confused with the fraction b/a.

Since $6 = 2 \cdot 3$, we have $2 \mid 6$. In the same way we can see that $-5 \mid 30$ and $7 \mid -21$ but $4 \nmid 9$. Any integer $a \neq 0$ is divisible by 1, -1, a, and $-a$.

2
Definition   An integer $p > 1$ is a *prime* if and only if the only divisors of p are 1, -1, p, and $-p$.

Examples of primes are 2, 3, 5, and 7.

EXERCISES

All problems refer to the set **Z** of integers.

1   Prove that in **Z** the relation "is a divisor of" is reflexive and transitive but not symmetric.

2   Prove that if a and b are positive integers such that $b\,|\,a$, then $b \leq a$.

3   Prove that if $a\,|\,1$, then $a = \pm1$.

*4   Prove that if $a\,|\,b$ and $b\,|\,a$, then $a = \pm b$.

5   For each of the following statements either construct a proof or find a counterexample.
a   If $a\,|\,b$ and $a\,|\,c$, then $a\,|\,(b+c)$.
b   If $a\,|\,(b+c)$, then $a\,|\,b$ or $a\,|\,c$.
c   If $a\,|\,c$ and $b\,|\,d$, then $(a+b)\,|\,(c+d)$.
d   If $a\,|\,c$ and $b\,|\,d$, then $ab\,|\,cd$.
e   If $a\,|\,b$, then $a\,|\,bc$ for any c.
f   If $a\,|\,bc$, then $a\,|\,b$ or $a\,|\,c$.

6   Find all primes less than 100. One way to do this is to make a table or list of the integers from 2 to 100. Circle the 2 and cross out all the other multiples of 2. Repeat this process with 3 and then continue the process. When can you stop? This method of finding primes is known as the sieve of Erathosthenes.

B. The Division Algorithm

If a and b are integers with $b > 0$, we can express a as a multiple of b plus a remainder term. This result is known as the *division algorithm*, which is formally stated as follows:

3
Theorem   If $a, b \in \mathbf{Z}$ with $b > 0$, then there exist unique integers q and r such that $a = bq + r$ and $0 \leq r < b$. The integer q is called the *quotient* and the integer r is called the *remainder*.

For example, if $a = 14$ and $b = 3$, then $14 = 3 \cdot 4 + 2$. This result can be illustrated on the number line by locating the integer a between consecutive multiples of b. The remainder is then pictured as the distance between a and the largest multiple of b to the left of a (see Figure A1).

Figure A1

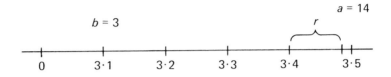

$$-25 = 7(-3) + (-4)$$

Note that when dividing -25 by 7 with the division algorithm it is not correct to write the answer as

$$-25 = 7(-3) + (-4)$$

The remainder r must satisfy the inequality $0 \leq r < 7$. Thus the correct answer is

$$-25 = 7(-4) + 3$$

Exercise — As further examples find the quotient and the remainder in the division algorithm for each given pair of values of a and b. Illustrate the result on the number line.

a:	25	-25	3	-3	24	-24	0
b:	7	7	4	4	8	8	5

Let $a, b \in \mathbf{Z}$ with $b > 0$. In proving the division algorithm we first establish the existence of the integers q and r such that $a = bq + r$ and $0 \leq r < b$. Once that has been accomplished we prove the uniqueness of these integers.

Case 1
Assume $a \geq 0$; in fact, let $a = n$. We prove the existence of q and r by induction on n with b fixed.

Let P_n be the proposition that for the fixed positive integer b there exist integers q and r such that $n = bq + r$ and $0 \leq r < b$.

Since $0 = b \cdot 0 + 0$, P_0 is true. (If you prefer to start with $n = 1$, prove that P_1 is true.) Assume that P_k is true for some integer $k \geq 0$ (that is, assume that there exist integers q and r such that $k = bq + r$ and $0 \leq r < b$. We must now prove that P_{k+1} is true.

First let us note that

$$k + 1 = bq + r + 1$$

If $r + 1 < b$, then P_{k+1} is true. If $r + 1 = b$, then

$$k + 1 = b(q+1) + 0$$

and again P_{k+1} is true. Thus by induction P_n is true for every integer $n \geq 0$.

Case 2

Assume that $a < 0$; set $a = -\alpha$, where $\alpha > 0$. As a consequence of case 1 there exist integers q and r such that $\alpha = bq + r$ and $0 \leq r < b$. But then

$$a = -\alpha = b(-q) + (-r)$$

If $r = 0$, then $a = b(-q) + 0$ and we have finished. If $0 < r < b$, then

$$a = b(-q-1) + (b-r)$$

and the new remainder $b - r$ satisfies the inequality $0 < b - r < b$.

The existence of q and r can also be proved using the well-ordering principle or the second induction principle.

Now let us prove the uniqueness of the integers q and r in the division algorithm. To this end suppose that $a, b, q, q_1, r, r_1 \in \mathbf{Z}$ with $b > 0$:

$$\begin{aligned} a &= bq + r & (0 \leq r < b) \\ a &= bq_1 + r_1 & (0 \leq r_1 < b) \end{aligned}$$

We must prove that $q = q_1$ and $r = r_1$.

We assume that $r \leq r_1$ (that's merely a matter of labeling). As a consequence of our hypothesis we have

$$bq + r = bq_1 + r_1$$

from which it follows that

$$b(q-q_1) = r_1 - r \geq 0$$

Since $r_1 < b$, $r_1 - r < b$. Thus

$$0 \leq r_1 - r = b(q-q_1) < b$$

and hence $q-q_1 \geq 0$ (remember $b > 0$). In fact, the integer $q-q_1$ must be zero (if $q-q_1 \geq 1$, then $b > b(q-q_1) \geq b$). But then $r_1 - r = 0$ and we are done.

EXERCISES 1   Let $a, b \in \mathbf{Z}$ with $b > 0$. Show that if the restriction $0 \leq r < b$ is removed in the division algorithm, then there are infinitely many values possible for q and r with $a = bq + r$. •

2   Use Theorem 3 to prove the following more general form of the division algorithm: If $a, b \in \mathbf{Z}$ with $b \neq 0$, then there exist unique integers q and r such that $a = bq + r$ and $0 \leq r < |b|$.

C. Greatest Common Divisors

In this section we prove that any two nonzero integers have a greatest common divisor and that this divisor can be expressed as a linear combination of the integers. In Section D an algorithm is given for finding this greatest common divisor and the specific linear combination. But first we tackle the existence proof.

Throughout Sections C, D, and E letters such as a, b, c, p, q, r (with or without subscripts) denote integers.

4
Definition   Let a and b be nonzero integers. An integer d is a *greatest common divisor* (abbreviated g.c.d.) of a and b if and only if

a d is positive,
b d is a divisor of both a and b, and
c   every divisor of a and of b is also a divisor of d.

The conditions defining a greatest common divisor of a and b can be written in symbols as follows:

a $d > 0$,
b $d \mid a$ and $d \mid b$, and
c   if $c \mid a$ and $c \mid b$, then $c \mid d$.

The greatest common divisor d of the integers a and b is often denoted by $d = \gcd(a, b)$.

5
Definition   The integers a and b are said to be *relatively prime* if and only if $\gcd(a, b) = 1$.

6
Example   The common divisors of 20 and 30 are ± 1, ± 2, ± 5, and ± 10. From this listing we see that if $c \mid 20$ and $c \mid 30$, then $c \mid 10$. Therefore 10 is the g.c.d. of 20 and 30.

Exercise   For each of the following number pairs find all common divisors and a greatest common divisor and determine whether or not the numbers are relatively prime:

a: 20 -30 -60 -20 15
b: 24 -36 90 -29 34

Use the definition to show that 2 is not a g.c.d. of 20 and 24.

Before proving the existence of a greatest common divisor for the integers a and b, we establish a useful auxiliary theorem.

7
Theorem   Let S be a nonempty subset of the integers such that S is closed under subtraction. Then either $S = \{0\}$ or S contains a smallest positive element d and S is the set of all integral multiples of d:

$$S = \{nd: n \in \mathbf{Z}\}$$

Proof
From the hypothesis we see that there exists some $a \in S$ and that $0 = a - a \in S$. Then for every $a \in S$ we have $0 - a = -a \in S$ and thus for every $a, b \in S$, $a - (-b) = a + b \in S$. This shows that S is a group under addition (addition is associative on S since the elements of S are integers).

Suppose $S \neq \{0\}$. Then S contains a positive element. (Why?) As a consequence of the well-ordering principle (Appendix 5A) the nonempty set

$$\{x: x \in S \text{ and } x > 0\}$$

has a smallest element $d \in S$. Since S is a group under addition, the set $\{nd: n \in \mathbf{Z}\}$ is contained in S. We wish to show that $S \subseteq \{nd: n \in \mathbf{Z}\}$. Let $x \in S$. We will show that $x \in \{nd: n \in \mathbf{Z}\}$. Since $x \in \mathbf{Z}$, the division algorithm implies that there exist integers n and r such that $x = nd + r$ and $0 \leq r < d$. Since $nd \in S$ and $x \in S$, $r = x - nd \in S$ also. But d is the smallest positive element of S and $0 \leq r < d$. Thus $r = 0$ and $x = nd$ for some integer n. Hence $S \subseteq \{nd: n \in \mathbf{Z}\}$. This completes the proof that $S = \{nd: n \in \mathbf{Z}\}$.

The existence and uniqueness of the greatest common divisor of two nonzero integers are guaranteed by the following theorem:

**8
Theorem**

Any two nonzero integers a and b have a unique greatest common divisor. Moreover, there are integers j and k such that

$$\gcd(a, b) = ja + kb$$

(i.e., the greatest common divisor of a and b can be expressed as a linear combination of a and b).

**9
Example**

The g.c.d. of 6 and 27 is 3. Since

$$3 = (-4)6 + 1 \cdot 27$$

we can write

$$\gcd(6, 27) = j \cdot 6 + k \cdot 27$$

with $j = -4$ and $k = 1$. Note also that

$$3 = 5 \cdot 6 + (-1)\, 27$$

Thus j and k are *not* unique.

Proof of Theorem 8

Let

$$S = \{ja + kb: j, k \in \mathbf{Z}\}$$

The set S is closed under subtraction since for integers j, k, j_1, and k_1,

$$(ja+kb) - (j_1 a + k_1 b) = (j-j_1)\, a + (k-k_1)\, b$$

and the latter expression is an element of S. By Theorem 7 there exists a positive integer $d \in S$ such that

$$S = \{nd: n \in \mathbf{Z}\}$$

Since $d \in S$, the definition of S guarantees that there exist integers j and k such that $d = ja + kb$.

Both a and b are elements of S. (Why?) But since $S = \{nd: n \in \mathbf{Z}\}$, $a = md$ and $b = nd$ for some integers m and n. This proves that $d \mid a$ and $d \mid b$. To show that $d = \gcd(a, b)$, let us assume that $c \mid a$ and $c \mid b$. Then there are integers p and p_1 such that $a = cp$ and $b = cp_1$ and hence

$$d = ja + kb = j(cp) + k(cp_1) = (jp + kp_1)\, c$$

so that $c \mid d$. This completes the proof of the existence of $\gcd(a, b)$.

Finally, suppose that d and d_1 are greatest common divisors of a and b. Since d_1 is a divisor of a and b, and d is a greatest common divisor of a and b, we must have $d_1 \mid d$. Similarly, $d \mid d_1$. But then $d = \pm d_1$ (see Exercise 4 in Section A). Since $d > 0$ and $d_1 > 0$, we must have $d = d_1$.

EXERCISES   1   For every pair of integers a and b in the exercise following Example 6, express $\gcd(a, b)$ as a linear combination of a and b.

2 Let d be the greatest common divisor of the integers a and b. Prove that there are infinitely many integers j and k such that $d = ja + kb$.

3 Let S be a set of integers which is closed under addition. Does S necessarily consist of all integral multiples of some fixed integer?

4 Let $n \in \mathbf{Z}^+$. Prove that $\gcd(na, nb) = n(\gcd(a, b))$. •

5 Prove that the greatest common divisor of two nonzero integers a and b is the largest integer which divides both a and b.

*6 Let $a, b \in \mathbf{Z}$ and $d = \gcd(a, b)$. Show that if $a = jd$ and $b = kd$, then $\gcd(j, k) = 1$.

D. The Euclidean Algorithm

We have proved that any pair of nonzero integers has a greatest common divisor, but the proof gave no hint about a method for finding this divisor or for expressing it as a linear combination of the given integers. There is a method, however, which gives both the greatest common divisor of the two integers and the expression as a linear combination. This method is known as the euclidean algorithm.

Let a and b be positive integers. (The situation with negative integers is dealt with in the exercises.) The technique of the algorithm is to perform successive divisions as follows: Divide a by b to obtain a remainder r_1. Divide b by r_1 with remainder r_2. Continue this process until a remainder of zero is obtained. Thus if a is not divisible by b,

$$
\text{A} \quad
\begin{aligned}
a &= bq_1 + r_1 & (0 < r_1 < b) \\
b &= r_1 q_2 + r_2 & (0 < r_2 < r_1) \\
r_1 &= r_2 q_3 + r_3 & (0 < r_3 < r_2) \\
&\ \vdots \\
r_{n-2} &= r_{n-1} q_n + r_n & (0 < r_n < r_{n-1}) \\
r_{n-1} &= r_n q_{n+1} + r_{n+1} & (r_{n+1} = 0)
\end{aligned}
$$

The greatest common divisor of a and b is then the last nonzero remainder, i.e., the number r_n in the sequence of divisions outlined above. (Why must the process terminate?) The proof of the euclidean algorithm follows Lemma 11.

10
Example

Find the g.c.d. of 105 and 28.

Carrying out the successive divisions, we have

$$105 = 28 \cdot 3 + 21 \qquad \text{(dividing 105 by 28)}$$
$$28 = 21 \cdot 1 + 7 \qquad \text{(dividing 28 by 21)}$$
$$21 = 7 \cdot 3 + 0 \qquad \text{(dividing 21 by 7)}$$

Thus the g.c.d. of 105 and 28 is 7.

Note that at each stage of the computation in the algorithm the previous divisor must be divided by the previous remainder. The quotients are irrelevant.

As a first step in the proof of the euclidean algorithm we prove the following lemma:

11
Lemma

Let $a, b > 0$. If $a = bq + r$ with $0 < r < b$, then the greatest common divisor of a and b is the same as the greatest common divisor of b and r:

$$\gcd(a, b) = \gcd(b, r)$$

Proof
We will demonstrate that the pair a and b has the same common divisors as the pair b and r. Suppose that $c \mid b$ and $c \mid r$. Then $b = cm$ and $r = cn$ for some integers m and n. As a consequence,

$$a = bq + r = cmq + cn = c(mq + n)$$

Thus $c \mid a$. Similarly, if $c \mid a$ and $c \mid b$, then $c \mid r$. Thus the set of common divisors of a and b is the same as the set of common divisors of b and r. It readily follows that the pairs a, b and b, r have the same greatest common divisor.

We now prove the euclidean algorithm (i.e., we prove that if r_n is the last non-zero remainder in the sequence of divisions (A), then r_n is the greatest common divisor of a and b).

Proof
In the sequence of nonnegative remainders $r_1 > r_2 > r_3 > \cdots$ there must be some remainder r_{n+1} which is 0, since there are only a finite number of integers m such that $0 < m < r_1$. Repeated application of Lemma 11 shows that

$$\gcd(a,b) = \gcd(b,r_1) = \gcd(r_1,r_2) = \cdots = \gcd(r_{n-1},r_n)$$
$$= r_n$$

The euclidean algorithm also can be used to represent the greatest common divisor of a and b as a linear combination of a and b. To do so start at the top of the sequence of divisions and represent in turn each remainder as a linear combination of a and b. Thus we have

$$\begin{aligned} r_1 &= a - q_1 b \\ r_2 &= b - q_2 r_1 = b - q_2(a - q_1 b) \\ &= (-q_2)a + (1 + q_2 q_1)b \\ r_3 &= r_1 - r_2 q_3 = \cdots \end{aligned}$$

As an example let us find the linear combination of 28 and 105 which represents the g.c.d. of 28 and 105. The divisions in Example 10 give us the following:

$$\begin{aligned} 21 &= 105 - 28 \cdot 3 \\ 7 &= 28 - 21 \cdot 1 = 28 - (105 - 28 \cdot 3) \end{aligned}$$

Thus $7 = 4 \cdot 28 - 1 \cdot 105$.

EXERCISES 1   Use the euclidean algorithm to find the following greatest common divisors:

a $\gcd(374, 51)$ c $\gcd(8766, 345)$
b $\gcd(9843, 334)$ d $\gcd(4673, 893)$

2   For each of the pairs in Exercise 1 use the euclidean algorithm to represent the greatest common divisor of a and b as a linear combination of a and b.

3   Let a or b be a negative integer. Show that the euclidean algorithm, when applied to a suitable pair of integers, can still be used to find the greatest common divisor of a and b. Provide one particular example of your procedure.

E. The Fundamental Theorem of Arithmetic

In working with the division algorithm and the euclidean algorithm, one quickly observes that the positive integers appear to fall into three groups: the integer 1, the prime numbers, and the positive integers which are products of primes. You may even have wanted to use the prime factors of integers a and b in order to find the greatest common divisor of a and b. The fact that every positive integer other than 1 is a prime or a (unique) product of primes is the result of the Fundamental Theorem of Arithmetic. We see in Exercise 7 that as a consequence of this theorem it is possible to use common prime factors of two integers, a and b, to find their greatest common divisor. We also see in Exercise 8 how to use all the prime factors of a and b to find their least common multiple (i.e, the smallest integer divisible by both a and b).

We first prove two results which are useful by themselves and also in the proof of the Fundamental Theorem of Arithmetic.

12
Theorem   If p is a prime and $p \mid ab$, then $p \mid a$ or $p \mid b$.

Proof
Let $p \mid ab$, where p is a prime, and assume that $p \nmid a$. Then $\gcd(a, p) = 1$ since p is prime, and there exist integers j and k such that $1 = ja + kp$. But then $b = b \cdot 1 = jab + kpb$. Since $p \mid ab$, there exists an integer m such that $ab = pm$. Then

$$b = jab + kpb = jpm + kpb = p(jm + kb)$$

Thus $p \mid b$.

13
Theorem   If p is a prime and $p \mid (a_1 a_2 \cdots a_n)$, then $p \mid a_i$ for some i, $1 \le i \le n$.

The proof of Theorem 13 is left for Exercise 1.

14
Theorem *The Fundamental Theorem of Arithmetic—First Form.* Any integer greater than 1 either is a prime or can be expressed as a product of primes. The expression of any positive integer which is not a prime as a product of primes is unique except for the order of the factors.

Proof

We prove the first statement of the theorem by using the second form of the principle of induction. For every integer $n \geq 2$ let P_n be the proposition: n is a prime or n can be expressed as a product of primes.

Since 2 is a prime, P_2 is true. For an integer $k \geq 2$ let us assume that the propositions $P_2, P_3, \ldots, P_k$ are all true. We must prove the proposition P_{k+1}: $k+1$ is a prime or $k+1$ can be expressed as a product of primes.

If $k+1$ is a prime, then P_{k+1} is true. If $k+1$ is not a prime, there exist integers i and j such that $k+1 = ij$, $1 < i < k+1$, and $1 < j < k+1$. As a result of the induction assumption P_i and P_j are true. Therefore there exist prime numbers $p_1, p_2, \ldots, p_r$ and $q_1, q_2, \ldots, q_s$ such that $i = p_1 p_2 \cdots p_r$ and $j = q_1 q_2 \cdots q_s$. Then

$$k + 1 = ij = p_1 p_2 \cdots p_r q_1 q_2 \cdots q_s$$

and hence P_{k+1} is true. Thus by the second principle of induction P_n is true for every integer $n \geq 2$.

To prove the uniqueness of the prime factorization of any integer $n \geq 2$, let P_n be the proposition: Either n is a prime or n can be expressed uniquely as a product of primes $p_1, p_2, \ldots, p_r$ such that $p_1 \leq p_2 \leq \cdots \leq p_r$.

The integer 2 is a prime, so P_2 is true. Let $k \geq 2$ be an integer and assume that $P_2, P_3, \ldots, P_k$ are all true. We must prove P_{k+1}.

If $k+1$ is a prime, then P_{k+1} is true. If $k+1$ is not a prime, there exist two or more primes $p_1, p_2, \ldots, p_r$ such that

$$k + 1 = p_1 p_2 \cdots p_r \qquad \text{and} \qquad p_1 \leq p_2 \leq \cdots \leq p_r$$

Suppose that $k+1$ also has the prime factorization

$$k + 1 = q_1 q_2 \cdots q_s$$

where

$$q_1 \leq q_2 \leq \cdots \leq q_s$$

Without loss of generality, we can assume that $p_1 \leq q_1$. Then, since $p_1 | k+1$, $p_1 | (q_1 q_2 \cdots q_s)$ and hence, by Theorem 13, $p_1 | q_i$ for some integer i, $1 \leq i \leq s$. But q_i is also a prime, so $p_1 = q_i$. Thus, as a consequence of the ordering $p_1 \leq q_1 \leq q_i$, we must also have $p_1 = q_1$.

Let

$$m = p_2 p_3 \cdots p_r = q_2 q_3 \cdots q_s$$

Then $2 \leq m < k+1$ and hence P_m is true by the induction assumption. This implies either that m is a prime, in which case $r = s = 2$ and $p_1 = q_1$, $p_2 = q_2$, or that the prime factorization of m is unique. Hence in the second case we must also have $r = s$ and $p_j = q_j$ for each $j = 1, 2, \ldots, r$.

**15
Theorem**   *Fundamental Theorem of Arithmetic—General Form.* Any integer different from 0, 1, or -1 is a prime or can be expressed as ± 1 times a product of primes or a prime. The expression of any nonprime number as a product of primes is unique except for the order of the factors.

The proof of Theorem 15 is left for Exercise 2.

It is frequently useful to write the prime factorization of an integer in the form

$$\pm p_1^{n_1} p_2^{n_2} \cdots p_r^{n_r}$$

where $p_1, p_2, \ldots, p_r$ are primes, $p_1 < p_2 < \cdots < p_r$, and $n_1, n_2, \ldots, n_r \in \mathbf{Z}^+$.

EXERCISES 1   Prove Theorem 13.

          2   Prove Theorem 15.

          3   Using the notation following Theorem 15, write the prime factorization of the integers 560, -693, 950, and -1278.

         *4   Prove that if r and s are relatively prime integers (that is $\gcd(r, s) = 1$) and $r | st$, then $r | t$.

5a If $r|t$ and $s|t$, does it necessarily follow that $rs|t$? Give examples.

b Complete the following proposition and prove it: Let r, s, and t be nonzero integers. If $r|t$, $s|t$, and _____ _____ , then $rs|t$.

6a Let $p_1, p_2, ..., p_k$ be primes. Prove by contradiction that none of these primes is a factor of the integer $(p_1 p_2 \cdots p_k) + 1$.

b Using the result of part a, prove that there are infinitely many prime numbers. (This argument is due to Euclid.) ●

7 State a technique for using the Fundamental Theorem of Arithmetic to find the greatest common divisor of two integers. Illustrate with some examples.

*8 **Definition** An integer m is a *least* (smallest) *common multiple* of two integers a and b if and only if (i) both a and b divide m and (ii) m divides any other integer which is a multiple of both a and b. We denote the least common multiple m of a and b by $m = \text{lcm}(a, b)$. In symbols we write $m = \text{lcm}(a, b)$ if and only if (i) $a|m$ and $b|m$ and (ii) if $a|c$ and $b|c$, then $m|c$.

a Find each of the following least common multiples:

lcm$(20, 24)$ lcm$(-20, -29)$
lcm$(-30, -36)$ lcm$(15, 34)$
lcm$(-60, 90)$

b Prove that any two positive integers have a least common multiple. ●

c Is the positive least common multiple of positive integers a and b unique? Justify your answer.

d Let a and b be integers and let $d = \gcd(a, b)$. Show that if $a = dm$ and $b = dn$, then $\gcd(m, n) = 1$ and the least common multiple of a and b is the integer dmn.

e Let a and b be integers. Then prove that

$$\gcd(a, b) \cdot \text{lcm}(a, b) = ab$$

f State a technique for using the Fundamental Theorem of Arithmetic to find the least common multiple of two positive integers. Illustrate with some examples.

Section 1.2 18b Set the product

$$\begin{pmatrix} a & b \\ c & d \end{pmatrix} \cdot \begin{pmatrix} w & x \\ y & z \end{pmatrix}$$

equal to the identity matrix and solve some linear equations for w, x, y and z.

Section 1.3 25c Assume that there are two identity elements e and e_1 and prove that they must be equal.

25g First display a solution and then prove that it is unique.

Section 1.4 46 Prove that $[h \circ (g \circ f)(w)] = [(h \circ g) \circ f](w)$ for every $w \in W$.

Section 1.5 59 To quickly determine the inverse of a permutation $f \in S_3$, note that $f^{-1}(y) = x$ if and only if $f(x) = y$. For example, if $f(1) = 3$, then $f^{-1}(3) = $ _____ .

61 Let $n \geq 3$ be a fixed integer. Choose two permutations which do not commute in S_3. Show how to expand these into two permutations which do not commute in S_n.

Section 1.6 63 A given vertex can be carried into _____ possible positions. With that vertex fixed in one of these positions, how many symmetries occur?

Section 1.8 83 You must prove that $(a+b)_n = (\bar{a}+\bar{b})_n$. To do so translate the lemma into statements involving congruences (for example, $a_n = \bar{a}_n$ so $a \equiv \bar{a} \pmod{n}$). Use prior results on congruences.

Section 2.1 12 The hypothesis asserts that for every $a, b \in H$ we have $a \circ b' \in H$. This hypothesis allows us to make specific choices for the elements a and b. Prove (i) $e \in H$, (ii) if $b \in H$, then $b' \in H$, and (iii) H is closed under $\circ$.

Section 2.3 31c Show that $a \circ H \subseteq b \circ H$ and vice versa.

31d Let $c \in a \circ H \cap b \circ H$.

35 See Problem 24.

Section 2.4 49 Use the statement that ϕ is one-to-one if and only if for every $a, b \in G$, $\phi(a) = \phi(b)$ implies $a = b$. First assume that ϕ is one-to-one. To prove that $\ker(\phi) = \{e\}$, let

$x \in \ker(\phi)$ and show that $x = e$. To prove the converse statement, let $\ker(\phi) = \{e\}$ and prove that ϕ is one-to-one. First show that $\phi(a \circ b') = e$ if $\phi(a) = \phi(b)$.

Section 2.6 71 First list the distinct elements of G.

Section 2.7 79 The definition of normality of a subgroup is equivalent to the statement $K \circ a \subseteq a \circ K$ and $a \circ K \subseteq K \circ a$ for every $a \in G$.

81 Use Theorem 80b.

83a First look at some cosets from Problem 77. Assume that $k \circ a \in K$.

84 Find the index of K. Use this index and perhaps the result of Problem 83 to describe the cosets of K.

Section 2.8 89 Show that if $k_1 \in K$, then $a_1 \circ b_1 \circ k_1 = a_1 \circ b_2 \circ k_2$ for some $k_2 \in K$. Then use the normality of K and the equality $a_1 \circ K = a_2 \circ K$ to obtain $a_1 \circ b_1 \circ k_1 = a_2 \circ b_2 \circ \underline{\hspace{1cm}}$.

94c In finding $\ker(\phi)$ remember that the identity element of G/K is the coset $\underline{\hspace{1cm}}$.

Section 3.2 7a Consider the sum $(a \cdot 0) + (a \cdot 0)$ and use property b in Proposition 6.

Section 3.6 43 To prove the implication a $\Rightarrow$ b let statement a be given and prove statement b. Since statement b is itself a conditional statement, assume the hypothesis of statement b and prove its conclusion.

51 Prove the two implications: If n is not $\underline{\hspace{2cm}}$, then $\mathbf{Z}_n$ is not an integral domain. If n is $\underline{\hspace{2cm}}$, then $\mathbf{Z}_n$ is an integral domain.

Section 3.7 63b See Theorem 35 in Chapter 2.

64b Show that $(a_p)^{p-1} = (a^{p-1})_p$.

Section 4.2 25 If $\theta = (s\ t)$, what factor in $P_\theta^{(n)}$ corresponds to the factor $x_s - x_t$ in $P^{(n)}$? If $i < s < t$, then $x_i - x_s$ and $x_i - x_t$ both appear as factors in the polynomial $P^{(n)}$. What factors correspond to these in the polynomial $P_\theta^{(n)}$? Consider other pairs of factors in $P^{(n)}$ and $P_\theta^{(n)}$ for the situations $s < j < t$ and $s < t < k$.

29 Use Problem 26 or Theorem 28.

30 Solve the equation $\alpha = \beta \circ \theta$ for $\theta \in S_n$ and show that $\theta \in A_n$.

Section 4.3 41   Remember that an automorphism of G is a homomorphism from G into G which is both one-to-one and onto. All these conditions must be taken into account in your proof.

Section 4.4 58a   Note that if $(h, k) \in H \times K$, then we want $\phi(h, k)$ to be an element of H.

Section 4.5 60   Use Lemma 79 in Chapter 2 to interchange elements of the composite $h \circ k \circ (h_1 \circ k_1)'$. Use Theorem 80b in Chapter 2 to prove that $H \circ K$ is normal.

       63   Show that $h' \circ k' \circ h \circ k \in H \cap K$.

       66   For one direction assume that G is the internal direct product of normal subgroups H and K. Define a function from $H \times K$ into $H \circ K$ and prove that it is an isomorphism. Feel free to use Theorems 64 and 56.

Section 5.1 9   Apply Theorem 6 several times.

       13a   Choose particular polynomials $f(x)$ and $g(x)$ to show that 2 is in this ideal.

       15   You may wish to refer to some ideas in Theorem 7 in Appendix 6. First do the proof if $S = \{0\}$ or $S = F$. Then let $S \neq \{0\}$ and $S \neq F$. Choose a nonzero polynomial $d(x)$ of lowest degree in S. (Why can this be done?) Show that $\deg(d(x)) \geq 1$. To do so assume $\deg(d(x)) = 0$, which implies that $1 \in S$. (Why?) Let $f(x) \in S$. We wish to prove that $f(x) = d(x) g(x)$ for some $g(x)$ in $F[x]$. Assume not. Then $f(x) = d(x) q(x) + p(x)$ for some $q(x), p(x) \in F[x]$, where $\deg(p(x)) < \deg(d(x))$ but $p(x) \neq 0$. Is $p(x)$ in S? What is $\deg(p(x))$?

Section 5.2 18   Assume that multiplication is properly defined. To show that S is an ideal let $r \in R$ and $s \in S$. Then $r + S = r + S$ and $s + S = 0 + S$, so $(rs) + S = $ _____ .

Section 5.3 26   First choose some small values for $a, b \in \mathbf{Z}$ and test the following implication: If $a, b \in S$, then $a \in S$ or $b \in S$. It may help you to use divisibility notation from Appendix 6A or Theorem 12 in Appendix 6.

       30b   Use Theorem 23.

Section 5.4 35   Show $S \neq R$. Then assume J is an ideal such that $S \subseteq J \subseteq R$. Use Lemma 34.

Section 1.2 4   To show that multiplication is a binary operation on $\mathscr{I}$, you must prove that if $A, B \in \mathscr{I}$, then $AB \in \mathscr{I}$. To do so prove that if $\det A \neq 0$ and $\det B \neq 0$, then $\det AB \neq 0$. To show that an identity matrix is in $\mathscr{I}$, you must first define it and show that it is nonsingular and then prove it is an identity. A similar procedure is necessary for inverses.

Section 1.3 6   Use Exercise 5.

Section 1.6 5a   To describe the elements of D_n, begin by making sketches of the polygons for D_3 and D_5 and the polygons for D_4 and D_6.

       5c   To demonstrate that composition ($\circ$) is a binary operation on D_n, it may help to use a counting argument similar to the one in Problem 63.

       5d   Fix n and explicitly describe two elements of D_n which do not commute with each other.

Section 1.7 3d   See Theorem 12 in Appendix 6.

       4   Assume that there exists $x \in a_n$ such that $0 < x < r$. Note that $0 < r - x < r < n$ (why?) and that $a = nq_1 + x$ for some $q_1 \in \mathbf{Z}$ (why?).

Section 1.8 2a   Try a few values of p.

       4d   First note that $\gcd(j, k_1) = 1$. Use Exercise 4 in Appendix 6E.

Section 2.1 11   Use Theorem 7 in Appendix 6.

       15b   See Exercise 8 in Appendix 6E.

       16c   See Theorem 8 in Appendix 6.

Section 2.2 3   The integers m and n may be negative. First prove the proposition for $n = -1$ and $m \in \mathbf{Z}$. Then consider the case for $n > 0$ and $m \in \mathbf{Z}$ and prove the proposition by induction on one variable with the other variable fixed.

       4   Is it possible that $a, a^2, a^3, \ldots$ are all different? Show that there exist integers j and k such that $a^j = a^k$ and $1 \leq j < k$. Prove that $e \in H$ and finally prove that $a' \in H$.

       11a   If $\gcd(m, n) = 1$, then there exist integers j and k such that $1 = jn + km$. Consider $b_1 = b^{jn}$ and $b_2 = b^{km}$.

       11c   Do this proof by induction on r, the number of primes.

12b See Exercise 7.

13a Prove that $b^n = e$ and that if k is the order of b, then $k \mid n$ so $k = n/x$ for some $x \in \mathbf{Z}^+$. In order to find x you might want to consider several values for n and s and look for a pattern.

13b Use the result of part a.

Section 2.3 8 Use Theorem 35 to show that if $(a \circ b)^k = e$, then the order of b^k divides both m and n. Do this by considering the groups $\langle a \rangle$ and $\langle b \rangle$ which have orders _____ and _____, respectively.

13a See Exercise 1.3–6.

14e Assume that A_4 does have a subgroup G of order six. Use Exercise 13 to determine which elements of A_4 must be in this proposed subgroup G.

Section 2.4 8b For one direction suppose $k \nmid n$. Then $n = kq + r$ for some $q \in \mathbf{Z}^+$ and $0 < r < k$. Consider $\phi(0_n)$ and $\phi(n_n)$ using the definition of ϕ. For the other direction assume that $k \mid n$ and $a_n = b_n$. Then $n \mid (b - a)$ and $k \mid (b - a)$. (Why?) Now show $\phi(a_n) = \phi(b_n)$.

Section 2.5 6 Suppose that ϕ is an isomorphism from $\mathbf{Z}$ onto $\mathbf{Q}$. To see how ϕ "works" let $\phi(1) = q \in \mathbf{Q}$. Then $\phi(n) = $ _____ for $n \in \mathbf{Z}$.

Section 2.6 3 Let H be a subgroup, $a \in G$ a generator of G, and s the smallest integer such that $a^s \in H$. Let $a^k \in H$. Since $k \in \mathbf{Z}$, $k = sq + r$ for $0 \le r < s$. Show that $a^r \in H$.

Section 2.7 2 Use Theorem 84 to find some of the normal subgroups and then use Proposition 82 to find at least one other.

12b Let $x \in C$ and $a \in G$. Show that $a' \circ x \circ a \in C$.

14 Prove that $h' \circ k' \circ h \circ k = e$.

16a To show that $(h \circ k) \circ (h_1 \circ k_1)'$ is in $H \circ K$ if $h, h_1 \in H$ and $k, k_1 \in K$, use Lemma 79.

Section 2.8 5 Examine a commutator in G/C.

8 Assume that $(a \circ K, b \circ K) \to (a \circ b) \circ K$ is a properly defined binary operation. Choose $a \in G$ and $k \in K$ and show that $a' \circ k \circ a \in K$. To do so consider the pairs $(k \circ K, a \circ K)$ and $(e \circ K, a \circ K)$.

9b See Theorems 71 and 72 and Exercise 4 above.

11 Prove the theorem using the second principle of induction. Let P_n be the proposition: For every commutative group G of order n, if p is a prime which divides n, then there exists $a \in G - \{e\}$ such that $a^p = e$. To prove the proposition when the order of G is $n+1$, assume that it is true for every group whose order is $k \leq n$. First consider the case in which G is a cyclic group (that is, $G = \langle a \rangle$ for some $a \in G$). Then consider the case of a noncyclic group and choose a proper subgroup K. (Why does K exist?) Show that if p does not divide the order of K, then p divides the order of G/K. Use Exercise 10.

Section 3.1 3 Use Venn diagrams and the familiar properties of intersection and union.

5 It is possible that ab can be the same element of G for every $a \in G$.

6e To show that R is commutative if $F(X,R)$ is commutative, you must show that for every $a, b \in R$ you have $ab = ba$. Find functions $f, g \in R$ such that $f(x_0) = a$ and $g(x_0) = b$ for some $x_0 \in X$.

6f To show that $F(X,R)$ has a multiplicative identity, you must first define a function $E: X \to R$. To show that if $F(X,R)$ has a multiplicative identity E, then R has a multiplicative identity, you must first find a candidate for the identity and then prove that it works. See the hint for Exercise 6e.

Section 3.4 5 See Exercise 1.4–5b.

6 Use Exercise 3.3–9.

Section 3.7 6b Factor $2^8 - 2^2$ into powers of distinct primes. Use Theorem 64 to show that one of these primes divides $x^6 - 1$.

11b Assume $n = \deg(r(x))$ and $m = \deg(g(x))$ with $n \geq m$. Let

$$r(x) = \sum_{k=0}^{n} r_k x^k \quad \text{and} \quad g(x) = \sum_{j=0}^{m} b_j x^j$$

Consider the polynomial

$$\bar{r}(x) = r(x) - (r_n b_m^{-1} x^{n-m}) g(x)$$

Show that $\bar{r}(x) \in S$.

12 Use Theorem 8 in Appendix 6.

Section 3.8 5   If $b \neq 0$ is an element of D, then b^{-1} exists in F (but not necessarily in D). Let

$$F' = \{ab^{-1}: a, b \in D, \, b \neq 0\}$$

Then $F' \subseteq F$.

Section 4.1 10   Let $f = (a_1 \; a_2 \; \ldots \; a_k)$. Compute $f^2(a_1)$, $f^3(a_1)$, etc.
         14   First look at examples.

Section 4.2 2a   The group A_4 has _____ elements. In S_4 are the cycles $(a \; b \; c)$ of length three elements of A_4?

Section 4.3 5   If ϕ is an automorphism of $\mathbf{Z}$ and $\phi(1) = k$, then $\phi(n) =$ _____ for $n \in \mathbf{Z}$. Find the possible values of k.
         6   Use the technique of Exercise 5.
         11   Define a function from G onto $\mathscr{H}$ such that a is mapped onto ϕ_a for every $a \in G$.

Section 4.5 11   To show uniqueness of a representation consider

$$a_1 + a_2 + \cdots + a_r = b_1 + b_2 + \cdots + b_r$$

where $a_j, b_j \in H_j$. What are the orders of $a_1 - b_1$ and

$$(b_2 - a_2) + \cdots + (b_r - a_r)?$$

(See Exercise 2.3–8.)

Section 5.1 7a   Suppose

$$f(x) = \sum_{k=0}^{n} a_k x^k \qquad \text{and} \qquad g(x) = \sum_{j=0}^{m} b_j x^j$$

are elements of $R[x]$ such that $f(r) = g(r)$ for every $r \in R$. Show that $f(r) - a_0 = g(r) - b_0$ for every $r \in R$ and then that

$$\sum_{k=1}^{n} a_k r^{k-1} = \sum_{j=1}^{m} b_j r^{j-1}$$

for every $r \in R - \{0\}$. Use Theorem 9.

9   Let $f(x), g(x) \in F[x]$ be fixed. Let

$$S = \{f(x)\,p(x) + g(x)\,q(x): p(x), q(x) \in F[x]\}$$

Show that S is an ideal in $F[x]$. Then use Theorem 15.

11   What is the greatest common divisor of $p(x)$ and $f(x)$ if $p(x)$ does not divide $f(x)$? Use Exercise 9.

13a   First prove the theorem for the subgroup

$$H_p = \{x: x \in G \text{ and order of } x \text{ is a power of } p\}$$

where p is a prime which divides the order of G. (See Exercise 2.2–12 for the definition of this group and examples.) You might begin by choosing $a \in H_p$ such that a has maximal order. Then construct a possible generator of G using the generators of the subgroups H_p and use Exercises 2.2–11 and 2.3–8 and a counting argument to complete the proof.

Section 5.2   5   See Exercise 3.3–9.

             9a   Use Theorem 23. See Exercise 5.1–12.

Section 5.3   2b   Prove by induction on the degree of the polynomial $g(x)$ that $g(x)$ has an irreducible factor.

Section 5.4   5   See Exercise 5.2–9.

             7c   Use Theorem 23.

             7d   See Exercise 5.3–2 or Exercise 5.1–11.

             8   Let J be an ideal such that $(p(x)) \subseteq J \subseteq F[x]$. Use Theorem 15.

Appendix 5B

             7   First look at the cases $n = 1, 2, 3, 4$. Then if the nth set is $\{x_1, x_2, ..., x_n\}$, develop a systematic procedure for obtaining all subsets of $\{x_1, x_2, ..., x_{k+1}\}$ by making use of the subsets of $\{x_1, x_2, ..., x_k\}$.

Appendix 5C

             4   For every integer $n \geq 1$ let Q_n be the proposition $P_{n_0 + n - 1}$. Show that the propositions Q_n, $n \in \mathbf{Z}^+$, satisfy both parts of the hypothesis of the first principle of induction.

Appendix 6B

    1   First look at some examples.

Appendix 6C

    4   Start with $d = \gcd(a, b)$.

Appendix 6E

    6b   Do a proof by contradiction.
    8b   Use the Fundamental Theorem of Arithmetic.

This bibliography is by no means complete. We have tried to include books which will complement the text of this book, give further insights into the topics included here, or provide new topics related to those of this book. Many of these books are accessible to the student with a modest background in abstract algebra; others are more advanced (e.g., Jacobson, Kurosh, van der Waerden). We have also included two books which give a picture of the men and the development of abstract algebra.

General Theory

Ames, Dennis B. *An Introduction to Abstract Algebra*. International, Scranton, Pa., 1969.

Birkhoff, Garrett, and Saunders MacLane. *A Survey of Modern Algebra*, 3d ed. Macmillan, New York, 1965.

Dean, Richard A. *Elements of Abstract Algebra*. Wiley, New York, 1966.

Dubisch, Roy. *Introduction to Abstract Algebra*. Wiley, New York, 1965.

Fraleigh, John B. *A First Course in Abstract Algebra*. Addison-Wesley, Reading, Mass., 1967.

Goldstein, Larry J. *Abstract Algebra: A First Course*. Prentice-Hall, Englewood Cliffs, N.J., 1973.

Herstein, I. N. *Topics in Algebra*. Blaisdell, New York, 1964.

Jacobson, Nathan. *Lectures in Abstract Algebra*. Van Nostrand, New York, Vol. I, 1951; Vol. II, 1953; Vol. III, 1964.

Johnson, Richard E. *University Algebra*. Prentice-Hall, Englewood Cliffs, N.J., 1966.

Kurosh, A. G. *Lectures on General Algebra*. Chelsea, New York, 1963.

Larsen, Max D. *Introduction to Modern Algebraic Concepts*. Addison-Wesley, Reading, Mass., 1969.

McCoy, Neal H. *Fundamentals of Abstract Algebra*. Allyn and Bacon, Boston, 1972.

Van der Waerden, B. L. *Modern Algebra*, rev. English ed. Ungar, New York, 1953.

Warner, Seth. *Modern Algebra*, Vol. I. Prentice-Hall, Englewood Cliffs, N.J., 1965.

Group Theory

Burnside, William. *Theory of Groups of Finite Order*, 2d ed. Dover, New York, 1955.

Fuchs, L. *Infinite Abelian Groups*, Vol. I. Academic Press, New York, 1970.

Hall, Marshall, Jr. *The Theory of Groups*, rev. ed. Macmillan, New York, 1959.
Lederman, Walter. *Introduction to the Theory of Finite Groups*, 4th ed. Interscience, New York, 1961.
Rotman, Joseph J. *The Theory of Groups: An Introduction*. Allyn and Bacon, Boston, 1965.

Ring Theory

Artin, E., C. J. Nesbitt, and R. M. Thrall. *Rings with Minimum Condition*. University of Michigan Press, Ann Arbor, 1944.
Burton, David M. *A First Course in Rings and Ideals*. Addison-Wesley, Reading, Mass., 1970.
McCoy, Neal H. *The Theory of Rings*. Macmillan, New York, 1964.

Galois Theory and Field Theory

Artin, Emil. *Galois Theory*, 2d ed. (Notre Dame Mathematical Lecture no. 2). University of Notre Dame Press, Notre Dame, Ind., 1944.
Postnikov, N. N. *Foundations of Galois Theory*. Macmillan (Pergamon Press), New York, 1962.
Several of the books listed under General Theory also contain brief descriptions of the elements of Galois Theory. These include Birkhoff and MacLane, Goldstein, and Herstein, each of which might serve as a good introduction to this topic.

Number Theory

Hardy, G. H., and E. M. Wright. *An Introduction to the Theory of Numbers*, 4th ed. Oxford University Press, Oxford, 1960.
LeVeque, William J. *Elementary Theory of Numbers*. Addison-Wesley, Reading, Mass., 1962.
Ore, Oystein. *Number Theory and Its History*. McGraw-Hill, New York, 1948.

History

Bell, E. T. *Men of Mathematics*. Simon and Schuster, New York, 1937.
Kline, Morris. *Mathematical Thought from Ancient to Modern Times*. Oxford University Press, New York, 1972.
Abstract Algebra: A First Course by Goldstein also contains historical comments.

$\exists x \in X \ P(x)$, there exists $x \in X$ such that $P(x)$ is true, 275

$\varnothing$, empty or null set, 271

δ_i, μ_i, ρ_i, symmetries of the square, 45–46

$\phi_a : G \to G$, inner automorphism on G, 220

$\phi_c : C[0, 1] \to \mathbf{R}$, point-evaluation homomorphism, 265

$\phi : G \to \overline{G}$, homomorphism or isomorphism, 88, 96, 160

$\phi(G)$, image set of homomorphism ϕ, 92

$\phi^{-1}(\overline{H})$, inverse image of set $\overline{H}$, 95

$\pi : G \to G/K$, canonical homomorphism of G onto quotient group G/K, 120

$\sum\limits_{j=0}^{n} a_j x^j$, polynomial in x over ring R, 168

$\circ, *, \square, +, \cdot$, binary operations, 5